Progress in Mathematics

2   GENERAL

Progress in Mathematics

Pupils' Book 1G
1G Mental Tests and Phase Tests
Pupils' Book 2G
2G Mental Tests and Phase Tests

Pupils' Book 1C
1C Mental Tests and Phase Tests
Pupils' Book 2C
2C Mental Tests and Phase Tests

3rd, 4th and 5th-year volumes are in preparation, as is a third 'layer'—the 'E' ('extension') books.

Progress in Mathematics

2   GENERAL

Les Murray BA

Senior Teacher and Head of Mathematics, Garstang County High School

Stanley Thornes (Publishers) Ltd

First published in 1985 by Stanley Thornes (Publishers) Ltd, Old Station Drive, Leckhampton, Cheltenham GL53 0DN, UK

British Library Cataloguing in Publication Data

Murray, Les
  Progress in mathematics.
  Bk. 2G
  1. Mathematics–Examinations, questions, etc.
  I. Title
  510′.76   QA43

  ISBN 0-85950-176-0

Typeset by Grafikon Ltd, Oostkamp, Belgium.
Printed and bound in Great Britain at Bath Press Ltd, Bath.

Preface

As with the first-year books, I have written numerous, carefully graded questions, so the teacher must again be selective. Few worked examples have been given thus allowing for alternative methods of introducing topics.

Where necessary, revision exercises covering first-year work have been provided: such exercises have been labelled $\boxed{\textbf{R}}$. A revision section has been inserted after every six chapters, questions being based on those chapters.

Once again, photocopy masters are available to the teacher for exercises where pupils may benefit by their provision. Such exercises have been labelled $\boxed{\textbf{M}}$.

The completion of this book has been dependent on the valued help and advice given to me by many people, in particular Mr Roger Wilson, Head of Mathematics at Parklands High School, Chorley, who has carefully and painstakingly worked through the whole text and has provided the answers as well as giving welcome advice; and to Mr J. Britton, Head of Mathematics at Copthall School, London, for his most useful comments. My thanks also go to staff and pupils of Garstang High School, for their interest and co-operation while writing has been in progress; to Carol A. R. Andrews, Research Assistant at the Department of Egyptian Antiquities at the British Museum, for the invaluable information provided; and to Vehicle Foreman Mr John Patrick, and Mr Fred Watson of Pandoro Ltd, Fleetwood, for their help with the section on containers.

Les Murray
1985

Acknowledgements

Dover Publications Inc for the hieroglyphic notation, on p. 46.
British Rail (Western) for the timetables, on p. 146.
Guinness Superlatives for the records of memorising π, on p. 244.
Mathematical Pie Ltd for the mnemonics for π, on p. 245.

To BAM and LM

Contents

1 Sets

Sets

Exercise 1

1. Here is a *set* of even numbers that are less than 19. One *member* (or *element*) of the set is missing. What is the missing member?

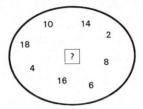

2. Consider the set of multiples of 3 that are less than 23.
   The set can be listed in curly brackets.
   Copy this set and fill in the missing members.
   The set of multiples of 3 that are less than
   23 = {3, ⬚? , 15, 6, ⬚? , 18, 12}.

3. List these sets. Use curly brackets.
   (a) The set of odd numbers that are bigger than 40 but less than 50
   (b) The set of capital letters that are formed with just straight lines. (Use the capital letters in the appendix on p. 427.)
   (c) The set of days of the week
   (d) The set of divisors of 24

4. If A = {months with 31 days}, then list the members of set A. Use curly brackets.
   Set out your work like this:
   $$A = \{ \qquad\qquad\qquad\qquad \}$$

5. List these sets as in question 4:
   (a) R = {odd numbers less than 14}
   (b) S = {suits in a pack of cards}

(c) V = the set of vowels

(d) M = {months that begin with the letter M}

(e) N = the set of natural numbers* that are less than 10

(f) L = the set of capital letters that have exactly one axis of bilateral symmetry. (Use the capital letters in the appendix on p. 427.)

6. Describe these sets in words:

(a) Q = {rectangle, square, rhombus, parallelogram, kite, trapezium}

Q = the set of $\boxed{?}$

(b) A = {Constable, Rembrandt, Van Gogh}

(c) P = {2, 3, 5, 7, 11, 13, 17, 19, 23, 29}

(d) D = {1, 2, 3, 6, 9, 18}

(e) C = {cumulus, nimbus, cirrus, stratus}

(f) M = {5, 10, 15, 20, 25, 30, 35, ... }

(g) F = {$\frac{2}{3}, \frac{4}{6}, \frac{6}{9}, \frac{8}{12}, \frac{10}{15}, \frac{12}{18}, \frac{14}{21}$, ... }

In parts (f) and (g) the lists *do not finish*.

They are called *infinite* sets.

The dots can be read as 'and so on'.

7. G = {3, 6, 8}

List set T where T = the set of 3-digit numbers formed by using all 3-digits in set G. (No digit should be repeated in any of these 3-digit numbers.)

8. V = {8, 10, 42, 18, 36, 22, 100, 54}

(a) List set D whose members are double all those in set V.

(b) List set H whose members are all half those in set V.

9. Q = the set of quadrilaterals in which opposite sides are equal

Draw one member of set Q.

10. Mark a point P on your page using a cross.

C = {points that are 25 mm from point P}

Make a drawing to show set C.

---

*See the glossary.

$\in$ means 'is a member of' (or 'belongs to').

$\notin$ means 'is not a member of' (or 'does not belong to').

Exercise 2

For each question, write the symbol ($\in$ or $\notin$) that would make the sentence correct:

1. 9   ?   {odd numbers}

2. 12   ? $\{1, 3, 5, 7, 9, 11, 13, \ldots\}$

3. 4   ? A where $A = \{\text{divisors of } 28\}$

4. 5   ? B where $B = \{\text{prime numbers}\}$

5. parallelogram   ?   {triangles}

6. kite   ?   {quadrilaterals}

7. 3546   ?   {numbers exactly divisible by 9}

8. 31 254   ?   {numbers exactly divisible by 4}

9. Paris   ?   {cities in Europe}

10. 25   ? S where $S = \{\text{square numbers}\}$

11. Y ?   {vowels}

12. square-based pyramid   ?   {solids with 6 vertices}

Exercise 3

$X = \{2, 4, 6, 8, 10\}$; $Y = \{\text{multiples of } 3\}$; $Z = \{4, 8, 12, 16, 20, \ldots\}$

Copy each of the following. Replace the boxes by the symbols $\in$ or $\notin$ to make the sentences true.

1. 6   ? X

2. 6   ? Y

3. 6   ? Z

4. 8   ? Y

5. 40   ? X

6. 40   ? Y

7. 40   ? Z

8. 84   ? Y

9. 106   ? Z

10. 236   ? Y

11. 3513   ? Y

12. 7268   ? Z

An *empty set* is a set with no members.

It is written as $\varnothing$ or { }.

{0} is not an empty set (zero is a member).

{$\varnothing$} is not an empty set (it has one member, namely $\varnothing$).

Exercise 4

A Which of these are empty sets?

Write $\varnothing$ or { } if a set is empty, otherwise write 'is not an empty set'.

1. The set of empty milk cartons
2. The set of even prime numbers
3. {tins of spotted paint}
4. {polygons with ten sides}
5. {quadrilaterals containing four right-angles}
6. {triangles containing three right-angles}
7. {straight lines that can be drawn on the curved face of a sphere}
8. {straight lines that can be drawn on the curved face of a cylinder}

B State whether each of the following is true or false:

1. {triangles with four sides} = $\varnothing$
2. {squares with perpendicular diagonals} = $\varnothing$
3. The set of even numbers that are multiples of 5 = $\varnothing$
4. The set of triangles containing two obtuse angles = { }
5. {quadrilaterals containing three obtuse angles} = { }

Venn Diagrams and the Intersection and Union of Sets

The *intersection* of sets A and B is the set of elements in both A and B. The symbol $\cap$ stands for intersection.

The *union* of sets A and B is the set of elements in either A or B or both A and B. The symbol $\cup$ stands for union.

$\cap$ is often pronounced as 'cap' and $\cup$ pronounced as 'cup'.

e.g. If $A = \{2, 4, 6, 8, 10, 12\}$

and $B = \{3, 6, 9, 12\}$

then $A \cap B = \{6, 12\}$

and $A \cup B = \{2, 3, 4, 6, 8, 9, 10, 12\}$

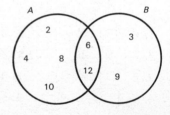

4

1. If $P = \{1, 3, 5, 7, 9\}$ and $Q = \{3, 4, 5, 6, 7, 8\}$, find:
   (a) $P \cap Q$ (b) $P \cup Q$

2. $D = \{2, 4, 6, 8\}$ and $F = \{2, 8, 32\}$. Find:
   (a) $D \cap F$ (b) $D \cup F$

3. $L = \{5, 10, 15, 20\}$ and $M = \{10, 20, 30, 40\}$. Find:
   (a) $L \cap M$ (b) $L \cup M$

4. $N = \{a, e, i, o, u\}$ and $P = \{a, b, c, d, e\}$. Find:
   (a) $N \cap P$ (b) $N \cup P$

5. $F = \{a, c, g\}$ and $G = \{b, c, h, k\}$. Find:
   (a) $F \cap G$ (b) $F \cup G$

6. $J = \{$Ann, Bina, John, Karen, Pat$\}$ and $K = \{$Pat, Peter, Jane, Asif, Ann$\}$. Find:
   (a) $J \cap K$ (b) $J \cup K$

7. $M = \{4, 8, 12, 16, 20, 24\}$ and $N = \{20, 15, 18, 12, 6, 16\}$. Find:
   (a) $M \cap N$ (b) $M \cup N$

8. $R = \{5, 10, 15, 20, 25, 30\}$ and $W = \{20, 25, 30\}$. Find:
   (a) $R \cap W$ (b) $R \cup W$

9. $J = \{1, 3, 5, 7\}$ and $K = \{2, 4, 6, 8\}$. Find:
   (a) $J \cap K$ (b) $J \cup K$

10. $F = \{1, 2, 3, 4, 5, 6, 7\}$ and $V = \{a, e, i, o, u\}$. Find:
   (a) $F \cap V$ (b) $F \cup V$

11. $A = \{l, m, p, t\}$ and $Z = \{m, p, t\}$. Find:
   (a) $A \cap Z$ (b) $A \cup Z$

12. $W = \{$even numbers less than 15$\}$ and $X = \{$even numbers between 9 and 21$\}$. Find:
   (a) $W \cap X$ (b) $W \cup X$

13. $M = \{$even numbers between 10 and 30$\}$ and $P = \{$even numbers between 20 and 29$\}$. Find:
   (a) $M \cap P$ (b) $M \cup P$

14. C = {multiples of 5 that are less than 30}
and D = {multiples of 8 that are less than 30}. Find:
(a) $C \cap D$ (b) $C \cup D$

15. X = $\{1, 3, 5, 7, 9\}$ and Y = {prime numbers less than 20}. Find:
(a) $X \cap Y$ (b) $X \cup Y$

16. T = {triangles} and R = {plane figures containing a right-angle}.
Find: $T \cap R$

17. A = {points on line JG}
B = {points on line LM}
Find: $A \cap B$

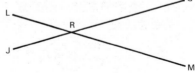

18. V = {factors of 12} and W = {factors of 20}. Find:
(a) $V \cap W$ (b) $V \cup W$

Exercise 6

A 1. (a) Write set A.
(b) Write set B.
(c) Write set $A \cap B$.
(d) Write set $A \cup B$.

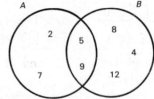

2. (a) Write set P.
(b) Write set Q.
(c) Write set $P \cap Q$.
(d) Write set $P \cup Q$.

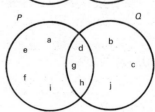

3. (a) Write set X.
(b) Write set Y.
(c) Write set $X \cap Y$.
(d) Write set $X \cup Y$.

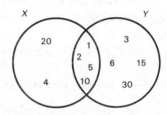

B 1. G = $\{1, 4, 6, 7, 9, 11, 15\}$ and H = $\{3, 6, 9, 12, 15\}$.
Draw a Venn diagram to show these two sets. Find:
(a) $G \cap H$ (b) $G \cup H$

2. $R = \{c, h, o, r, d\}$ and $S = \{s, e, c, t, o, r\}$.
Draw a Venn diagram to show these two sets. Find:
(a) $R \cap S$ (b) $R \cup S$

3. $W = \{\text{natural numbers less than } 12\}$ and $X = \{\text{odd numbers between 6 and 18}\}$.
Draw a Venn diagram to show these two sets. Find:
(a) $W \cap X$ (b) $W \cup X$

4. $D = \{\text{divisors of } 42\}$ and $P = \{\text{prime numbers less than } 15\}$.
Draw a Venn diagram to show these two sets. Find:
(a) $D \cap P$ (b) $D \cup P$

Exercise 7

A   **1.** $T = \{\text{divisors of } 18\}$ and $F = \{\text{divisors of } 24\}$.
     (a) List set T.
     (b) List set F.
     (c) Find $T \cap F$.
     (d) Find the common factors of 18 and 24.
     (e) What is the HCF (highest common factor) of 18 and 24?

   2. $A = \{\text{divisors of } 42\}$ and $B = \{\text{divisors of } 28\}$.
     (a) Find $A \cap B$.
     (b) Find the common factors of 42 and 28.
     (c) What is the HCF of 42 and 28?

   3. $R = \{\text{divisors of } 36\}$ and $L = \{\text{divisors of } 48\}$.
     (a) Find $R \cap L$.
     (b) Find the HCF of 36 and 48.

B   **1.** $Y = \{\text{the first ten multiples of } 6\}$ and $Z = \{\text{the first eight multiples of } 8\}$.
     (a) Find $Y \cap Z$.
     (b) List the set of common multiples of 6 and 8 that are less than 60.
     (c) What is the LCM (lowest common multiple) of 6 and 8?

   2. $P = \{\text{the first twelve multiples of } 10\}$ and $Q = \{\text{the first eight multiples of } 15\}$.
     (a) Find $P \cap Q$.
     (b) What is the LCM of 10 and 15?

The Universal Set and the Complement of a Set

The *universal* set is the set of all elements being considered.

The symbol $\mathscr{E}$ is used ('$\mathscr{E}$' for '$\mathscr{E}$verything') to stand for the universal set.

On a Venn diagram, a rectangle is used for the universal set.

The *complement* of a set A is written as A'. It is the set of elements of $\mathscr{E}$ that are not in set A.

e.g.　If　　$\mathscr{E}$ = {natural numbers less than 10}
　　　and　A = {even numbers less than 10}
　　　then　A' = {1, 3, 5, 7, 9} as shown in the diagram.

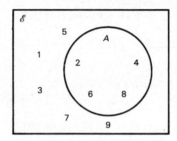

Exercise 8

A Draw Venn diagrams to show the following:

1. Universal set $\mathscr{E}$ = {5, 10, 15, 20, 25, 30, 35, 40}
and A = {5, 15, 25, 35}

2. $\mathscr{E}$ = {the first ten letters of the alphabet} and B = {a, e, i}

3. $\mathscr{E}$ = {factors of 64} and C = {2, 64}

B Suggest a possible universal set for each of the following sets:

1. {rectangle, parallelogram, trapezium}
2. {2, 4, 6, 8, 10}
3. {cod, haddock, plaice}
4. {potatoes, carrots, peas, cabbage}
5. {hexagon, pentagon, octagon}
6. {3, 6, 9, 12, 15, 18, 21, 24, ... }

Exercise 9

1. (a) Draw a Venn diagram as shown.
   (b) Complete it where:
      $\mathcal{E}$ = {even numbers less than 20}
      A = {2, 4, 6, 8}
   (c) List A'.
   (d) Describe A' in words.

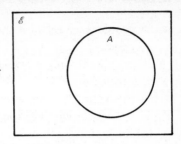

2. $\mathcal{E}$ = {natural numbers between 30 and 50} and
   B = {odd numbers between 30 and 50}.
   (a) List B'.   (b) Describe B' in words.

3. $\mathcal{E}$ = {the last fifteen letters of the alphabet} and
   C = {l, p, r, u, v, w, y, z}.
   List C'.

4. $\mathcal{E}$ = {divisors of 48} and D = {divisors of 16}.
   (a) List D'.   (b) Show this on a Venn diagram.

5. $\mathcal{E}$ = {natural numbers less than 30}
   F = {multiples of 6} and G = {prime numbers}.
   (a) List F'.   (b) List G'.

Exercise 10

Given a universal set $\mathcal{E}$, and another set A, describe in words the set A'.

Universal set $\mathcal{E}$	Set A
1. {letters of the alphabet}	{consonants}
2. {three and four-sided plane shapes}	{quadrilaterals}
3. {natural numbers}	{even numbers}
4. {whole numbers*}	{whole numbers less than 49}
5. {trees}	{coniferous trees}

* See the glossary.

Exercise 11 Logic Problems

A 1. 34 people were asked if they ate a cereal or toast for breakfast this morning.
16 people ate only a cereal. 15 people had toast. 6 had both cereal and toast.
In the Venn diagram shown, C = {people who ate a cereal} and T = {people who ate toast}.
(*a*) How many ate only toast?
(*b*) How many had either a cereal or toast or both?
(*c*) How many had neither?
(*d*) How many altogether ate a cereal?

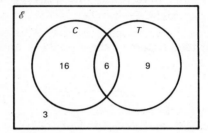

2. Copy this Venn diagram:

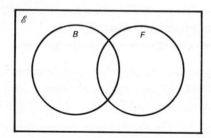

Now complete your copy using the following information.
40 people were asked what sort of pen they owned.
B = the set of people who owned a ball-point pen, and
F = the set of people who owned a fountain pen.
30 said they owned a ball-point pen, while 7 people said they owned both. (Complete two parts of your Venn diagram now.) 15 people altogether owned a fountain pen. (Now complete the rest of your Venn diagram.)
(*a*) How many owned only a ball-point pen?
(*b*) How many did not own either type of pen?
(*c*) How many did not own a fountain pen?

B Draw Venn diagrams to help you to solve these questions. (Any letters may be used to label the sets.)

1. 25 pupils were asked whether they belonged to the chess club or the computer club. 13 said they were members of the chess club, 16 were members of the computer club, while 5 were in both clubs. How many belonged to neither club?

2. 32 children were asked whether they liked jelly, ice cream or both. 3 liked only jelly, 21 liked both, while 2 liked neither.
   (a) How many liked only ice cream?
   (b) How many liked ice cream?

3. In a survey, people were asked whether they watched BBC1 or BBC2 on TV last night. 29 watched BBC1, 25 watched BBC2, 16 watched both, while 12 watched neither. How many people were questioned in the survey?

4. 43 people were asked whether they liked to drink tea or coffee. A total of 16 liked tea, 9 liked both, while only 1 liked neither.
   (a) How many liked only coffee?
   (b) How many did not like coffee?

5. Out of 68 people, all owned a cassette recorder or a record player and 12 of them owned both. 37 owned a cassette recorder.
   (a) How many owned a record player?
   (b) How many owned only a cassette recorder?

6. 80 people were asked whether they liked a comedy film or a thriller. All liked one or the other or both. 56 liked a comedy, while 42 liked a thriller. How many liked both?

Exercise 12   Miscellaneous Questions

1. Here is a set of numbers:

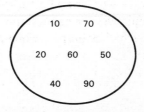

The members are the same in some way.
Give two more members of this set and describe the set in words.

11

2. Using this Venn diagram: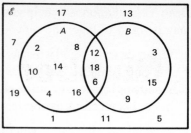
  (a) List set A.
  (b) List set B.
  (c) List set A'.
  (d) List $A \cap B$.
  (e) List $A \cup B$.
  (f) List $(A \cup B)'$.

3. $N = \{$natural numbers less than 30$\}$
  $P = \{$prime numbers less than or equal to 31$\}$
  $O = \{$odd numbers less than 31$\}$
  $M = \{$multiples of 3 that are less than or equal to 30$\}$
  (a) In which set or sets is the number 23?
  (b) List the members of M that are even.
  (c) List the members of $M \cap O$.
  (d) List the members of $N \cap P$.
  (e) Find the members of set P that are not in set O.

4. Copy this set of numbers:

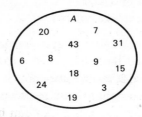

Split the set A into two parts in some way using a single line (the line need not be straight).
Write why you split the set in the way you did. (Describe in words the two sets obtained by your *partition* line.)

5. Two dice are thrown. List the set of totals obtained by adding all possible pairs of numbers that can appear on the dice.

6. $R = \{$right-angled triangles$\}$
  $I = \{$isosceles triangles$\}$
  $S = \{$scalene triangles$\}$
  (a) Describe in words set $R \cap I$.
  (b) What can you say about set $S \cap I$?

$\overset{\displaystyle 2}{}$ Number

1. (a) 700 + 20 + 5000 + 8
   (b) 60 + nine hundred + four

2. (a) Write 3049 in words.
   (b) Write one thousand, five hundred and seventy-six in figures.

3. From the given set of numbers, find the odd numbers and write them in order of size, largest first:
   {85, 6, 19, 23, 46, 98, 153, 7, 61, 104}

4. Copy these, but fill in the correct sign < or > :
   (a) 2036 ? 2360   (b) 96 231 ? 147 982

5. Using any of the digits 2, 5, 7 and 8 once only in each number, write:
   (a) the largest 4-digit number that can be made,
   (b) the largest 4-digit odd number that can be made.

Carry out these calculations:

1. 6147
   + 2396

3. 7006
      25
   + 193

5. 6436
   − 1540

7. 8204
   − 3195

2.   79
    364
   + 408

4. 927
   − 264

6. 7261
   − 6867

8. 4007
   − 1639

13

9. 4531 + 2496
10. 7290 + 493 + 1847
11. 6005 + 75 + 719 + 2640
12. 846 + 274

13. 5384 − 1968
14. 3062 − 1875
15. 5003 − 2127
16. 7065 − 986

Exercise 3 R

Copy these and fill in the missing digits:

1.
```
   4 ? 5 7
 + 2 6 ? ?
 ─────────
   ? 9 0 2
```

2.
```
   8 0 7 3
 + ? ? ? ?
 ─────────
   9 7 5 8
```

3.
```
   ? ? ? ?
 +   6 5 8
 ─────────
   5 2 3 7
```

4.
```
   6 ? ? 0
 − 2 5 9 ?
 ─────────
   ? 4 3 4
```

5.
```
   6 1 3 2
 − ? ? ? ?
 ─────────
   4 1 8 6
```

6.
```
   ? ? ? ?
 − 4 1 9 2
 ─────────
   2 0 3 5
```

Exercise 4 R

Answer these. Look for quick methods.

1. 8 + 7 + 2
2. 15 + 36 + 25
3. 84 + 49 + 16
4. 39 + 46 + 21
5. 69 + 38 − 19

6. 47 + 88 − 27
7. 79 + 34 − 24
8. 467 + 388 − 167
9. 509 + 365 + 491
10. 842 + 466 + 534

Exercise 5 R

1. 532 people were at a concert. If 189 of these were in the more expensive seats, how many were in the cheaper seats?

2. If 23 + 24 + 25 + 26 + 27 + 28 + 29 = 182, find the value of 73 + 74 + 75 + 76 + 77 + 78 + 79.

3. A girl guessed that there were 347 marbles in a jar.
If the actual number was 298 marbles, by how many was she wrong?

4. In an election there were two candidates. The loser got 5827 votes. If he lost by 2796 votes, how many voters were there?

5. 27 cm more string will give me a length that is 19 cm shorter than 62 cm. How long is the string I have got?

Exercise 6 $\boxed{\text{R}}$

1. Round 48 correct to the nearest ten.
2. Round 384 correct to the nearest hundred.
3. Round 627 correct to the nearest ten.
4. Round 2392 correct to the nearest thousand.
5. Round 5215 correct to the nearest ten.
6. Round 7096 correct to the nearest hundred.
7. Round 4899 correct to the nearest hundred.
8. Round 4899 correct to the nearest ten.
9. Round 4899 correct to the nearest thousand.
10. Round 7499 correct to the nearest thousand.

Exercise 7

e.g. Find $1 + 2 + 3 + 4 + 5 + 6$.

$$1 + 2 + 3 + 4 + 5 + 6$$
$$= (1 + 6) + (2 + 5) + (3 + 4)$$
$$= 7 + 7 + 7$$
$$= \underline{\underline{21}}$$

Find:

1. $1 + 2 + 3 + 4 + 5 + 6 + 7 + 8 + 9 + 10$
2. $7 + 8 + 9 + 10 + 11 + 12 + 13 + 14$
3. $29 + 30 + 31 + 32 + 33 + 34 + 35 + 36$
4. $5 + 7 + 9 + 11 + 13 + 15$
5. the sum of the first 10 odd numbers
6. the sum of the first 20 even numbers
7. the sum of the numbers from 1 to 100 inclusive

Darts

Brief rules (There are other versions.)

1. Scoring starts at 301, and the total score at each turn is subtracted until zero is reached.

2. Players take it in turn to throw 3 darts.

3. To begin, a player must score a double.

4. Also, to end, a player must score a double.

5. The bull's eye in the centre scores 50.

6. The narrow band around the bull's eye scores 25.

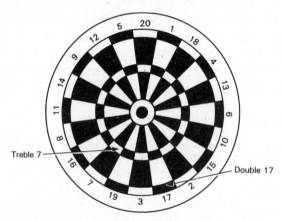

A sample game showing scoring

(a) John starts. He misses with his first dart and scores double 5 and 18 with his other darts.
    (Score = 10 + 18 = 28. 301 − 28 = 273.)
(b) Jim scores double 20 and 5 = 45. (256)
(c) John scores treble 20, 20 and 1 = 81. (192)
(d) Jim scores 100. (256 − 100 = 156)
(e) John scores 84.
(f) Jim scores 79.
(g) John scores 66 (42 needed to win).
(h) Jim scores 38 (39 needed to win).
(i) John scores 36.
(j) Jim scores 7, 16 and then double 8 to win.

John	Jim
273	256
192	156
108	77
42	39
6	0

1. What is the highest score that a player can obtain with a single dart?

2. If Jane needs to score 39 to win and scores 7 with her first dart, which double does she obtain if she wins with her next dart?

3. Frank scores double 17, treble 3 and 19 with three darts. What total score was that?

4. Copy and complete the following table:

| | \multicolumn{3}{|c|}{Score from} | |
	First dart	Second dart	Third dart	Total
(a)	17	15	2	
(b)	12		9	26
(c)	double 20	5	treble 1	
(d)	treble 18	double 4	13	
(e)	treble 6	13		48
(f)		double 19	18	67
(g)	bull's eye	treble 20	double 20	
(h)	double ?	14	treble 16	88
(i)	18	double 17	treble ?	109
(j)	double 16		14	67

5. Paul scores double 14 and 13. If with his third dart he reaches a total of 48, what did the third dart score?

Exercise 9

e.g. John scores 56, 43, 87, and 76.
Make out a table for him:

245 ← (301 − 56)
202   In a darts match, earlier scores are normally crossed out.
115   To avoid untidiness DO NOT cross out scores.
 39

1. If Polly scores 46, 62, 38, 85 and 49, how many more does she need for 301?
Make out a table for her.

2. Alec scores 87, 34, 12, 56 and 72.
Make out a table for him.

3. From the table shown for Fritz, write down the scores he obtained.

265
202
176
 98
 43
  2

4. Make out a table for Asif who scores 78, 39, 64, 55 and 61.

5. George scores 93, 108 and 84.
Make out a table for him.

Exercise 10

For each of the given tables produced during various darts matches, find the scores obtained by the particular players.

e.g. 214   scores obtained were 87 (301 − 214)
       102   112 (214 − 102)
        41   61 (102 − 41)
         4   37 (41 − 4)

1. 246	**2.** 281	**3.** 205	**4.** 219
192	205	126	143
103	174	89	68
64	97	57	51
12	29	2	10
	6		

5. 172	**6.** 216	**7.** 237	**8.** 141
23	159	167	21
2	68	104	14
	8	22	

Exercise 11

1. Alan has 207 entered on the board after throwing three darts to start the game. If two of the darts scored treble 19 and 3, what double did he score?

2. Lynne needs 129. Her previous required total was 165. With two darts she had obtained a double 8 and a 13. What did the third dart score?

3. Nick scored 49 with three darts. If two of the darts scored 18 and 19, what could the third dart have scored?

4. Tony prefers to aim for the right-hand side of a dartboard. He also finds the 20-sector easy but has difficulty with the 3-sector. If at least one of his throws hits a double, list six possible ways he can score 44 with only two darts. (He only tries for his preferred sectors.)

5. Kim requires 29 with three darts (all darts should score). She prefers to aim for the top part of the board and since she finds the 6-sector and the 11-sector difficult, she does not aim for these.
List 12 possible ways in which she can score 29 if she aims for her preferred sectors and if she scores exactly one double.

Exercise 12   Magic Square Puzzles   M

Where possible, copy and complete each of the following magic squares. (Rows, columns and diagonals should each have the same total.) Note that in each magic square, each number is used once only and zero is not allowed. Note also that one of the given magic squares is impossible to complete.

1.

3	5	7

2.

3		
5		
		7

3.

4		
3		
8		

4.

	4	
10	6	2
	8	

5.

	17	
13	9	
	1	

6.

12	10	8
	6	

7.

	9	
	7	
	5	

8.

2		
		5
		8

Exercise 13

Carry out the calculations as quickly as possible. (Working need not be shown.)

1.	700 – 248	**9.**	600 – 333	**17.**	18 000 – 6541
2.	500 – 395	**10.**	900 – 514	**18.**	12 000 – 5009
3.	600 – 183	**11.**	2000 – 817	**19.**	6000 – 964
4.	800 – 79	**12.**	5000 – 1832	**20.**	4000 – 1076
5.	600 – 452	**13.**	6000 – 3720	**21.**	7000 – 3131
6.	700 – 476	**14.**	8000 – 2806	**22.**	10 000 – 4993
7.	200 – 108	**15.**	900 – 642	**23.**	20 000 – 17 607
8.	400 – 236	**16.**	10 000 – 5321	**24.**	14 000 – 6094

Exercise 14   Difference Tables

```
2
   3                 These are called     2   5   13   28   52   87
5     5              difference tables.      3   8   15   24   35
   8     2           Try to work out          5   7   9   11
13     7             how they have              2   2   2
   15    2           been made.
28     9
   24    2
52    11
   35
87
```

Now make difference tables for the sequences of numbers given in these questions. (Some of them have been started for you.)

1. 5 9 14 23 39 65 104 159 . . .

```
  4   5       16   26
    1           10
```

20

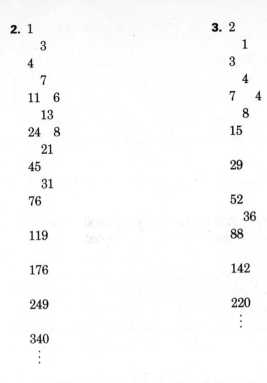

2. 1
 3
 4
  7
 11 6
  13
 24 8
  21
 45
  31
 76

 119

 176

 249

 340
  ⋮

3. 2
  1
  3
  4
  7 4
  8
  15

  29

  52
   36
  88

  142

  220
   ⋮

4. 1 2 5 13 29 56 97 155 233 334 461 617 805
 1 3   41 58 78
     17

Exercise 15 Number Puzzle ▬▬▬▬▬▬▬ **M**

For each of these puzzles, start at the arrow and continue from square to square adding the first square, subtracting the second, adding the third, subtracting the fourth, and so on, adding and subtracting alternately, until you obtain the answer at the end. You must find the numbers that are missing from some of the boxes, which will give you the correct answer at the end.

Copy each puzzle and fill in the missing numbers:

e.g. → | 7 | 2 | 4 | 5 | 6 | 3 | ? | 4 | 1 | 2 | 6 | ? | 3 | 2 | 5 | = 17

$7 - 2 + 4 - 5 + 6 - 3 + \mathbf{5} - 4 + 1 - 2 + 6 - \mathbf{2} + 3 - 2 + 5 = 17$

The missing numbers could be 5 and 2.

1. → | 6 | 1 | ? | 2 | 3 | 4 | 3 | = 9 **2.** → | 4 | 2 | 7 | ? | 1 | 3 | ? | 2 | = 8

3. → | 9 | 3 | 8 | 5 | ? | 5 | 7 | 4 | 8 | ? | 1 | 3 | 5 | 8 | 5 | = 13

4. → | 8 | 2 | ? | 5 | 2 | 8 | 9 | ? | 4 | 3 | 7 | 6 | 5 | 1 | ? | 4 | 6 | 2 | 1 |

= 19

5. | 6 | 2 | 1 | ? | 8 | 4 | ? | 1 | 3 | ? | 4 | 5 | ? | 2 | 2 | = 12
| 5 |
| 7 |

↑

6. | 9 | 2 | 5 | ? | 4 | 2 | 3 | 5 | ? | 6 | 7 | 4 | 6 | 2 | 9 | ←
| 4 |
| 2 |
| 5 | 4 | 3 | ? | ? | 1 | 2 | 4 | 3 | 5 | ? | 2 | 4 | 1 | = 20

Exercise 16

Copy and complete:

1. $43 + 28 = \boxed{?} + 30$

2. $56 - 37 = \boxed{?} - 40$

3. $71 + 54 = \boxed{?} + 60$

4. $87 + 43 = \boxed{?} + 40$

5. $89 - 45 = \boxed{?} - 50$

6. $74 + 62 = 80 + \boxed{?}$

7. $93 - 49 = 100 - \boxed{?}$

8. $65 - 36 = 60 - \boxed{?}$

9. $94 + 72 = 90 + \boxed{?}$

10. $83 - 34 = \boxed{?} - 30$

11. $653 - 279 = \boxed{?} - 280$

12. $946 - 487 = 956 - \boxed{?}$

13. $205 + 568 = 200 + \boxed{?}$

14. $814 + 352 = \boxed{?} + 360$

15. $814 - 352 = \boxed{?} - 360$

16. $4006 - 2791 = \boxed{?} - 2800$

17. $4006 + 2791 = \boxed{?} + 2800$

18. $7615 + 2385 = 7625 + \boxed{?}$

19. $9268 + 5479 = 10\,000 + \boxed{?}$

20. $8543 - 6194 = 10\,000 - \boxed{?}$

Exercise 17 R

Answer these:

1.
$$427 \atop \times 6$$

2.
$$3709 \atop \times 4$$

3. 162×9

4. 380×7

5. 2151×8

6. 5337×3

7.

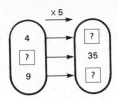

8.

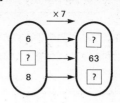

9. Find the product of 87 and 4.

10. I have 7 packets of stamps with 36 stamps in each packet. How many stamps is that?

11. How many minutes are there in 9 hours?

12. Write 8349 correct to the nearest thousand. Now use this to help you to estimate the answer to 8349 × 6.

Exercise 18   R

Answer these:

1. (a) 700 × 40   (b) 263 × 100   (c) 300 × 481

2. (a) 46 × 31   (b) 309 × 42   (c) 726 × 201

3. A car can travel 18 km on 1 litre of petrol. How far can it travel on 34 litres?

4. How many hours are there in 19 days?

Exercise 19   Long Multiplication

Try this method:

e.g.   63 × 27 = (63 × 20) + (63 × 7)
            =   1260   +   441
            =   1701

Check the answer using long multiplication.

Now try these using the method on the previous page:

1. 19×14 6. 78×64
2. 26×15 7. 97×57
3. 38×27 8. 172×43
4. 49×23 9. 79×950
5. 65×34 10. 324×607

Exercise 20   Russian Multiplication

e.g. 38×27

1. Write down the two numbers side by side.

2. Divide one of the numbers by 2, ignoring any remainders. (Note that $38 \div 2 = 19$, and $19 \div 2 = 9$ if the remainder is ignored. Also, $9 \div 2 = 4$.) Stop at 1.

38	27
19	54
9	108
4	216
2	432
1	864

3. Multiply the other number by 2. Repeat this and write each answer next to the answers in the first set of numbers.
Stop when you write down a number alongside the 1.

4. Now cross out each pair of numbers where there is an even number in the first set.

5. Add together the numbers that remain in the second set (in this example, $54 + 108 + 864$).

6. The answer you obtain is the answer to the given product. So $38 \times 27 = 1026$.

Now try these using the same method:

1. 48×33 6. 32×19
2. 44×57 7. 64×35
3. 14×81 8. 63×42
4. 36×78 9. 61×27
5. 33×69 10. 85×52

Exercise 21   Number Patterns ━━━━━━━

Use a calculator to help with these. Look for patterns.

1. 9999 × 1
    9999 × 2
    9999 × 3
    9999 × 4
    9999 × 5
    9999 × 6
    9999 × 7
    9999 × 8
    9999 × 9
    9999 × 10
    9999 × 11
    9999 × 12
    9999 × 13
    9999 × 14
    9999 × 15

2. 142 857 × 1
    142 857 × 2
    142 857 × 3
    142 857 × 4
    142 857 × 5
    142 857 × 6
    142 857 × 7

Exercise 22 ━━━━━━━

Try to find some 3-digit numbers which can be divided by the sum of their digits.

For example, 342 is one such number. The sum of the digits is 3 + 4 + 2 = 9 and 342 is exactly divisible by 9.

285 is another example. 2 + 8 + 5 = 15 and 285 is exactly divisible by 15.

Calculations (Division) ━━━━━━━

Exercise 23 ━━━━━━━ R

Answer these:

1. 3 ⟌ 78

2. 2 ⟌ 56

3. 92 ÷ 4

4. 133 ÷ 7

5. 4224 ÷ 6

6. 3177 ÷ 9

7. 5072 ÷ 8

8. 9145 ÷ 5

9. How many days will 192 tablets last if I need to take 3 each day?

10. Find the remainder when 8237 is divided by 9.

Exercise 24

Copy and complete these calculations:

1.
```
         3 ?
    12  4 5 6
        3 6
        9 6
        9 6
            0
```

4.
```
          1 ? ?
     42  4 4 1 0
         4 ?
         ? 1 0
         ? 1 0
         0 0 0
```

2.
```
           5 ?
    23  1 3 1 1
        1 1 ?
        ? 6 1
        ? ? ?
        0 0 0
```

5.
```
           ? 1 ?
    64  2 0 1 6 0
        ? 9 ?
        ? ?
        6 4
        ? ? 0
        ? ? 0
        0 0 0
```

3.
```
          ? 3 ?
    31  7 3 4 7
        6 2
        ? ? 4
        9 ?
        ? ? ?
        2 ? 7
        0 0 0
```

Exercise 25

Carry out these calculations:

1. 714 ÷ 21   **3.** 3618 ÷ 54   **5.** 8946 ÷ 71
2. 2656 ÷ 32   **4.** 6536 ÷ 43   **6.** 7252 ÷ 28

7. $9296 \div 13$ **9.** $5738 \div 19$ **11.** $9072 \div 84$
8. $1813 \div 37$ **10.** $9706 \div 46$ **12.** $46\,170 \div 95$

Exercise 26

1. 3073 matches are packed in boxes so that there are 49 matches in each box.
   (a) How many boxes of matches are there?
   (b) How many matches are left over?

2. How many lengths of 24 cm can be cut from a length of 3.12 m?

3. 294 pupils go on a school trip. How many coaches are needed if each coach holds 39 people?

4. What is the remainder when 29 364 is divided by 25?

5. How many times can 26 be subtracted from 2704?

Exercise 27

A Use a calculator for this part of the exercise.
Find the value of:

1. (a) $396\,000 \div 10$
   (b) $396\,000 \div 100$
   (c) $396\,000 \div 1000$

2. (a) $210\,000 \div 100$
   (b) $210\,000 \div 1000$
   (c) $21\,000 \div 100$

3. (a) $543 \div 3$
   (b) $54\,300 \div 30$
   (c) $54\,300 \div 300$

4. (a) $646 \div 17$
   (b) $6460 \div 170$
   (c) $64\,600 \div 170$

2. (a) $70\,380 \div 460$
   (b) $7038 \div 46$
   (c) $70\,380 \div 46$

6. (a) $3\,255\,000 \div 35\,000$
   (b) $3255 \div 35$
   (c) $325\,500 \div 35$

7. (a) $8673 \div 21$
   (b) $867\,300 \div 21$
   (c) $86\,730\,000 \div 210\,000$

8. (a) $4717 \div 89$
   (b) $471\,700 \div 890$
   (c) $47\,170\,000 \div 8900$

Compare your answers to parts (a), (b) and (c) of each of the questions above. What do you notice?

B Copy these and fill in the missing numbers:

1. $\dfrac{6720}{70} = \dfrac{672}{\boxed{?}}$

2. $\dfrac{76\,800}{2400} = \dfrac{\boxed{?}}{24}$

3. $\dfrac{576\,000}{32\,000} = \dfrac{576}{\boxed{?}}$

4. $\dfrac{79\,800}{1400} = \dfrac{798}{\boxed{?}}$

5. $90\,300 \div 4300 = \boxed{?} \div 43$

6. $37\,740 \div 510 = 3774 \div \boxed{?}$

7. $617\,700 \div 2900 = \boxed{?} \div 29$

8. $387\,000 \div 8600 = \boxed{?} \div 86$

9. $24\,700\,000 \div 38\,000 = \boxed{?} \div 38$

10. $98\,700\,000 \div 4700 = \boxed{?} \div 47$

C Answer these:

1. $97\,200 \div 1800$
2. $999\,000 \div 27\,000$
3. $114\,800 \div 41$
4. $100\,700 \div 530$
5. $217\,000 \div 6200$

6. $278\,800\,000 \div 34\,000$
7. $162\,000\,000 \div 150\,000$
8. $834\,300\,000 \div 810\,000$
9. $2\,622\,000\,000 \div 760\,000$
10. $44\,110\,000\,000 \div 220\,000$

Exercise 28

For each question, select the one correct answer:

1. $58 \times 34 = \boxed{?}$
   A. 1970
   B. 1972
   C. 1974
   D. 1976

2. $39 \times 26 = \boxed{?}$
   A. 1325
   B. 874
   C. 1014
   D. 674

3. $25 \times 87 \times 4 = \boxed{?}$
   A. 8528
   B. 3825
   C. 8700
   D. 87 000

4. $36 \times 48 = \boxed{?}$
   A. 18×60
   B. 72×24
   C. 18×24
   D. 72×96

5. $420 \times 1900 = \boxed{?}$
  A. 78 900
  B. 789 000
  C. 79 800
  D. 798 000

6. $24\,480\,000 \div 720 = \boxed{?}$
  A. 34
  B. 340
  C. 3400
  D. 34 000

7. $64 \times 28 = \boxed{?}$
  A. 16×56
  B. 128×7
  C. 56×32
  D. 32×14

8. $2368 \div 74 = \boxed{?}$
  A. $1184 \div 148$
  B. $1184 \div 37$
  C. $592 \div 37$
  D. $4736 \div 37$

9. $12 \times 8 \times 28 \times 9 = \boxed{?}$
  A. $24 \times 16 \times 14 \times 3$
  B. $36 \times 4 \times 56 \times 3$
  C. $48 \times 4 \times 14 \times 3$
  D. $6 \times 24 \times 14 \times 3$

10. $21 \times 32 \times 18 \times 12 = \boxed{?}$
  A. $42 \times 8 \times 6 \times 72$
  B. $42 \times 16 \times 3 \times 36$
  C. $7 \times 64 \times 9 \times 24$
  D. $42 \times 8 \times 9 \times 72$

Miscellaneous Questions

Exercise 29

1. Is 38×49 greater than or less than 2000?

2. $39 \times 6\blacksquare = 2613$
Unfortunately, one digit is smudged. What should it be?

3. A girl, when asked to multiply 46 by 25, divided 4600 by 4. Would her answer be correct? Give a reason.

4. If $42 \times 68 = 2856$, find the value of:
  (a) 4200×680
  (b) 21×68
  (c) 84×34
  (d) $2100 \times 68\,000$
  (e) $2856 \div 42$
  (f) $2856 \div 68$
  (g) $2856 \div 21$
  (h) $285\,600 \div 420$

5. (a) $4 \times 9 = \boxed{?} \times 18$ (c) $108 \div 12 = \boxed{?} \div 6$

    (b) $240 \times 460 = 12 \times \boxed{?}$ (d) $50\,400 \div 360 = 1680 \div \boxed{?}$

Exercise 30   M

In the following football matches, 3 points are awarded for a win, 1 for a draw and 0 for losing.

1. Girls United played 24 games, drew 6 of them and gained 45 points. How many games did they lose?

2. Rotten Rovers won only 3 matches after playing 29. If they gained 21 points altogether, how many games did they lose?

3. Copy and complete the following table:

	Number of games played	Number of wins	Number of draws	Number of games lost	Total points
(a)	13	7			25
(b)		12		5	45
(c)			11	13	95
(d)	35			10	53

Exercise 31

1. In certain league football matches, 3 points are awarded for a win, 1 for a draw, and 0 for losing.

(a) If Clever United played 19 games and obtained 38 points having lost only 3 of those games, how many games did they win?

(b) Brilliant Rovers played 37 matches and lost 9 of them. If their points totalled 62, how many of their matches were draws? How many did they win?

(c) Pathetic City, after playing 42 matches, had lost 9 of them and gained 53 points. How many games did they win?

(*d*) After playing 16 games, Midville Town had a total of 29 points. List all the possible ways that Midville could do this (*i.e.* list all possible wins, draws and losses).

2. In a rugby league match, Rovers scored a total of 24 points. If they took only one penalty, how many tries and how many conversions did they have in that match? (A try = 3 points, a conversion = 2 points, a penalty = 2 points.)
Note There must be the same number (or more) of tries than conversions in a game.

3. In rugby union, a try is worth 4 points, a penalty is worth 3 points, while a conversion is worth 2 points. Again, there must be the same number (or more) of tries than conversions in a game. If the Grasshoppers obtained 19 points in a particular game, list all the possible ways they could do so.

4. Park obtained 17 points in a rugby union match. List all the possible ways in which they could get such a score.

Exercise 32　　Calculator Investigations

	e.g.
A 1. Select any 3 digits (all different).	3, 9, 0

2. Enter on your calculator the biggest 3-digit number you can make with your selected digits.　　930

3. Subtract the smallest number you can make.　　$-\,\underline{039}$
　　891

4. Note the 3 digits in the answer; clear the display, then enter the largest number you can make with the digits obtained in that answer.　　981

5. Subtract the smallest number you can make with these 3 digits.　　$-\,\underline{189}$
　　792

6. Continue doing this (*i.e.* repeat steps 4 and 5) until you keep obtaining the same 3-digit number.　　972
　　$-\,\underline{279}$
　　etc.

7. What is the final 3-digit number obtained?

8. Repeat the steps using different 3-digit numbers.
   Note   Note the answer obtained at each stage. Watch how the first (or last) digits change in successive answers. Add the digits.

9. Write what you notice.

B **1.** Enter on your calculator the biggest 4-digit number you can make using any 4 digits (not all the same).

e.g.
8631

2. Subtract the smallest number you can make using the same 4 digits.

– 1368

7263

3. Re-arrange the 4 digits in your answer to form the biggest number possible using all 4 digits. Enter this number into the calculator after clearing the display.

7632

4. Now subtract the smallest number that can be made using the same 4 digits.

– 2367

5265

5. Repeat steps 3 and 4 over and over again until you repeatedly obtain the same 4-digit answer.

6552
– 2556

3996

6. What is the final 4-digit number that you repeatedly obtain?

9963

7. Try all the steps above again using different digits (still use 4 digits).

– 3699
etc.

C At each stage of your answers to part B:

1. Find the sum of the digits.

2. Add the first and last digits.

3. Add the middle 2 digits.

4. Look for patterns.

5. Try to find 4 digits that do not give the patterns that are usually obtained.

6. Write about your findings.

D **1.** Test 5-digit and 6-digit numbers as in parts A and B.

2. In each case, do you eventually obtain a certain answer whatever the starting digits?

3. Note your answers at each stage and look for patterns.

4. Write about your findings.

3 Symmetry

Bilateral Symmetry

Exercise 1 — R

A For each shape, write its number of axes of bilateral symmetry (the answer may be 'none'):

1.

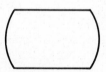

4.

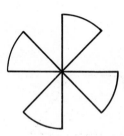

2.

5.

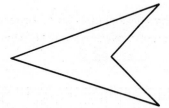

3.

6.

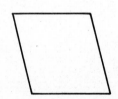

B Copy these.

Where possible, draw the axis of symmetry for each shape. A shape may have one axis, more than one, or none.

1.

2.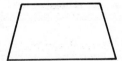

3.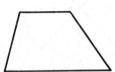

4.

5.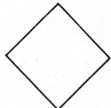

6.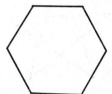

C Copy these shapes on to squared paper. **M**

Complete each one so that the broken line is an axis of symmetry.

1.   **2.**

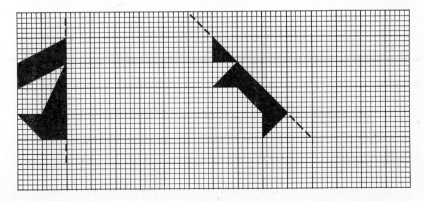

Exercise 2 ━━━━━━━━━━━━━━━━━━━━━━━━━━━━━━━ R

1. Using the letters of the alphabet in the appendix on p. 427, write:
   (a) 3 letters that have no axes of symmetry,
   (b) 3 letters that have exactly one axis of symmetry,
   (c) 2 letters that have exactly two axes of symmetry.

2. (a) Name a triangle with exactly one axis of symmetry.
   (b) Name two quadrilaterals that have exactly two axes of symmetry.

Exercise 3 ━━━━━━━━━━━━━━━━━━━━━━━━━━━━━━━ M

In this 5 × 5 grid of squares, 4 squares have been shaded to give a pattern so that the whole grid has exactly two axes of bilateral symmetry.

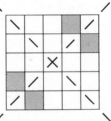

A Copy each of the following grids. Shade the given square in each grid.

1.

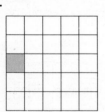

3.

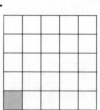

5.

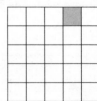

2.

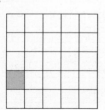

4.

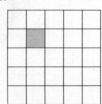

6.

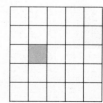

7. 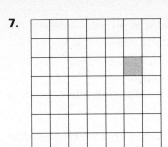   **8.**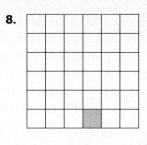

Shade 3 more squares in each grid to give a pattern so that the whole grid has *at least two axes* of bilateral symmetry (there may be more than one answer).

B Copy the grids again and shade the given squares. This time, shade 3 more squares in each grid to give a pattern so that the whole grid has *exactly two axes* of bilateral symmetry (there may be more than one answer).

Rotational Symmetry

Exercise 4 To Make a Windmill

1. Cut out a square from a piece of paper (about 15 cm square).

2. Draw the two diagonals.

Fig. 1

3. Cut along the diagonals from each vertex. Stop when you are about 15 mm from the centre of the square (fig. 1).

4. Put pin-pricks through the paper as shown in fig. 1.

Fig. 2

5. Fold the four parts as shown in fig. 2 and fig. 3 but *do not crease* the paper. These are the windmill's sails.

Fig. 3

37

6. Pin, or nail the sails to a stick. If you put a small bead between the stick and the sails, the sails will turn more easily.

The windmill's sails have *rotational symmetry*.
A shape has rotational symmetry if it can be rotated to a new position to fit exactly on top of itself.

When a shape is rotated, the number of times it fits exactly on top of itself is called the *order of rotational symmetry*. The windmill in Exercise 4 has rotational symmetry of order 4.

Exercise 5

1. (*a*) Draw an equilateral triangle.

(*b*) Cut an equilateral triangle out of card or paper. (It should be the same size as the triangle you have drawn.) Colour one side.
(*c*) Keeping the coloured side uppermost, in how many different ways can the cut-out triangle fit exactly on top of the triangle you have drawn?
(*d*) What is the order of rotational symmetry of an equilateral triangle?

2. What is the order of rotational symmetry of a rectangle? Make a cardboard cut-out and test it.

3. What is the order of rotational symmetry of a square?

Exercise 6

1. Which of these shapes have rotational symmetry of order greater than 1?

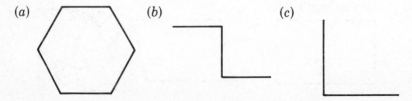

(*a*) (*b*) (*c*)

(d)   (e) 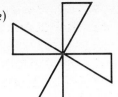   (f)

2. What is the order of rotational symmetry of:
   (a) a parallellogram?   (d) a regular octagon?
   (b) a rhombus?   (e) a regular pentagon?
   (c) a kite?

3. Write the order of rotational symmetry for each shape:
   (a)    (b)   (c)

4. Which letters of the alphabet have rotational symmetry of order 2 when printed in block capitals? (Use the letters in the appendix on p. 427.)

Exercise 7 ════════════════════════════════ **M**

Copy each shape. If it has rotational symmetry of order greater than 1, mark on your copy its centre of rotation. Use a dot.

1. 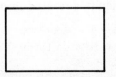   2. 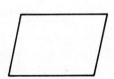   3.

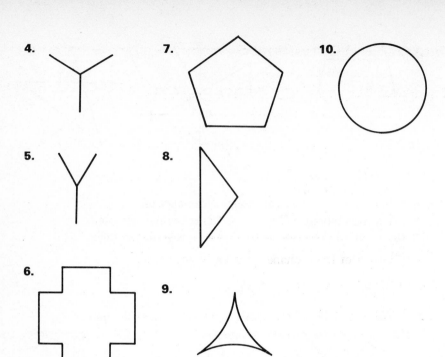

4. **7.** **10.**

5. **8.**

6. **9.**

Exercise 8

Using this shape as many times as required, draw diagrams that have the following orders of rotational symmetry:

Centre of symmetry

1. Order 2   **3.** Order 4   **5.** Order 6
2. Order 3   **4.** Order 5   **6.** Order 8

Exercise 9

A square looks the same if it is rotated through 90°, 180° or 270°.

1. Draw another shape that looks the same when it is rotated through 90°.

2. Draw a shape that looks the same when it is rotated through 60°.

3. Draw a shape that looks the same when it is rotated through 120°.

Bilateral and Rotational Symmetry

Exercise 10

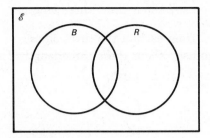

$\mathscr{E}$ = {letters of the alphabet written in capitals}

(Use the letters in the appendix on p. 427.)

B = {letters with bilateral symmetry}

R = {letters with rotational symmetry}

Draw a Venn diagram as shown (but make it larger than this one). Write each letter of the alphabet in the correct part of your diagram.

Exercise 11

1. 'Any plane shape with more than one axis of bilateral symmetry must have rotational symmetry.'
   Check the statement above. Try to find out whether it is true or false.

2. 'Any plane shape that has rotational symmetry must also have bilateral symmetry.'
   Try to find out whether the statement above is true or false.

Exercise 12

1. Cut an equilateral triangle out of paper.

2. Mark the centre of rotational symmetry on your triangle.

3. On the same triangle draw in its three axes of bilateral symmetry. (You can find them by folding the triangle.)

4. What do you notice about your answers to questions 2 and 3?

5. (a) If C is the centre of rotational symmetry, how far is C from each of the three vertices?

   (b) What can you say about these three lengths?

6. (a) How far is C from each of the three sides?

   (b) What can you say about these three lengths?

4 Fractions

1. Copy the circle. Shade $\frac{2}{3}$.

2. (a) Write seven-sixteenths in figures.
   (b) Write $\frac{5}{8}$ in words.

3. Draw a straight line 120 mm long.
   Divide the line into eighths.

4. How many sixteenths make a whole?

5. (a) Write the numerator of the fraction $\frac{9}{10}$.
   (b) Write the denominator of the fraction $\frac{3}{8}$.

6. Copy these and fill in the missing numbers:

   (a) $\dfrac{3}{5} = \dfrac{\boxed{?}}{20}$ (b) $\dfrac{10}{16} = \dfrac{\boxed{?}}{8}$ (c) $\dfrac{24}{32} = \dfrac{3}{\boxed{?}}$

7. Here is a set of equivalent fractions. Copy it and give the next three
   members of the set.
   $F = \left\{ \dfrac{3}{4}, \dfrac{6}{8}, \dfrac{9}{12}, \dfrac{12}{16}, \boxed{?}, \boxed{?}, \boxed{?} \right\}$

8. Simplify these fractions:
   (a) $\frac{16}{32}$ (b) $\frac{15}{18}$ (c) $\frac{95}{105}$ (d) $\frac{240}{360}$ (e) $\frac{65}{104}$

9. Write as improper fractions:
   (a) $1\frac{1}{3}$ (b) $2\frac{3}{5}$ (c) $5\frac{3}{4}$ (d) $3\frac{7}{8}$ (e) $2\frac{7}{12}$

10. Write as mixed numbers:
   (a) $\frac{5}{2}$ (b) $\frac{11}{4}$ (c) $\frac{17}{5}$ (d) $\frac{79}{10}$ (e) $\frac{41}{16}$

11. Find the smaller fraction:
   (a) $\frac{1}{8}$ or $\frac{1}{9}$ (b) $\frac{3}{8}$ or $\frac{3}{7}$ (c) $\frac{7}{9}$ or $\frac{5}{6}$ (d) $\frac{5}{8}$ or $\frac{7}{12}$

12. Find a fraction that lies between $\frac{3}{8}$ and $\frac{2}{5}$.

13. Write these fractions in order of size, smallest first:

$$\frac{4}{7}, \frac{6}{6}, \frac{9}{4}, 4\frac{1}{4}, \frac{8}{5}, \frac{9}{3}, \frac{3}{7}, 1\frac{4}{5}, \frac{35}{8}, \frac{3}{8}$$

Exercise 2 R

A Answer these. Where possible, simplify your answers.

1. (a) $\dfrac{3}{5} + \dfrac{1}{5}$ (c) $\dfrac{4}{12} + \dfrac{5}{12}$ (e) $\dfrac{7}{10} + \dfrac{2}{10}$ (g) $\dfrac{5}{20} + \dfrac{7}{20}$

   (b) $\dfrac{3}{8} + \dfrac{1}{8}$ (d) $\dfrac{7}{16} + \dfrac{5}{16}$ (f) $\dfrac{2}{6} + \dfrac{3}{6}$ (h) $\dfrac{5}{8} + \dfrac{3}{8}$

2. (a) $\dfrac{1}{4} + \dfrac{1}{8}$ (c) $\dfrac{1}{12} + \dfrac{2}{3}$ (e) $\dfrac{7}{20} + \dfrac{3}{10}$ (g) $\dfrac{7}{10} + \dfrac{3}{5}$

   (b) $\dfrac{2}{5} + \dfrac{3}{10}$ (d) $\dfrac{1}{2} + \dfrac{5}{16}$ (f) $\dfrac{5}{9} + \dfrac{1}{3}$ (h) $\dfrac{7}{8} + \dfrac{1}{2}$

3. (a) $\dfrac{2}{3} + \dfrac{1}{4}$ (c) $\dfrac{3}{4} + \dfrac{4}{5}$ **4.** (a) $2\dfrac{3}{8} + 3\dfrac{1}{2}$ (c) $3\dfrac{7}{10} + 2\dfrac{1}{2}$

   (b) $\dfrac{2}{3} + \dfrac{1}{2}$ (d) $\dfrac{9}{10} + \dfrac{3}{4}$ (b) $4\dfrac{1}{5} + 1\dfrac{7}{10}$ (d) $1\dfrac{3}{10} + 3\dfrac{1}{8}$

B Answer these. Where possible, simplify your answers.

1. (a) $\dfrac{7}{9} - \dfrac{2}{9}$ (c) $\dfrac{7}{8} - \dfrac{1}{8}$

   (b) $\dfrac{15}{16} - \dfrac{9}{16}$ (d) $\dfrac{8}{10} - \dfrac{3}{10}$

2. (a) $\dfrac{7}{10} - \dfrac{3}{5}$ (c) $\dfrac{5}{8} - \dfrac{7}{16}$

   (b) $\dfrac{13}{16} - \dfrac{1}{4}$ (d) $\dfrac{9}{10} - \dfrac{1}{2}$

3. (a) $\dfrac{1}{2} - \dfrac{1}{5}$ (c) $\dfrac{9}{10} - \dfrac{3}{4}$

(b) $\dfrac{7}{8} - \dfrac{2}{3}$ (d) $\dfrac{4}{5} - \dfrac{3}{8}$

4. (a) $3 - \dfrac{5}{8}$ (c) $5 - \dfrac{2}{5}$

(b) $7 - \dfrac{9}{16}$ (d) $10 - \dfrac{7}{10}$

5. (a) $5\dfrac{3}{5} - \dfrac{2}{5}$ (c) $3\dfrac{5}{8} - 1\dfrac{3}{8}$

(b) $5\dfrac{9}{10} - \dfrac{3}{10}$ (d) $7\dfrac{11}{16} - 4\dfrac{5}{16}$

6. (a) $3\dfrac{7}{8} - 1\dfrac{1}{2}$ (c) $4\dfrac{27}{32} - \dfrac{1}{4}$

(b) $6\dfrac{7}{8} - 2\dfrac{5}{16}$ (d) $5\dfrac{11}{12} - 4\dfrac{3}{4}$

7. (a) $8\dfrac{3}{4} - 1\dfrac{1}{6}$ (c) $7\dfrac{5}{8} - 5\dfrac{5}{12}$

(b) $2\dfrac{4}{5} - 1\dfrac{1}{2}$ (d) $5\dfrac{2}{3} - 2\dfrac{1}{2}$

8. (a) $2\dfrac{2}{5} - \dfrac{4}{5}$ (c) $6\dfrac{3}{8} - 2\dfrac{5}{8}$

(b) $4\dfrac{2}{9} - 2\dfrac{7}{9}$ (d) $7\dfrac{3}{10} - 4\dfrac{7}{10}$

9. (a) $4\dfrac{1}{2} - \dfrac{4}{5}$ (c) $7\dfrac{1}{6} - 5\dfrac{1}{4}$

(b) $6\dfrac{1}{3} - 1\dfrac{3}{4}$ (d) $5\dfrac{3}{8} - 4\dfrac{2}{3}$

C **1.** I need two pieces of washing line, one $3\frac{5}{8}$ m long and the other $2\frac{9}{10}$ m long. What is the total length needed?

2. John walked $5\frac{2}{5}$ km while Ann walked $2\frac{3}{4}$ km. How much further did John walk?

Exercise 3

Copy and complete these magic squares:

1.

$\frac{3}{4}$	$\frac{7}{8}$	
	$\frac{5}{8}$	
		$\frac{1}{2}$

3.

		$2\frac{9}{10}$
$4\frac{1}{10}$	$3\frac{3}{10}$	$2\frac{1}{2}$

5.

	$1\frac{1}{20}$	
	$5\frac{1}{4}$	
$4\frac{1}{5}$	$9\frac{9}{20}$	

2.

	1	
$\frac{5}{6}$	$1\frac{2}{3}$	$\frac{1}{2}$

4.

$2\frac{4}{5}$		$2\frac{1}{10}$
	$1\frac{3}{4}$	
$1\frac{2}{5}$		

6.

		$4\frac{3}{4}$
$3\frac{1}{6}$	$2\frac{3}{8}$	$6\frac{1}{3}$

History of Fractions

Hieroglyphic notation from the Rhind Papyrus (1580 BC):

46

When fractions were first used, they were not written in the way we write them. The Egyptians, as shown in the Rhind Papyrus (about 1580 BC) wrote their fractions with 1 in the numerator (called unit fractions).

The fraction $\frac{1}{7}$ was written as $\overset{\circ}{\underset{\shortmid\shortmid\shortmid\shortmid}{}}$. The only fractions that were not written in this way were $\frac{1}{2}$ and $\frac{2}{3}$.

$\frac{1}{2}$ was written as $\Rightarrow$ or $\sqsubset$ and $\frac{2}{3}$ as $\curlyvee$.

If we wrote our fractions as unit fractions, we could write $\frac{2}{7}$ as $\frac{1}{4} + \frac{1}{28}$ (since $\frac{2}{7} = \frac{8}{28} = \frac{7}{28} + \frac{1}{28} = \frac{1}{4} + \frac{1}{28}$).

The unit fractions to be used were given in a table. The table had been produced by a scribe. He followed certain rules in producing the table. For example, consider the fraction $\frac{2}{15}$.

$\frac{1}{15} + \frac{1}{15}$ was not acceptable since fractions were repeated.

$\frac{1}{9} + \frac{1}{45}$ was not acceptable since the denominators were odd numbers. (Even numbers were preferred.)

$\frac{1}{10} + \frac{1}{30}$ was acceptable (written as $\overset{\circ}{\sqcap}$ $\overset{\circ}{\sqcap\sqcap\sqcap}$).

$\frac{1}{8} + \frac{1}{120}$ was not acceptable ($\frac{1}{8}$ was better than $\frac{1}{10}$ but $\frac{1}{120}$ was too big).

$\frac{1}{12} + \frac{1}{20}$ was a possibility, but $\frac{1}{10} + \frac{1}{30}$ was preferred.

Exercise 4

Write these fractions as the sum of different unit fractions:

e.g. $\frac{5}{9} = \frac{1}{2} + \frac{1}{18}$

(This is a better answer than $\frac{1}{3} + \frac{1}{6} + \frac{1}{18}$ since fewer fractions are used.)

1. $\frac{4}{9}$ **3.** $\frac{7}{12}$ **5.** $\frac{2}{9}$ **7.** $\frac{4}{7}$

2. $\frac{5}{8}$ **4.** $\frac{2}{5}$ **6.** $\frac{7}{8}$ **8.** $\frac{5}{6}$

47

Exercise 5　Fractions and Formulae

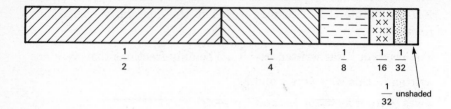

The diagram above shows that:

$$\frac{1}{2} + \frac{1}{4} + \frac{1}{8} + \frac{1}{16} + \frac{1}{32} = 1 - \frac{1}{32} = \frac{32-1}{32} = \frac{31}{32}$$

We can write:

$$\frac{1}{2} + \frac{1}{4} + \frac{1}{8} + \ldots + \frac{1}{n} = 1 - \frac{1}{n} = \frac{n-1}{n}$$

A Test the formula for:

1. $n = 4$ **2.** $n = 8$ **3.** $n = 16$ **4.** $n = 256$

B Use the formula to find:

$$\frac{1}{2} + \frac{1}{4} + \frac{1}{8} + \frac{1}{16} + \frac{1}{32} + \frac{1}{64} + \frac{1}{128} + \frac{1}{256} + \frac{1}{512} + \frac{1}{1024}$$

Multiplication of Fractions

Exercise 6

A Copy and complete:

1. (a) 2×4 apples = ☐?

    (b) 2×4 ninths = ☐?

    (c) 2×4 sevenths = ☐?

    (d) $2 \times \frac{4}{5}$ = ☐?

2. (a) 3×5 eggs = ☐?

    (b) 3×5 sixteenths = ☐?

    (c) 3×5 eighths = ☐?

    (d) $3 \times \frac{5}{4}$ = ☐?

B Work these out:

1. (a) $\dfrac{3}{7} + \dfrac{3}{7}$

    (b) $2 \times \dfrac{3}{7}$

2. (a) $\dfrac{2}{15} + \dfrac{2}{15} + \dfrac{2}{15} + \dfrac{2}{15}$

    (b) $4 \times \dfrac{2}{15}$

3. (a) $\dfrac{3}{16} + \dfrac{3}{16} + \dfrac{3}{16}$

    (b) $3 \times \dfrac{3}{16}$

4. (a) $\dfrac{3}{16} + \dfrac{3}{16} + \dfrac{3}{16} + \dfrac{3}{16} + \dfrac{3}{16}$

    (b) $5 \times \dfrac{3}{16}$

5. (a) $\dfrac{1}{2} + \dfrac{1}{2} + \dfrac{1}{2} + \dfrac{1}{2} + \dfrac{1}{2} + \dfrac{1}{2} + \dfrac{1}{2}$

    (b) $7 \times \dfrac{1}{2}$

6. (a) $\dfrac{5}{4} + \dfrac{5}{4} + \dfrac{5}{4}$

    (b) $3 \times \dfrac{5}{4}$

C Copy and complete:

1. $3 \times \dfrac{3}{10} = \dfrac{\boxed{?}}{10}$

2. $5 \times \dfrac{3}{7} = \dfrac{\boxed{?}}{7}$

3. $2 \times \dfrac{3}{5} = \dfrac{\boxed{?}}{5}$

4. $4 \times \dfrac{2}{3} = \dfrac{\boxed{?}}{3}$

5. $7 \times \dfrac{1}{4} = \dfrac{\boxed{?}}{4}$

6. $5 \times \dfrac{7}{8} = \dfrac{\boxed{?}}{8}$

7. $9 \times \dfrac{3}{4} = \dfrac{\boxed{?}}{4}$

8. $5 \times \dfrac{11}{12} = \dfrac{\boxed{?}}{12}$

9. $8 \times \dfrac{4}{9} = \dfrac{\boxed{?}}{9}$

D Work these out:

1. (a) $2 \times \dfrac{4}{9}$

    (b) $\dfrac{4}{9} \times 2$

2. (a) $3 \times \dfrac{5}{7}$

    (b) $\dfrac{5}{7} \times 3$

3. (a) $7 \times \dfrac{3}{8}$

    (b) $\dfrac{3}{8} \times 7$

4. (a) $9 \times \dfrac{3}{2}$

    (b) $\dfrac{3}{2} \times 9$

5. $\dfrac{3}{4} \times 5$

6. $\dfrac{7}{4} \times 7$

7. $\dfrac{4}{9} \times 10$

8. $\dfrac{9}{16} \times 7$

Exercise 7

A Work these out:

1.

    (a) $\frac{1}{2}$ of 6 = $\boxed{?}$

    (b) $6 \div 2$ = $\boxed{?}$

2. (a) $\frac{1}{4}$ of 12 = $\boxed{?}$ (b) $12 \div 4$ = $\boxed{?}$

3.

    (a) 6 lots of $\frac{1}{2}$ = $\boxed{?}$

    (b) $6 \times \frac{1}{2}$ = $\boxed{?}$

4. (a) $12 \div 3$ (b) $\frac{1}{3}$ of 12   (c) $\frac{1}{3} \times 12$

    (d) 12 lots of $\frac{1}{3}$ (e) $12 \times \frac{1}{3}$

5. (a) $30 \div 5$ (b) $\frac{1}{5}$ of 30   (c) $\frac{1}{5} \times 30$

    (d) 30 lots of $\frac{1}{5}$ (e) $30 \times \frac{1}{5}$

B Work these out:

1. (a) $\frac{1}{3} \times 15$ **3.** (a) $\frac{1}{3} \times 21$ **6.** $24 \times \frac{3}{8}$ **9.** $12 \times \frac{5}{6}$

    (b) $\frac{2}{3} \times 15$ (b) $\frac{2}{3} \times 21$ **7.** $\frac{1}{2} \times 10$ **10.** $10 \times \frac{7}{5}$

2. (a) $20 \times \frac{1}{4}$ **4.** $\frac{4}{5} \times 30$ **8.** (a) $8 \times \frac{1}{2}$ **11.** $\frac{7}{4} \times 12$

    (b) $20 \times \frac{3}{4}$ **5.** $28 \times \frac{3}{7}$ (b) $8 \times \frac{3}{2}$ **12.** $\frac{6}{5} \times 25$

Exercise 8

Work these out. Simplify your answers.

1. $2 \times \dfrac{1}{4}$

3. $\dfrac{1}{8} \times 6$

5. (a) $8 \times \dfrac{3}{10}$

7. $\dfrac{7}{10} \times 15$

2. (a) $2 \times \dfrac{3}{4}$

4. (a) $\dfrac{5}{8} \times 6$

(b) $3 \times \dfrac{8}{10}$

8. $6 \times \dfrac{5}{4}$

(b) $3 \times \dfrac{2}{4}$

(b) $\dfrac{6}{8} \times 5$

6. (a) $\dfrac{9}{16} \times 12$

9. $\dfrac{10}{9} \times 12$

(c) $3 \times \dfrac{1}{2}$

(c) $\dfrac{3}{4} \times 5$

(b) $\dfrac{12}{16} \times 9$

10. $9 \times \dfrac{7}{12}$

Exercise 9

1. $\frac{5}{8}$ of 32 pupils were boys.
   (a) What fraction were girls?
   (b) How many were girls?

2. £91 is shared between Tom and Margaret so that Tom receives $\frac{4}{7}$.
   How much does Tom receive?

3. The petrol tank of my car holds 15 gallons when full. If I use $\frac{5}{6}$ of
   the petrol in a full tank, how many gallons are left?

4. Mr Bell travelled $\frac{8}{9}$ of his journey of 54 km by train. How far was
   that?

5. Karen spent $\frac{7}{12}$ of £15 and saved the rest. How much did she spend?

6. The current carried by a conductor is $\frac{3}{4}$ of 6 amperes. What current
   does it carry?

7. $\frac{9}{16}$ of the 48 patients in a ward are over 40 years of age. How many
   is that?

8. About $\frac{2}{3}$ of the mass of an adult is water. How many litres of water
   are there in the body of an adult who weighs 75 kg? (1 litre of water
   has a mass of 1 kg.)

51

Exercise 10

1. Brass is an alloy made of $\frac{3}{5}$ copper and $\frac{2}{3}$ zinc. If the mass of 100 brass screws is 225 g, how heavy is the copper that is in them?

2. British 'silver' coins are made from cupro-nickel. This is an alloy containing $\frac{3}{4}$ copper and $\frac{1}{4}$ nickel. £2.90 worth of these coins have a mass of 328 g. How heavy is the copper in £2.90 worth of cupro-nickel coins?

3. My electric drill only works at $\frac{7}{10}$ efficiency. It needs a power supply of 350 W (watts) to work. What power (in watts) is obtained from the electric motor of my drill when it is used?

4. A transformer is designed to step down from 240 V (volts) to 6 V. There are 1920 turns on the primary (input) coil. The number of turns on the secondary (output) coil is $\frac{6}{240}$ of the number of primary turns. How many turns are there on the secondary coil?

5. Add $\frac{3}{8}$ of 236 to $\frac{5}{8}$ of 236.

6. Which is larger, $\frac{11}{16}$ of 40 or $\frac{8}{15}$ of 54?

7. A gear wheel with 72 teeth, drives another gear wheel with 32 teeth. If the small gear wheel turns through 36 r.p.m. (revs per minute), through how many r.p.m. does the large gear wheel turn?

8. If $\dfrac{\boxed{?}}{8}$ of $\dfrac{\boxed{?}}{35} = \dfrac{2}{5}$, find the two missing numbers so that each fraction is in its simplest form.

Exercise 11

A 1. $\frac{1}{3}$ of a garden is used for vegetables.
$\frac{1}{2}$ of the vegetable patch is used to grow potatoes.
What fraction of the garden is used for potatoes?

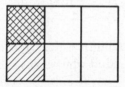

Vegetables

Potatoes

2.

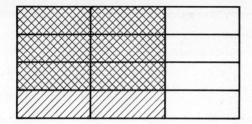

The diagram shows that $\frac{3}{4} \times \frac{2}{3} = \frac{6}{12} = \frac{1}{2}$.

Draw a diagram to show $\frac{1}{2} \times \frac{3}{5}$.

B Work these out:

1. $\frac{1}{3} \times \frac{1}{4}$ **4.** $\frac{1}{3} \times \frac{2}{5}$ **7.** $\frac{1}{8} \times \frac{3}{7}$ **10.** $\frac{7}{8} \times \frac{1}{5}$

2. $\frac{1}{5} \times \frac{1}{2}$ **5.** $\frac{3}{4} \times \frac{1}{4}$ **8.** $\frac{2}{3} \times \frac{2}{5}$ **11.** $\frac{9}{11} \times \frac{3}{4}$

3. $\frac{1}{4} \times \frac{1}{2}$ **6.** $\frac{5}{12} \times \frac{1}{4}$ **9.** $\frac{6}{7} \times \frac{4}{5}$ **12.** $\frac{7}{12} \times \frac{5}{8}$

C Work these out. Give your answers in their simplest form.

1. (a) $\frac{1}{4} \times \frac{2}{3}$ **3.** $\frac{3}{5} \times \frac{5}{11}$ **9.** $\frac{7}{12} \times \frac{8}{9}$ **15.** $\frac{15}{16} \times \frac{8}{9}$

  (b) $\frac{2}{4} \times \frac{1}{3}$ **4.** $\frac{5}{8} \times \frac{2}{5}$ **10.** $\frac{6}{7} \times \frac{1}{3}$ **16.** $\frac{9}{10} \times \frac{5}{6}$

  (c) $\frac{1}{2} \times \frac{1}{3}$ **5.** $\frac{2}{3} \times \frac{3}{8}$ **11.** $\frac{5}{7} \times \frac{3}{10}$ **17.** $\frac{7}{12} \times \frac{3}{14}$

2. (a) $\frac{1}{2} \times \frac{7}{8}$ **6.** $\frac{4}{9} \times \frac{3}{7}$ **12.** $\frac{9}{25} \times \frac{5}{12}$ **18.** $\frac{4}{9} \times \frac{9}{10}$

  (b) $\frac{5}{10} \times \frac{7}{8}$ **7.** $\frac{6}{11} \times \frac{2}{3}$ **13.** $\frac{8}{25} \times \frac{25}{48}$ **19.** $\frac{15}{16} \times \frac{12}{25}$

  (c) $\frac{7}{10} \times \frac{5}{8}$ **8.** $\frac{7}{20} \times \frac{4}{5}$ **14.** $\frac{6}{7} \times \frac{7}{12}$ **20.** $\frac{3}{4} \times \frac{8}{9}$

Exercise 12

Work these out. Simplify your answers.

1. (a) $\dfrac{1}{2} \times \dfrac{14}{3}$

(b) $\dfrac{1}{2} \times 4\dfrac{2}{3}$

2. (a) $\dfrac{3}{4} \times \dfrac{6}{5}$

(b) $\dfrac{3}{4} \times 1\dfrac{1}{5}$

3. $\dfrac{2}{3} \times 5\dfrac{1}{4}$

4. $4\dfrac{1}{6} \times \dfrac{4}{5}$

5. $\dfrac{3}{7} \times 5\dfrac{5}{6}$

6. $3\dfrac{3}{10} \times \dfrac{5}{6}$

7. $2\dfrac{4}{7} \times \dfrac{7}{12}$

8. $\dfrac{5}{7} \times 4\dfrac{1}{5}$

9. (a) $\dfrac{8}{3} \times \dfrac{5}{4}$

(b) $2\dfrac{2}{3} \times 1\dfrac{1}{4}$

10. $3\dfrac{1}{5} \times 3\dfrac{1}{3}$

11. $2\dfrac{2}{5} \times 4\dfrac{1}{6}$

12. $7\dfrac{1}{8} \times 3\dfrac{1}{9}$

13. (a) $3 \times \dfrac{19}{6}$

(b) $3 \times 3\dfrac{1}{6}$

14. $4\dfrac{2}{3} \times 3$

15. $2\dfrac{7}{10} \times 12$

16. $2\dfrac{3}{16} \times 2\dfrac{2}{15}$

Exercise 13

Work these out:

1. $\dfrac{1}{2} \times \dfrac{2}{1}$

2. $\dfrac{6}{1} \times \dfrac{1}{6}$

3. $\dfrac{3}{4} \times \dfrac{4}{3}$

4. $\dfrac{5}{8} \times \dfrac{8}{5}$

5. $\dfrac{6}{5} \times \dfrac{5}{6}$

6. $\dfrac{3}{2} \times \dfrac{2}{3}$

7. $\dfrac{5}{12} \times \dfrac{12}{5} \times \dfrac{3}{8}$

8. $\dfrac{7}{8} \times \dfrac{8}{7} \times \dfrac{4}{5}$

9. $\dfrac{2}{5} \times \dfrac{4}{9} \times \dfrac{5}{2}$

10. $\dfrac{9}{10} \times \dfrac{5}{3} \times \dfrac{3}{5}$

11. $\dfrac{5}{12} \times \dfrac{7}{10} \times \dfrac{12}{5}$

12. $3\dfrac{1}{5} \times \dfrac{5}{16}$

Exercise 14

Find the missing fractions:

1. $\dfrac{1}{4} \times \boxed{?} = 1$

2. $\dfrac{7}{1} \times \boxed{?} = 1$

3. $\dfrac{9}{4} \times \boxed{?} = 1$

54

4. $\boxed{?} \times \dfrac{12}{7} = 1$

7. (a) $\boxed{?} \times \dfrac{9}{4} = 1$

(b) $\boxed{?} \times 2\dfrac{1}{4} = 1$

10. $\dfrac{3}{8} \times \boxed{?} = 1$

5. $\boxed{?} \times \dfrac{8}{15} = 1$

8. $3\dfrac{5}{8} \times \boxed{?} = 1$

11. $\boxed{?} \times 2\dfrac{2}{3} = 1$

6. (a) $\dfrac{15}{2} \times \boxed{?} = 1$

9. $1\dfrac{7}{9} \times \boxed{?} = 1$

12. $\boxed{?} \times 3\dfrac{3}{4} = 1$

(b) $7\dfrac{1}{2} \times \boxed{?} = 1$

Division of Fractions

Exercise 15

Each of the sections A to C shows one approach to dividing fractions. Only ONE of the sections A to C needs to be answered.

A 1. (a) How many 4s are there in 24?

(b) $24 \div 4 = \boxed{?}$

(c) $\dfrac{24}{1} \div \dfrac{4}{1} = \boxed{?}$

(d) $\dfrac{24}{1} \times \dfrac{1}{4} = \boxed{?}$

2. (a) How many halves are there in four?

(b) $4 \div \dfrac{1}{2} = \boxed{?}$

(c) $\dfrac{4}{1} \div \dfrac{1}{2} = \boxed{?}$

(d) $\dfrac{4}{1} \times \dfrac{2}{1} = \boxed{?}$

3. (*a*) How many $\frac{3}{4}$ are there in 6?

(*b*) $\dfrac{6}{1} \div \dfrac{3}{4} = \boxed{?}$

(*c*) $\dfrac{6}{1} \times \dfrac{4}{3} = \boxed{?}$

4. (*a*) How many $\frac{2}{3}$ are there in $2\frac{2}{3}$?
(*i.e.* How many $\frac{2}{3}$ are there in $\frac{8}{3}$?)

(*b*) $\dfrac{8}{3} \div \dfrac{2}{3} = \boxed{?}$

(*c*) $\dfrac{8}{3} \times \dfrac{3}{2} = \boxed{?}$

5. (*a*) How many $\frac{3}{4}$ are there in $4\frac{1}{2}$?

(*b*) $\dfrac{9}{2} \times \dfrac{4}{3} = \boxed{?}$

B Copy and complete:

1. $24 \div 4 = \dfrac{24}{4} = \boxed{?}$

2. $4 \div \frac{1}{2} = \dfrac{4}{\frac{1}{2}} = \dfrac{4 \times \boxed{?}}{\frac{1}{2} \times 2} = \dfrac{8}{1} = \boxed{?}$

3. $6 \div \frac{3}{4} = \dfrac{6}{\frac{3}{4}} = \dfrac{6 \times \boxed{?}}{\frac{3}{4} \times 4} = \dfrac{\boxed{?}}{3} = \boxed{?}$

4. $2\frac{2}{3} \div \frac{2}{3} = \dfrac{2\frac{2}{3}}{\frac{2}{3}} = \dfrac{\frac{8}{3}}{\frac{2}{3}} = \dfrac{\frac{8}{3} \times \boxed{?}}{\frac{2}{3} \times 3} = \dfrac{\boxed{?}}{2} = \boxed{?}$

5. $4\frac{1}{2} \div \frac{3}{4} = \dfrac{4\frac{1}{2}}{\boxed{?}} = \dfrac{\boxed{?}}{\frac{3}{4}} = \dfrac{\frac{9}{2} \times \boxed{?}}{\frac{3}{4} \times 4} = \dfrac{\boxed{?}}{3} = \boxed{?}$

6. $\frac{2}{5} \div \frac{3}{4} = \dfrac{\frac{2}{5}}{\frac{3}{4}} = \dfrac{\frac{2}{5} \times \boxed{?}}{\frac{3}{4} \times 20} = \dfrac{8}{\boxed{?}}$

C Copy and complete:

1. (a) $24 \div 4 = \dfrac{24}{4} = \boxed{?}$

(b) $24 \div 4 = \dfrac{24}{\frac{4}{1}} = \dfrac{24 \times \frac{1}{4}}{\frac{4}{1} \times \frac{1}{4}} = \dfrac{24 \times \frac{1}{4}}{1} = 24 \times \frac{1}{4} = \boxed{?}$

2. $4 \div \frac{1}{2} = \dfrac{4}{\frac{1}{2}} = \dfrac{4 \times \boxed{?}}{\frac{1}{2} \times 2} = \dfrac{8}{1} = \boxed{?}$

3. $6 \div \frac{3}{4} = \dfrac{6}{\frac{3}{4}} = \dfrac{6 \times \boxed{?}}{\frac{3}{4} \times \frac{4}{3}} = \dfrac{6 \times \frac{4}{3}}{1} = 6 \times \frac{4}{3} = \boxed{?}$

4. $2\frac{2}{3} \div \frac{2}{3} = \dfrac{2\frac{2}{3}}{\frac{2}{3}} = \dfrac{\frac{8}{3}}{\frac{2}{3}} = \dfrac{\frac{8}{3} \times \boxed{?}}{\frac{2}{3} \times \frac{3}{2}} = \dfrac{\frac{8}{3} \times \frac{3}{2}}{1} = \frac{8}{3} \times \frac{3}{2} = \boxed{?}$

5. $4\frac{1}{2} \div \frac{3}{4} = \dfrac{4\frac{1}{2}}{\frac{3}{4}} = \dfrac{\frac{9}{2}}{\frac{3}{4}} = \dfrac{\frac{9}{2} \times \boxed{?}}{\frac{3}{4} \times \frac{4}{3}} = \dfrac{\frac{9}{2} \times \frac{4}{3}}{1} = \frac{9}{2} \times \frac{4}{3} = \boxed{?}$

6. $\frac{2}{5} \div \frac{3}{4} = \dfrac{\frac{2}{5}}{\frac{3}{4}} = \dfrac{\frac{2}{5} \times \boxed{?}}{\frac{3}{4} \times \frac{4}{3}} = \dfrac{\frac{2}{5} \times \frac{4}{3}}{1} = \frac{2}{5} \times \frac{4}{3} = \boxed{?}$

Compare these two stages.

(*i.e.* for each question, compare the question with the stage before the answer.)

Exercise 16

Work these out:

1. $5 \div \dfrac{1}{3}$ **4.** $\dfrac{2}{7} \div 4$ **7.** $\dfrac{3}{4} \div \dfrac{7}{8}$ **10.** $5\dfrac{5}{8} \div 2$

2. $5 \div \dfrac{2}{3}$ **5.** $\dfrac{5}{6} \div \dfrac{1}{6}$ **8.** $\dfrac{9}{10} \div \dfrac{3}{5}$ **11.** $3\dfrac{3}{4} \div \dfrac{3}{4}$

3. $\dfrac{8}{9} \div 4$ **6.** $\dfrac{5}{6} \div \dfrac{2}{3}$ **9.** $7\dfrac{1}{2} \div 3$ **12.** $2\dfrac{1}{12} \div \dfrac{5}{6}$

13. $4\dfrac{1}{2} \div 1\dfrac{1}{2}$ **15.** $9 \div 5\dfrac{5}{8}$ **17.** $\dfrac{3}{5} \div 2\dfrac{1}{10}$ **19.** $7\dfrac{1}{8} \div 12\dfrac{2}{3}$

14. $5\dfrac{3}{7} \div 1\dfrac{3}{7}$ **16.** $2\dfrac{1}{10} \div \dfrac{3}{5}$ **18.** $1\dfrac{7}{8} \div 2\dfrac{1}{4}$ **20.** $12\dfrac{2}{3} \div 7\dfrac{1}{8}$

Fractions and Formulae

Exercise 17

A Here is a formula that will help you to subtract two fractions:

$$\frac{k}{l} - \frac{m}{n} = \frac{(kn - lm)}{ln}$$

1. Test the formula for these questions:

(a) $\dfrac{2}{3} - \dfrac{2}{5}$ (b) $\dfrac{7}{9} - \dfrac{3}{4}$ (c) $\dfrac{5}{6} - \dfrac{2}{5}$ (d) $\dfrac{11}{12} - \dfrac{3}{8}$

2. Test the formula using fractions of your own choice.

B Try to find a formula that will help you to add two fractions.

C The formula $\dfrac{k}{l} \div \dfrac{m}{n} = \dfrac{kn}{lm}$ helps you to divide fractions.

1. Test the formula for these questions:

(a) $\dfrac{3}{10} \div \dfrac{2}{5}$ (b) $\dfrac{5}{8} \div \dfrac{3}{4}$ (c) $\dfrac{3}{4} \div \dfrac{5}{8}$ (d) $\dfrac{1}{2} \div \dfrac{7}{8}$

2. Test the formula using your own fractions.

D Try to find a formula that will help you to multiply two fractions.

E Try to use a calculator to add, subtract, multiply and divide fractions. Use the formulae. Choose your own fractions.

Miscellaneous Problems

Exercise 18

1. Consider the fractions $5\frac{1}{4}, 2\frac{5}{8}, 2\frac{1}{4}, 2\frac{2}{9}, 1\frac{7}{9}, 3\frac{3}{8}$.
   (a) Multiply the second fraction by the fourth.
   (b) Divide the sixth fraction by the third.

2. A circle has a diameter of $3\frac{7}{8}$ inches. Find its radius.

3. $2\frac{1}{4}$ l of milk are shared equally between 6 people. What fraction of a litre does each person get?

4. A joiner works for $7\frac{3}{4}$ h each day. Find the total number of hours he works in 5 days.

5. How many pieces of elastic $\frac{3}{4}$ m long can be cut from a $5\frac{1}{4}$ m length?

6. Find 8 times $\frac{3}{8}$ of 104.

7. Add $\frac{1}{3}$ of 114 to $\frac{2}{3}$ of 114.

8. $\frac{2}{5}$ of a class of 30 pupils were girls. How many were boys?

9. How many $\frac{3}{4}$ pints of milk can I get out of 9 pints?

10. Find the area of a rectangle measuring $3\frac{3}{5}$ m by $1\frac{1}{3}$ m.

11. Calculate the area of a square with side $2\frac{1}{2}$ cm.

12. Anna spent $\frac{5}{12}$ of £18 and saved the rest. How much did she save?

13. Caragh cycles $\frac{7}{12}$ of 156 km while Colin cycles $\frac{3}{5}$ of 145 km. Who cycles further, and by how many kilometres?

14. $\frac{8}{15}$ of my journey of 285 miles is by motorway. How far do I travel on other roads?

Exercise 19

1. $\frac{2}{5}$ of an 80-page exercise book have been used. How many pages have not yet been used?

59

2. In an election, Mr Hill polled $\frac{1}{6}$ of the total number of votes. Mrs Scott polled $\frac{1}{4}$, Mr Ward polled $\frac{1}{3}$ and Mrs Burns polled the remaining votes. If the total number of votes was 1644,
   (a) who won the election?
   (b) how many votes did each candidate poll?
   (c) what fraction of the total number of votes was for Mrs Burns?

3. 1 l of a liquid has a mass of $1\frac{3}{5}$ kg. Find the mass of $4\frac{1}{6}$ l.

4. On a car journey, 42 l of petrol were used. The tank was full at the start of the journey. If $\frac{3}{10}$ of the petrol was left, how many litres does the tank hold when full?

5. $\frac{1}{2}$ of John's mass is the same as $\frac{1}{3}$ of Mr Smith's. If Mr Smith weighs 72 kg, how heavy is John?

6. Paula spent $\frac{3}{8}$ of her money, then half the remainder. What fraction of the original amount was left?

7. My car's petrol tank holds 56 l and the petrol consumption is 15 km per litre. At the start of a journey the tank is $\frac{5}{7}$ full.
   (a) After travelling 480 km, how many litres will I have left?
   (b) How far will I have travelled when I run out of petrol?

5 Angles, Parallels and Constructions

Write whether each angle is an acute angle, an obtuse angle, a reflex angle or a right-angle:

1.

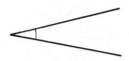

4.

2.

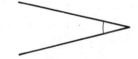

5.

3.

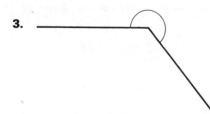

6.

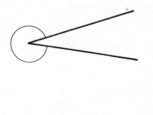

Write how many degrees there are in:

1. $\frac{1}{4}$ turn
2. $\frac{3}{4}$ turn
3. $\frac{3}{5}$ turn
4. $\frac{1}{8}$ turn

5. $\frac{5}{8}$ turn
6. $\frac{7}{12}$ turn
7. 2 turns
8. 6 turns

9. 8 turns
10. 10 turns
11. $\frac{23}{360}$ turn
12. $\frac{23}{36}$ turn

Exercise 3

Estimate the number of degrees in each of these angles:

1.

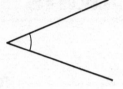

4.

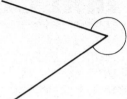

2.

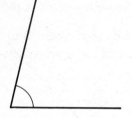

5.

3.

Exercise 4

A Draw a pair of axes as shown where x ranges from 0 to 14 and y from 0 to 18.

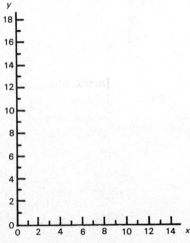

For each question, plot the points and join them in the given order. Measure each angle formed (the type of angle is stated in brackets). Use the same pair of axes for all the questions.

1. (5, 5) (1, 1) (6, 1)   [acute angle]
2. (8, 1) (14, 1) (12, 6)   [acute angle]
3. (0, 4) (4, 8) (9, 8)   [obtuse angle]
4. (1, 14) (4, 11) (9, 11)   [obtuse angle]
5. (6, 16) (8, 12) (12, 14)   [not a reflex angle]
6. (8, 10) (13, 7) (10, 12)   [acute angle]
7. (4, 17) (10, 17) (13, 14)   [reflex angle]

B Draw another pair of axes. This time, x should range from $^-8$ to $^+8$ and y from $^-10$ to $^+10$. Plot and join the points in the given order and measure each angle as in part A.

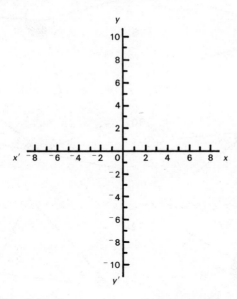

1. (8, 10) (2, 9) (8, 6)   [acute angle]
2. ($^-8$, 10) ($^-6$, 6) ($^-1$, 5)   [obtuse angle]
3. ($^-6$, 4) ($^-2$, 2) (2, 6)   [obtuse angle]
4. (5, 4) (6, $^-2$) (8, 4)   [acute angle]
5. ($^-2$, $^-2$) ($^-8$, $^-2$) ($^-2$, $^-4$) [acute angle]
6. ($^-2$, 1) (4, 4) (2, 0)   [reflex angle]
7. (6, $^-6$) (2, $^-2$) ($^-4$, 0)   [reflex angle]
8. ($^-8$, $^-6$) ($^-2$, $^-6$) ($^-8$, $^-10$) [acute angle]
9. (0, $^-9$) (7, $^-8$) (2, $^-6$)   [reflex angle]

Calculate the angles that are labelled with Greek letters.

1.

2.

3.
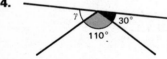

4.
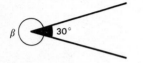

5.
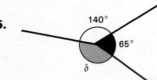

6.
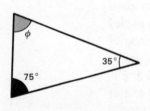

7.
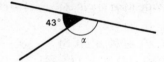

8.
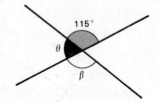

9.
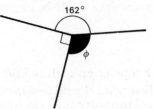

10.
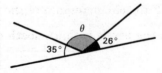

11.
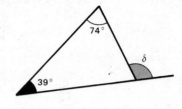

12.
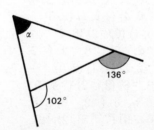

Exercise 6   Angles and Spirals

Draw a circle of radius 48 mm. (The drawing here is not full-size.)

Divide your circle into twelve equal parts (use a protractor to help you).

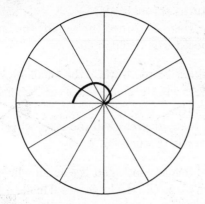

Mark a point on each radius:
the first point should be 2 mm from the centre of the circle, the second
4 mm, the third 6 mm, the fourth 8 mm, and so on. Continue until you
reach the circumference of the circle.

Join the points with a smooth curve.

Exercise 7   Gear Wheels

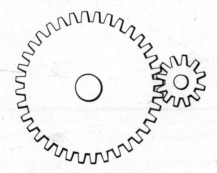

Examine the gear wheels in the drawing above.

1. If the small gear wheel turns anticlockwise, in which direction does
the large wheel turn?

2. If the large wheel has 36 teeth and the small wheel 12 teeth, work out:
   (a) the number of times the small wheel turns when the large wheel makes one full turn,
   (b) the number of degrees the small wheel turns through when the large wheel turns through 60°,
   (c) the number of degrees turned through by the large wheel when the small wheel turns through 60°.

3. If the large wheel has 36 teeth while the small wheel has 18 teeth:
   (a) how many times will the small wheel turn when the large wheel makes 4 full turns?
   (b) through how many degrees will the large wheel turn when the small wheel turns through 45°?

4. If the large wheel has 36 teeth and the small wheel 24 teeth:
   (a) how many full turns will the large wheel make if the small wheel turns 9 times?
   (b) through how many degrees will the small wheel turn when the large wheel turns through 60°?
   (c) through how many degrees will the small wheel turn when the large wheel turns through 50°?

Angles and Parallels

Adjacent angles are angles that lie next to each other.
In the diagram, a and c are adjacent angles.

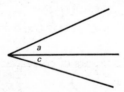

If the sum of two angles is 90°, the two angles are called *complementary angles*. Each of the angles is the *complement* of the other.

If the sum of two angles is 180°, the two angles are called *supplementary angles*. Each of the angles is the *supplement* of the other.

e.g. The angles 75° and 105° are supplementary angles.
     65° is the complement of 25°.

A Write the complement of each of these angles:

1. 40°	**4.** 35°	**7.** 81°	**10.** 22°
2. 20°	**5.** 75°	**8.** 19°	**11.** 45°
3. 90°	**6.** 64°	**9.** 57°	**12.** 36°

B Write the supplement of each of these angles:

1. 120°	**4.** 125°	**7.** 163°	**10.** 90°
2. 50°	**5.** 146°	**8.** 109°	**11.** 0°
3. 65°	**6.** 37°	**9.** 45°	**12.** 152°

A line that cuts a set of other lines is called a *transversal*.

In the diagram, PQ is a transversal.

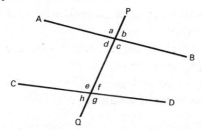

Angles *a*, *b*, *g* and *h* are called *exterior angles* while *c*, *d*, *e* and *f* are called *interior angles*.

Corresponding angles are in corresponding positions with regard to the transversal and the lines it cuts. They are both on the same side of the transversal and if one lies 'above' one of the lines cut by the transversal, the other angle lies 'above' the other line. (Both could lie 'below' instead of 'above'.)
In the diagram, there are four sets of corresponding angles: *a* and *e*, *d* and *h*, *b* and *f*, and *c* and *g*.
Corresponding angles are sometimes called F-angles.

Alternate angles lie in alternate positions. One lies to the left of the transversal while the other lies to the right. One lies 'above' one of the lines cut by the transversal while the other angle lies 'below' the other line.
In the diagram, *a* and *g*, *b* and *h*, *c* and *e*, and *d* and *f* are pairs of alternate angles. (*a* and *g* are called exterior alternate angles. Which others are exterior alternate angles?)

Alternate angles are sometimes called Z-angles.

Interior angles that lie on the same side of the transversal are called *co-interior (or allied) angles.*
In the diagram on p. 67, *c* and *f*, and *d* and *e* are co-interior angles.
Co-interior angles are sometimes called C-angles or U-angles.

Exercise 9

The following sentences all refer to this diagram:

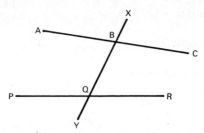

Copy and complete:

1. ∠ ABQ and ∠ ? are corresponding angles.

2. Angle BQR and angle ? are alternate angles.

3. One pair of co-interior angles is angle CBQ and angle ? .

4. ∠ PQY and ∠ ? are vertically opposite angles.

5. Angle XBC and angle BQR are ? angles.

6. Angle XBA and angle ? are alternate angles.

Exercise 10

Write whether each of the given pairs of angles are alternate, corresponding, co-interior or vertically opposite:

1.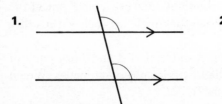

2.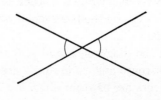

68

3.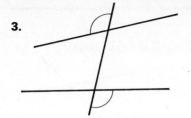

5.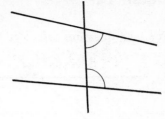

4.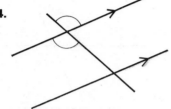

6.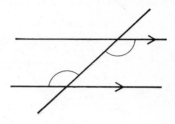

Exercise 11

1. Draw a pair of parallel lines.

2. Draw a transversal across the parallel lines.

3. (a) Measure any pair of corresponding angles.
   (b) What do you notice about the two angles?

4. (a) Measure other pairs of corresponding angles.
   (b) What do you notice about corresponding angles when lines are parallel?

5. (a) Measure any pair of alternate angles.
   (b) Measure other pairs of alternate angles.
   (c) What do you notice about alternate angles when lines are parallel?

6. (a) Measure any pair of co-interior angles.
   (b) Add them.
   (c) What do you notice?

7. (a) Measure, then add the other pair of co-interior angles.
   (b) What do you notice about co-interior angles when lines are parallel?

Exercise 12

For each question *calculate* the angles labelled with letters:

1.
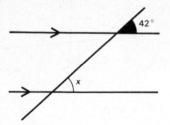
42°
x

6.
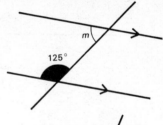
m
125°

2.
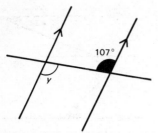
107°
y

7.
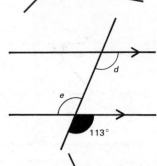
d
e
113°

3.
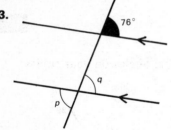
76°
q
p

8.
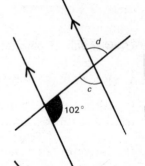
d
c
102°

4.
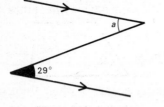
a
29°

9.
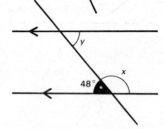
y
x
48°

5.
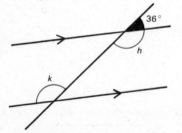
36°
h
k

10.
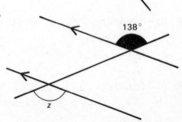
138°
z

11.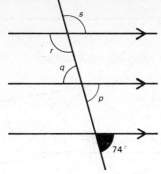

13.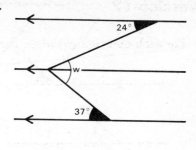

12.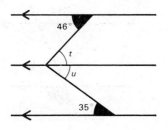

14.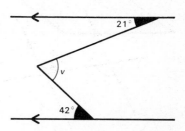

Exercise 13

Copy each diagram. Fill in all the missing angles on your copies.

1.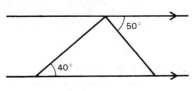

3.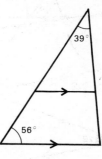

2.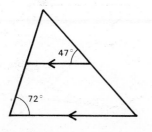

4.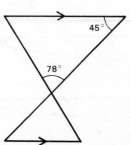

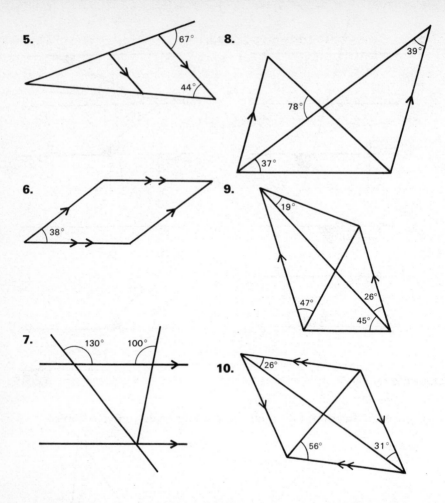

5. 67° 44°

6. 38°

7. 130° 100°

8. 39° 78° 37°

9. 19° 47° 26° 45°

10. 26° 56° 31°

Exercise 14

For each question, state whether or not AB is parallel to CD. Give reasons for your answers.

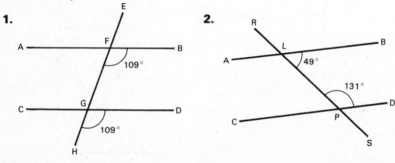

1.

E

A ———— F ———— B

109°

C ———— G ———— D

109°

H

2.

R

A ———— L ———— B

49°

131°

C ———— P ———— D

S

3.

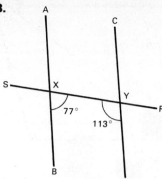

6.

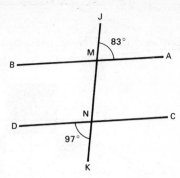

4.

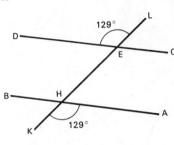

7.

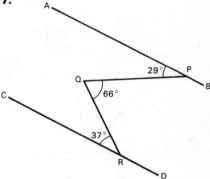

5.

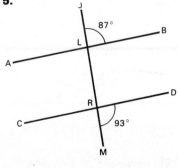

8.

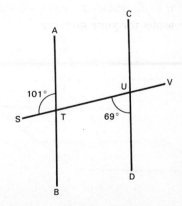

73

Copy and complete this crossnumber puzzle:

Across

1.

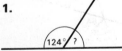

3.

5.

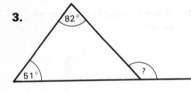

8.

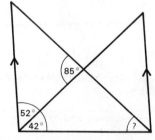

10.

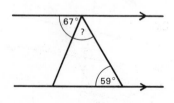

11. The complement of 28°.

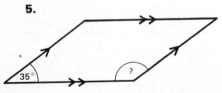

Across (contd)

13.

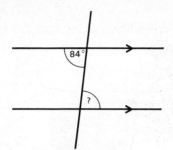

15.

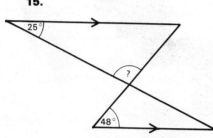

16.

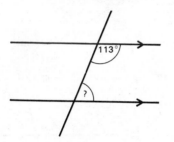

17. 26° and this angle are complementary angles.

19. 51° less than a full turn.

20. Eight right-angles.

22.

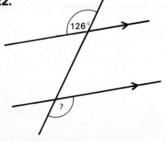

23. The angle turned through by the hour hand of a clock in 2 hours.

24. 80 right-angles.

26. $1\frac{2}{3}$ full turns plus 13°.

29.

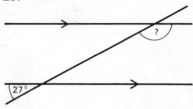

31. 79° more than the supplement of 51°.

33.

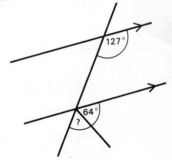

34. How many degrees are there in $1\frac{3}{4}$ full turns?

35.

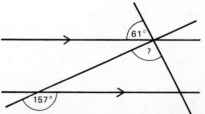

Down

2.

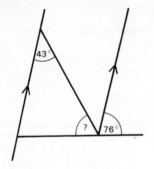

3.

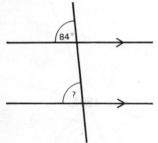

4.

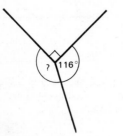

6. One of the angles in a right-angled isosceles triangle.

7.

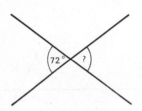

9. Angles at a point add up to ☐? degrees.

12. $\frac{3}{4}$ turn.

13.

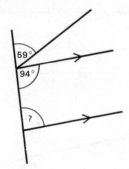

14. The supplement of $133°$.

15.

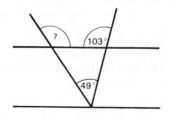

17. Each angle of an equilateral triangle.

18.

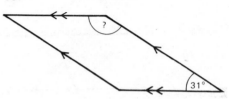

19.

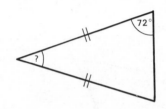

20. The sum of the interior angles of a hexagon.

76

Down (*contd*)

21.

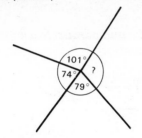

22.

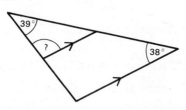

24. This angle added to 15° gives a right-angle.

25. The number of degrees the hour hand of a clock turns through in $\frac{1}{2}$ hour.

27. The number of degrees in $\frac{1}{3}$ of a full turn.

28. $\frac{1}{12}$ of a full turn in degrees.

29. You may be unlucky not to answer this.

30. (a rhombus)

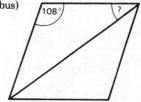

32. You could get this RIGHT if you were not 1 degree under while ANGLING.

Exercise 16

Copy and complete this proof:

Given △ABC.
To prove the sum of the angles of a triangle is 180°.
Construction Draw straight line DE through A and parallel to BC.

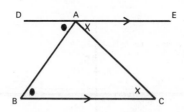

Proof ∠DAB = ∠ABC (alternate angles, DA // $\boxed{?}$)

∠EAC = ∠$\boxed{?}$ (alternate angles, AE // $\boxed{?}$)

but ∠DAB + ∠BAC + ∠EAC = $\boxed{?}$ (angles on a straight line)
hence ∠ABC + ∠BAC + ∠ACB = 180°
Therefore the sum of the angles of a triangle = 180°.

Exercise 17

To construct a line through a given point P and parallel to a given line AB (using a pair of compasses)

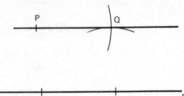

1. Draw the given line AB and mark the given point P.

2. Mark any two points, X and Y, on line AB.

3. With centre P and with radius XY, draw an arc as shown.

4. With centre Y and radius XP draw a second arc to cross the first arc. Label this new point, Q.

5. Join PQ.
   PQ is parallel to AB.

Exercise 18

To erect a perpendicular to a line from a point on the line (using a pair of compasses)

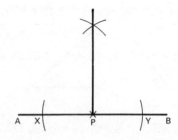

1. Let AB be the line, and P the point on it. With centre P and any convenient radius, draw arcs to cut the line AB at X and at Y (one at each side of P).

2. Now construct the perpendicular bisector of XY:

    (*a*) With centre X and radius bigger than $\frac{1}{2}$XY, draw an arc above AB.

    (*b*) With centre Y and using the *same* radius, draw an arc above AB to cross the previous one.

3. Join P to the point formed by the intersecting arcs. This line is the required perpendicular.

Exercise 19

A *To construct an angle of 60°*

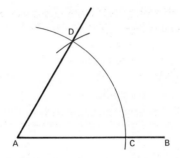

1. Draw a line AB.

2. With centre A and any radius, draw a long arc (as shown) to cut AB at C.

3. With C as centre, and using the *same* radius, draw a second arc to cut the first one at D.

4. Join AD.
    ∠ CAD = 60°

B Try to construct angles of:

1. 120°   **2.** 30°   **3.** 150°   **4.** 240°

C *To construct an angle of 90° (a right-angle) at one end of a straight line*

1. Draw a line AB.

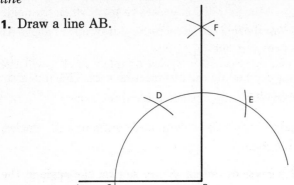

2. To construct a right-angle at B:
  (*a*) With B as centre, and any radius, draw a long arc (almost making a semi-circle) to cut AB at C.
  (*b*) *Using the same radius throughout*, with centre C, draw an arc to cross your long arc at D.
  (*c*) With D as centre, keeping the same radius, draw two arcs, one to cross your long arc at E and the other to be directly above B and also above your long arc.
  (*d*) With centre E, keeping the same radius, draw an arc to cut your previous arc at F.
  (*e*) Join FB.
      ∠ FBA = 90°.

D Try to construct angles of:

1. 45°   **2.** 135°   **3.** 225°   **4.** $22\frac{1}{2}°$

Exercise 20

You MUST NOT use a protractor to help with the constructions in this exercise. A protractor may only be used to measure angles after the construction has been completed.

1. Draw a straight line PQ, 50 mm in length. With a pair of compasses, construct a right-angle at Q. Complete your diagram to form a square PQRS. Bisect angle *P*. Where does this bisector meet the square again? What do you notice about the bisectors of the angles of a square?

2. A pair of compasses has two legs of equal length. Both are 70 mm long.
   (a) What radius will the pair of compasses be set at when the angle between the legs is 30°?
   (Find your answer by construction.)
   (b) When the angle between the legs is doubled to 60°, will the radius be doubled?
   (Check your answer using constructional methods.)

3. Construct a rhombus with sides 35 mm and containing 60° angles. Measure both diagonals.

4. Draw a sector of a circle of radius 48 mm so that the angle at the centre is 45°.
   Measure the length of chord XY, where X and Y are the end points of the radii forming the sector.

5. Construct a kite where the long diagonal measures 75 mm and where the angle between the two long sides is 60° and the angle between the two short sides is 90°. Measure the sides.

6. Draw a line JK, 70 mm long. At K, erect a perpendicular 40 mm in length. Use this construction to construct a rectangle of length 70 mm and breadth 40 mm. How long are the diagonals?

7. Construct an equilateral triangle with sides of 56 mm. Bisect all three angles. Let the bisectors meet at P. How far is P from each of the vertices?

8. Draw a line UV, 50 mm in length. By construction find a point W where $\angle$ VUW = 60° and $\angle$ UVW = 45°. Now construct line WX parallel to UV such that WX = 75 mm. Join VX. How long is VX?

6 Decimals

A Copy each pair of numbers and fill in the correct sign ($<$, $>$ or $=$):

1. 0.46 ? 0.5   **4.** 0.70 ? 0.7

2. 3.08 ? 3.1   **5.** $6\frac{3}{10}$? 6.3

3. 5.8 ? 5.75   **6.** 2.09 ? $2\frac{9}{10}$

B **1.** (a) Write $\frac{3}{10}$ as a decimal.

(b) Write $\frac{30}{100}$ as a decimal.

(c) $\frac{30}{100} = \frac{?}{10}$

2. (a) Write $2\frac{9}{10}$ as a decimal.

(b) Write $2\frac{90}{100}$ as a decimal.

(c) $2\frac{90}{100} = 2\frac{?}{10}$

3. Write as common fractions in their simplest form:

(a) 0.7   (b) 0.70   (c) 0.700

C **1.** Add one-tenth to 5.9.

2. $7\frac{9}{10} + \frac{1}{10} = $?

3. Add one-tenth to 6.9.

4. Add one-hundredth to 3.84.

5. Add one-hundredth to 3.9.

6. Add one-hundredth to 3.99.

D Write as decimals:

1. $\frac{26}{100}$ **3.** $\frac{32}{10}$ **5.** $\frac{51}{100}$ **7.** $\frac{11}{100}$

2. $7\frac{5}{10}$ **4.** $\frac{51}{10}$ **6.** $\frac{19}{10}$ **8.** $\frac{11}{10}$

E Write as decimals:

1. $\frac{1}{10}$ 3. $6\frac{3}{5}$ 5. $\frac{3}{8}$ 7. $\frac{9}{20}$ 9. $\frac{18}{25}$

2. $\frac{1}{5}$ 4. $\frac{1}{4}$ 6. $2\frac{7}{8}$ 8. $1\frac{19}{20}$ 10. $\frac{13}{16}$

F Write as common fractions in their simplest form:

1. 0.9   3. 0.4   5. 0.35   7. 0.125   9. 0.005

2. 0.5   4. 0.75   6. 0.85   8. 0.625   10. 0.68

Exercise 2 R

Carry out these calculations:

1.   1.63
      + 8.09

2.   78.60
      − 19.27

3. $80.07 + 26.5$
4. $7.682 + 15.73$
5. $31.02 − 24.65$
6. $407.2 − 19.75$
7. 8.13×4
8. 16.09×9

9. $4.734 \div 6$
10. $1.6 − 0.95$
11. 0.57×7
12. $42.72 \div 8$
13. $0.7105 \div 5$
14. $6.4 + 17 + 0.81$

Exercise 3 R

Answer these:

1. 2.76×10
2. 10×31.43
3. 100×2.876
4. 19.72×100
5. 9.803×1000

6. $72.5 \div 10$
7. $638.41 \div 100$
8. $846.73 \div 10$
9. $1984.5 \div 1000$
10. $7684 \div 100$

11. 100×20.64
12. $93.85 \div 10$
13. $106.71 \div 100$
14. 40.602×100
15. 9.672×1000

Exercise 4 R

Carry out these calculations:

1. (a) 4.638×3
   (b) 46.38×3
   (c) 46.38×30

2. (a) 81.54×7
   (b) 81.54×70

3. (a) 6.084×2
   (b) 6.084×200

4. 74.612×40 **8.** $680.48 \div 40$ **15.** 1.961×8000

5. (*a*) $826.8 \div 2$ **9.** 1.096×600 **16.** $8264 \div 8000$
    (*b*) $826.8 \div 20$ **10.** 89.7×90
    (*c*) $826.8 \div 200$

6. (*a*) $74.85 \div 5$ **11.** $408.36 \div 600$
    (*b*) $74.85 \div 50$ **12.** 23.841×500

7. (*a*) $1692.9 \div 3$ **13.** $807.3 \div 90$
    (*b*) $1692.9 \div 300$ **14.** $913.5 \div 700$

Estimating

To estimate an answer to a question, each number used in the question needs to be made as simple as possible. The calculation can then be worked out in your head.

For example, the number 7.132 would become 7. The number 7 has only one *significant figure*. 7.132 has four significant figures. We say that '7.132 = 7 correct to 1 sig. fig.' (Sig. fig. stands for significant figure. Sometimes the abbreviation s.f. is used.)

827.6 = 800 correct to 1 sig. fig. In this case, the zeros are not significant figures. 827.6 is approximately equal to 800. (827.6 is not approximately equal to 8 so the zeros must be written in the approximation.)

Exercise 5

A *e.g. 1*   108.6 = 100 correct to 1 sig. fig.

     e.g. 2   85.13 =   90 correct to 1 sig. fig.

     e.g. 3   0.048 = 0.05 correct to 1 sig. fig.

Write these numbers correct to 1 sig. fig.:

1. 79.6	**6.** 65.72	**11.** 0.716	**16.** 8640.5
2. 31.4	**7.** 12.96	**12.** 0.038	**17.** 0.006 84
3. 2.96	**8.** 2.085	**13.** 0.072	**18.** 1.452
4. 7.203	**9.** 6347.1	**14.** 0.0086	**19.** 0.099
5. 192.8	**10.** 3.707	**15.** 0.001 93	**20.** 0.973

B *e.g. 1* 648.2 = 648 correct to 3 s.f.

e.g. 2 648.2 = 650 correct to 2 s.f.

e.g. 3 0.0469 = 0.047 correct to 2 s.f.

Write these numbers correct to the number of significant figures given in the brackets:

1. 692 (2) **5.** 826.4 (3) **9.** 2937 (3) **13.** 0.564 (2)

2. 318 (2) **6.** 151.7 (3) **10.** 149.7 (2) **14.** 0.706 (2)

3. 27.7 (2) **7.** 286.3 (2) **11.** 5.692 (2) **15.** 0.4316 (3)

4. 416.6 (3) **8.** 193.6 (2) **12.** 0.1482 (3) **16.** 0.038 25 (2)

Exercise 6 ═══════════════════════════════ R

Estimate the answers to these. Work with one significant figure.

e.g. $3.8 \times 6.1 \approx 4 \times 6 = \underline{\underline{24}}$

1. 8.7 × 2.3 **5.** 8.16 ÷ 1.8 **9.** 38.4 × 4.9

2. 6.9 × 4.2 **6.** 8.78 ÷ 2.7 **10.** 9.1 × 78.6

3. 9.8 × 3.4 **7.** 5.92 ÷ 2.3 **11.** 49.1 ÷ 5.2

4. 6.79 × 5.8 **8.** 612.3 ÷ 3.9 **12.** 390 ÷ 7.9

Exercise 7 ═══════════════════════════════ R

Carry out these calculations. Check by estimating.

Estimate first. Then calculate

1. 2.9 × 1.6 **6.** 6.45 ÷ 1.5 **11.** 2.4 × 26.6

2. 30.6 × 5.2 **7.** 7.03 ÷ 3.7 **12.** 50.96 ÷ 9.1

3. 6.41 × 2.8 **8.** 5.29 ÷ 2.3 **13.** 61.5 × 3.4

4. 4.2 × 3.91 **9.** 17.28 ÷ 5.4 **14.** 4.67 × 8.7

5. 7.03 × 6.3 **10.** 338.4 ÷ 7.2 **15.** 7.072 ÷ 6.8

Exercise 8 ═══════════════════════════════ R

Answer these:

1. 0.82 × 10 **6.** 75.4 ÷ 100 **11.** 0.174 ÷ 30

2. 7.6 ÷ 10 **7.** 0.253 ÷ 10 **12.** 0.0469 ÷ 700

3. 8.59 ÷ 10 **8.** 0.006 × 100 **13.** 2.635 ÷ 500

4. 0.071 × 10 **9.** 0.27 × 20 **14.** 0.0207 × 900

5. 0.534 × 10 **10.** 0.093 × 400 **15.** 0.005 × 8000

Exercise 9

Estimate the answers to these. Work with one significant figure.

1. 0.27×0.4
2. 0.59×0.16
3. 0.72×0.051
4. 0.069×0.93

5. $6.34 \div 0.32$
6. $0.87 \div 0.34$
7. $0.793 \div 0.021$
8. $5.36 \div 0.49$

9. 0.056×0.72
10. 6.35×0.025
11. $1.872 \div 0.39$
12. $0.289 \div 0.057$

Exercise 10 $\boxed{\text{R}}$

Answer these:

A
1. 0.7×5
2. 0.04×0.2
3. 1.6×0.3
4. 0.24×0.6

5. 0.6×0.09
6. 0.19×0.5
7. 2.73×0.8
8. 14.8×0.7

9. 0.41×8.09
10. 3.9×0.045
11. 0.13×0.68
12. 0.023×5.89

B
1. $4.8 \div 0.2$
2. $0.415 \div 0.5$
3. $0.765 \div 0.9$
4. $0.152 \div 0.04$

5. $0.028 \div 0.07$
6. $0.462 \div 0.06$
7. $0.351 \div 0.003$
8. $7.04 \div 0.008$

9. $0.1846 \div 0.26$
10. $7.02 \div 0.18$
11. $0.1015 \div 0.035$
12. $0.3403 \div 8.3$

Exercise 11

1. A car averages 37.6 miles on 1 gallon of petrol. How far will it go on 7 gallons?

2. Mrs Charlton got $1.16 for each £1 she changed. How many dollars did she get for £8?

3. A roll of carpet 27.6 m long is cut into six equal lengths. How long is each length?

4. 9.35 l of creosote are poured into five containers. If all five containers contain the same amount, how many litres are in each?

5. 3 l of lemonade are shared equally among four people. Write as a decimal of a litre what each person receives.

6. Calculate the perimeter of a square with length of side 0.63 m.

7. The circumference of a circle is about 3 times its diameter. Calculate the circumference of a circle with a diameter of 1.84 m.

8. A circle has a circumference of 0.87 m. Find its diameter if its circumference is taken as 3 times its diameter.

9. 38 people are going to a party. How much orange drink is needed, if each person is allowed two drinks and the plastic cups used each hold 0.14 ℓ?

10. A car travelled 56 km in 32 minutes. If it travelled at a steady rate, how far did it travel in 1 minute?

11. Calculate the area of a wall measuring 3.4 m by 2.43 m.

12. (a) How many glasses, each holding 0.57 ℓ, can be filled from a 7 ℓ container?
    (b) What decimal of a litre is left over?

Exercise 12

1. If 70 sheets of paper weigh 0.35 kg, find the mass of one sheet.

2. The pitch of a certain screw thread is 2.3 mm. How far will the screw go into a piece of wood if it moves through a distance of 9 threads?

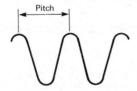

Pitch

3. A piece of sheet metal is 0.34 cm thick. Find the total thickness of a pile of 14 sheets.

4. A piece of copper tube expands by 0.008 35 mm for each °C rise in temperature. If the temperature of the tubing is increased from 20 °C to 100 °C, find its expansion.

5. A certain sort of wire has a resistance of 1.23 ohms per centimetre. Calculate the resistance of a 70 cm length of this wire.

Exercise 13

A 1. (a) 6 lots of 3 = $\boxed{?}$ (b) 6 × 3 = $\boxed{?}$

2. (a) How many threes are there in six?
   (b) 6 ÷ 3 = $\boxed{?}$

3. (a) 6 lots of $\frac{1}{2}$ = $\boxed{?}$ (b) 6 × $\frac{1}{2}$ = $\boxed{?}$

4. (a) How many halves are there in six?
   (b) 6 ÷ $\frac{1}{2}$ = $\boxed{?}$

5. (a) Which is larger, 6 × $\frac{1}{2}$ or 6 ÷ $\frac{1}{2}$?
   (b) Which is larger, 6 × 0.5 or 6 ÷ 0.5?

B Which gives the bigger answer:

1. (a) 18 × 3   or   18 ÷ 3?
   (b) 18 × 0.3   or   18 ÷ 0.3?

2. (a) 2.4 × 6   or   2.4 ÷ 6?
   (b) 2.4 × 0.6   or   2.4 ÷ 0.6?

3. (a) 5   × $\frac{5}{10}$ or   5   ÷ $\frac{5}{10}$?
   (b) 5   × 0.5   or   5   ÷ 0.5?

C 1. Does 3.7 × 5.4 = 15.28?

2. Does 5.8 × 0.19 = 1.103?

3. Does 0.79 × 0.85 = 6.715?

4. If 2.83 × 1.6 = 4.528, find the value of 28.3 × 0.016.

5. If 6.324 ÷ 3.1 = 2.04, find the value of 632.4 ÷ 0.31.

6. If ● 2.9 × 8.4 ● = 278.663, what are the two smudged digits?

Exercise 14   Addition and Subtraction of Money

1. Ron spent £8.40 at one shop and £6.80 at another. How much did he spend altogether?

2. A shopkeeper bought an article for £49. If she sold it at a profit of £14, find the selling price.

3. How much change is there from £10 if I spend £6.48?

4. My telephone bill came to £57.84 while my gas bill was £98.59. What did the two bills total?

5. I spent £8.63, £12.09, £15.71 and £3.97 while shopping. How much did I spend altogether?

6. The selling price of a TV set was £349.95. I paid £297.30 cash for it. How much did I save?

7. A cassette recorder costs £49.25. Ann has saved £34.80 towards it. How much more money does she need?

8. A car costs £7043. After paying a deposit of £1408.60, how much more has Mrs Dickson to pay?

9. Mr Wilson spent £8.27, £12.53 and £8.95 on petrol. How much was that altogether?

10. Mr Patel had £623.37 in his bank account. If he withdrew £176.58, how much was left in his account?

11 I had £291.18 in my bank account. I withdrew £58.69 but later deposited £37.42. How much was left in my account?

12. Mrs Grant went shopping and had £62.07 in her purse. She spent £18.70 at one shop and £33.16 at another. She called at her bank and made a withdrawal of £35. She then spent a further £26.85. How much did Mrs Grant have left in her purse?

Exercise 15   Multiplication and Division of Money

1. Two books cost £3.95 each. Find the total cost.

2. Find the cost of 5 m of material at £5.34 per metre.

3. John earns £2.70 per hour. What are his daily earnings if he works 8 hours each day?

4. The train fare for three adults on a certain journey was £23.40. What was the adult fare?

5. Mr Singh made six payments of £8.43 towards a washing machine. How much was that altogether?

6. Four tins of paint cost £29.28 altogether. Find the cost of each tin if they each cost the same.

7. My newspapers cost £7.35 for five weeks. What was the weekly cost?

8. A holiday costs £346.20 per person. How much would four people have to pay?

9. Jane saved £4.65 per week for seven weeks. How much was that?

10. Mrs Lee earned £4098 in six months. How much was that per month?

11. Coffee costs £2.79 per jar. Find the cost of three jars.

12. The adult fare for a certain journey was £3.75, while the children's fare was £1.88. Find the total fare paid by three adults and four children.

Exercise 16   Miscellaneous Questions

1. Mr Carr bought a bicycle for £79.34 then sold it for £93.21. How much profit did he make?

2. If turkey costs 74 p a pound, what would be the cost of a 13 lb turkey?

3. A bill for two items came to £6.73. If one of the items costs £4.87, what was the cost of the other?

4. A record player cost £64 to buy on hire purchase. If I must pay this in 25 weeks, what should the weekly payments be?

5. If Paula earns £73.82 per week, how much does she earn in a year?

6. Mrs Read bought two books. One cost £3.95 and the other £4.69. Find the total cost.

7. Seven people went out for a meal. The bill came to £35.70 plus a service charge of £3.57. What was the cost per person if they all ordered the same?

8. A calculator cost £9.20 plus £1.38 VAT. If it was sold for £8.95 in a sale, by how much was it reduced?

9. 5 m of brown material and 3 m of green material cost £57.46. If the green costs £6.92 per metre, find the cost per metre of the brown.

10. A video recorder can be bought on hire purchase for a deposit of £177.48 and twelve payments of £34.51. How much is saved by paying cash, if the cash price is £545.95?

Exercise 17 ▬▬▬▬▬▬▬▬▬▬▬▬▬▬▬▬ M

Copy and complete these invoices:

1.

			£	p
3	writing pads	@ 69 p		
4	packets of envelopes	@ 69 p		
1	pen	@ £8.95		
1	bottle of ink	@ 78 p		
3	packs of cartridges	@ 42 p		
		Total cost	£	

2.

			£	p
2	paintbrushes	@ £1.90		
4	tins of paint	@ £5.99		
8	rolls of wallpaper	@ £4.72		
2	packets of paste	@ £0.78		
		Total cost	£	

Exercise 18

Carry out these calculations using a calculator.
Round your answers to the given number of decimal places.

1. $8.28 \div 7$ (3 d.p.)
2. $98.3 \div 5.3$ (2 d.p.)
3. 6.2×3.4 (1 d.p.)
4. 5.63×2.8 (2 d.p.)
5. $98.6 \div 0.65$ (1 d.p.)
6. $2.3 \div 0.48$ (2 d.p.)

7. 5.27×1.25 (2 d.p.)
8. $87.3 \div 1.97$ (2 d.p.)
9. 7.46×0.27 (3 d.p.)
10. $28.46 \div 4.3$ (1 d.p.)
11. $84.6 \div 8$ (2 d.p.)
12. 2.31×5.87 (3 d.p.)

Recurring Decimals

The decimal 2.623 762 376 237 623 7 and so on is called a *recurring decimal*. The pattern of digits is repeated for ever. Some people call them *repeating decimals* and others *circulating decimals*.

The decimal above would usually be written as $2.\dot{6}23\dot{7}$ (in some countries it would be written as $2.\overline{6237}$). The dots above the 6 and 7 mean that all the digits from 6 to 7 inclusive should be repeated.
$0.\dot{3}5\dot{2}$ stands for 0.352 352 352 and so on,
$0.35\dot{2}$ stands for 0.352 222 2 and so on (since the dot is only above the 2, only the digit 2 is repeated),
$0.3\dot{5}\dot{2}$ stands for 0.352 525 252 and so on.

Exercise 19

1. Using a calculator, try to find some recurring decimals. (Key in a common fraction and see if it gives a recurring decimal.) Note the denominators that give recurring decimals.

e.g. $\frac{2}{3}$ is 0.6666 and so on $(\frac{2}{3} = 0.\dot{6})$

Note that $0.666\,666\,66 = 0.666\,666\,7$ correct to 7 decimal places.
Your calculator probably gives $\frac{2}{3}$ as 0.666 666 7. Key in
$\boxed{2}\,\boxed{\div}\,\boxed{3}\,\boxed{=}$ to check this.

2. By dividing, without using a calculator, try to find some more common fractions that give recurring decimals.

3. Make out a table of denominators up to and including 30. The table should show which denominators give recurring decimals when the numerator is 1.

Non-recurring	Recurring
2	3
4	and so on
and so on	

Exercise 20

A Change the following fractions into recurring (circulating) decimals. Set out your work carefully. Keep the decimal points in a straight line. Each digit should be written directly under another.

1. (a) $\frac{1}{7} = 0.14$? ? ? ?

  (b) $\frac{3}{7} = 0.$

  (c) $\frac{2}{7} = 0.$

  (d) $\frac{6}{7} =$

  (e) $\frac{4}{7} =$

  (f) $\frac{5}{7} =$

2. Look carefully at the pattern in the digits of these decimals. What do you notice?

3. Try to work out how to write down the fractions in the correct order to create a pattern.

4. (a) Copy this circle.

  (b) Compare the decimal for $\frac{1}{7}$ with the numbers on the circle.

  (c) Compare the decimals for $\frac{3}{7}, \frac{2}{7}, \frac{6}{7}, \frac{4}{7}$ and $\frac{5}{7}$ with the numbers on the circle.

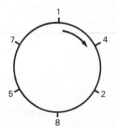

  (d) Try to work out why I listed the fractions in that order. 'Circulating' decimals is a good name for these decimals, isn't it?

5. (*a*) On your circle, join the numbers that are diametrically opposite.

(*b*) Add them.

(*c*) Write what you notice.

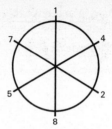

6. $\frac{1}{7} = 0 . 1\ 4\ 2\ \underline{8\ 5\ 7}$

$\phantom{\frac{1}{7} = 0 . 1\ 4\ 2\ }\underline{8\ 5\ 7}$

(*a*) Copy the decimal for $\frac{1}{7}$.

(*b*) Write the second half of the decimal under the first.

(*c*) Add the two digits in each column.

(*d*) Write what you notice.

B Answer the questions in part A for the thirteenths. (List the fractions in an order that will give a pattern. Note that you may need to make two lists for the thirteenths. Only one list was needed for the sevenths.)

Exercise 21

Use a calculator to help you to write $\frac{5}{17}$ as a recurring decimal. Explain your method.

Revision Exercises I to VI

Revision Exercise I

1. List the set of even numbers that lie between 45 and 65.

2. $M = \{3, 7, 9, 10, 12, 20, 25, 100\}$
   N is a set with members that are three times as big as the members of set M. List set N.

3. $Q = \{$quadrilaterals that contain exactly two right-angles$\}$
   Draw one member of set Q.

4. $P = \{$multiples of 5$\}$
   Copy the following. Replace the boxes by $\in$ or $\notin$ to make the statements true.
   (a) 15 $\boxed{?}$ P (b) 284 $\boxed{?}$ P (c) 590 $\boxed{?}$ P

5. Is the set of even numbers that are multiples of 3 empty?

6. Is the statement $\{$odd numbers that are multiples of 6$\} = \varnothing$ true or false?

7. If $A = \{2, 4, 6, 8, 10\}$ and $B = \{5, 6, 7, 8\}$ find $A \cup B$.

8. $C = \{$triangles having two equal sides$\}$
   $D = \{$triangles containing a right-angle$\}$
   Draw a member of the set $C \cap D$.

9. $P = \{$p, r, i, m, e$\}$
   $N = \{$n, u, m, b, e, r$\}$
   Draw a Venn diagram to show these two sets. Find:
   (a) $P \cap N$ (b) $P \cup N$

10. The universal set $\mathscr{E} = \{$odd numbers between 20 and 40$\}$
    $K = \{$multiples of 3$\}$
    Draw a Venn diagram to show these sets. List K'.

11. Draw a Venn diagram to help with this problem.

100 people were asked whether they would prefer a cat or a dog as a pet. 36 liked a cat, 59 liked a dog and 13 liked both. How many liked neither?

Revision Exercise II

1. Work out $7 + 8 + 9 + 10 + 11 + 12 + 13$.

2. Copy and complete:

(a) $79 + 47 = \boxed{?} + 50$

(c) $94 - 28 = 100 - \boxed{?}$

(b) $83 - 36 = \boxed{?} - 40$

(d) $189 + 265 = \boxed{?} + 260$

3. A box holds 48 books. How many similar boxes are needed to hold 5136 books?

4. Find the value of:

(a) 827×100

(e) $66\,300 \div 100$

(b) 396×4000

(f) $201\,000 \div 300$

(c) 2031×300

(g) $930\,000 \div 5000$

(d) 5100×3206

(h) $100\,700 \div 190$

5. For each statement, write whether it is true or false:

(a) $39 \times 26 = 1012$

(d) $11\,610\,000 \div 430 = 270$

(b) $68 \times 23 = 4564$

(e) $1488 \div 24 = 744 \div 12$

(c) $48 \times 32 = 24 \times 64$

(f) $5 \times 869 \times 20 = 86\,900$

6. If $3952 \div 52 = 76$, find the value of:

(a) $39\,520\,000 \div 7600$

(b) $5200 \times 76\,000$

Revision Exercise III

1. Draw a regular hexagon and show its axes of bilateral symmetry.

2. (a) What is the order of rotational symmetry of the given shape?

(b) Copy it and mark its centre of rotational symmetry.

3. Name the type of triangle that has the given number of axes of bilateral symmetry. If no such triangle exists, say so.
   (a) 0   (b) 1   (c) 2   (d) 3

4. A plane shape has exactly two axes of bilateral symmetry. Must the two axes be perpendicular? Investigate this.

Revision Exercise IV

1. Which is the smaller fraction:
   (a) $\frac{1}{10}$ or $\frac{1}{12}$?   (b) $\frac{5}{8}$ or $\frac{5}{9}$?   (c) $\frac{3}{5}$ or $\frac{5}{8}$?

2. Draw a straight line 90 mm in length. Divide the line into sixths.

3. Draw a rectangle 4 cm by 3 cm. Divide the rectangle into six equal parts. Shade $\frac{1}{3}$.

4. The given rectangle measures 4 cm by 3 cm and $\frac{2}{3}$ has been shaded. Copy it.

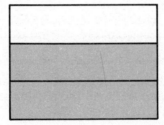

   Using a different shading, shade $\frac{1}{4}$ of the shaded part of your copy. What fraction of the whole rectangle has been shaded in two different ways?

5. $\frac{1}{4} \times \frac{2}{3}$ = $\boxed{?}$

6. (a) $2\frac{3}{8} \times 4$ = $\boxed{?}$ (b) $2\frac{3}{16} \div \frac{5}{8}$ = $\boxed{?}$

7. Which gives the bigger answer, $2\frac{5}{8} \times \frac{3}{4}$ or $2\frac{5}{8} \div \frac{3}{4}$?

8. $\frac{3}{8}$ of 56 pupils were boys. How many girls were there?

9. An electric motor works at $\frac{4}{5}$ efficiency. What power, in watts, does it give if it works on a power supply of 320 watts?

10. How many $\frac{5}{8}$ ℓ bottles can be filled from $7\frac{1}{2}$ ℓ?

Revision Exercise V

1. Calculate the missing angles:

   (a)   (b)

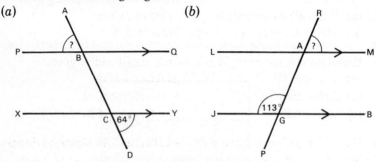

2. (a) What is the complement of 38°?

   (b) What is the supplement of 65°?

3. Calculate the missing angles:

   (a)   (b)

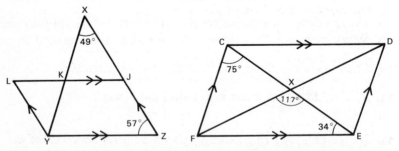

4. Copy each diagram. Write all the missing angles on your copies:

   (a)   (b)

5. Carry out this construction using a ruler, a pencil and a pair of compasses only:

   Draw a straight line, MN, 65 mm in length. Construct a right-angle at N. Construct angle NMP equal to 30° where MP = 50 mm. Construct a line PQ parallel to MN.

   X lies on PQ and angle XNM = 90°. How long is PX?

Revision Exercise VI

1. Is $0.29 > 0.4$?

2. Add one-tenth to 3.9.

3. Write as decimals:
(a) $\frac{53}{100}$ (b) $\frac{1}{2}$ (c) $\frac{3}{4}$ (d) $\frac{1}{8}$ (e) $\frac{5}{8}$

4. Answer these:

(a) $61.9 + 7 + 0.82$ (f) 4000×2.912
(b) $300.6 - 142.8$ (g) $865.9 \div 100$
(c) $43.2 - 13.86$ (h) $43.56 \div 9$
(d) 21.65×7 (i) $562.8 \div 400$
(e) 1.384×100 (j) $2.92 \div 200$

5. (a) Write 63.84 correct to 1 significant figure.
(b) Write 7.5 correct to 1 significant figure.

6. Estimate the answers. Work with 1 significant figure.
(a) 4.62×8.39 (d) $0.084 \div 0.196$
(b) $56.5 \div 2.81$ (e) 6.305×0.0074
(c) 0.67×0.21 (f) $0.917 \div 0.0325$

7. If the circumference of a circle is taken as 3.14 times its diameter, find the circumference of a circle with a diameter of 4.6 cm.

8. An 80 cm length of wire has a resistance of 107.2 ohms. Calculate the resistance of 1 cm of the wire.

9. Which is bigger, 16×0.4 or $16 \div 0.4$?

10. Paint costs £4.86 per tin. Find the cost of three tins.

11. Find $12.523 \div 2.6$ correct to 2 decimal places.

12. If $\dfrac{1}{a}$ gives a recurring decimal, give nine possible values of a.

7 Ratio

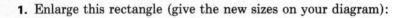

Exercise 1

1. Enlarge this rectangle (give the new sizes on your diagram):

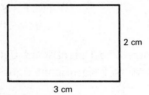

2 cm

3 cm

2. Enlarge this square (give the new sizes on your diagram):

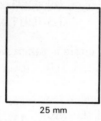

25 mm

3. Reduce the size of this rectangle (give the new sizes on your diagram):

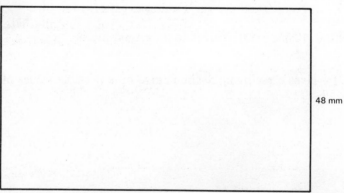

48 mm

84 mm

Exercise 2

Enlarge rectangle ABCD:

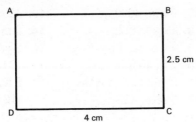

1. Make the new length CD 8 cm long.

2. Make the new length CD 6 cm long.

3. Make the new length CD 4.8 cm long.

Exercise 3

For each question, write how many times as big the first quantity or drawing is compared with the second:

1. £12, £4

2. 10 km, 2 km

3. 36 s, 4 s

4. 48 m, 6 m

5. 8 inches, 2 inches

6. 18, 3

7. 70, 10

8. 42 cm, 7 cm

9. 72 p, 12 p

10. 75, 15

11. 25 kg, 10 kg

12. 8 h, 16 h

13.

14.

15.

Exercise 4

How many times as big is the first quantity compared with the second?

1. £4, £2
2. £4, 50 p
3. 6 cm, 3 cm
4. 6 cm, 3 mm
5. 3 cm, 6 mm
6. 8 km, 2 m

7. 8 km, 4000 m
8. 1 day, 12 h
9. 4 weeks, 4 days
10. 2 h, 40 min
11. 2 years, 8 months
12. 6 min, 45 s

13. 12 cm, 5 mm
14. 3 m, 60 cm
15. 2 yd, 2 ft
   (3 ft = 1 yd)
16. 2 ft, 6 in
   (12 in = 1 ft)

Exercise 5

Write these ratios in their simplest form:

e.g. $8 : 4 = \frac{8}{4} : \frac{4}{4}$
$\qquad = 2 : 1$

1. 10 : 5
2. 6 : 2
3. 6 : 4
4. 4 : 6
5. 4 : 8
6. 10 : 6
7. 12 : 9
8. 9 : 12
9. 12 : 8
10. 40 : 10

11. 40 : 5
12. 40 : 30
13. 28 : 4
14. 28 : 8
15. 12 : 28
16. 24 : 36
17. 24 : 16
18. 15 : 10
19. 5 : 5
20. 12 : 21

21. 60 : 48
22. 46 : 46
23. 35 : 28
24. 32 : 56
25. 63 : 42
26. 96 : 72
27. 39 : 52
28. 5 : 2.5
29. $\frac{1}{4} : \frac{3}{4}$
30. 1.8 : 0.6

Exercise 6

Write the following as ratios in their simplest form:

1. 16 kg to 4 kg
2. 20 p to 5 p
3. £5 to £15
4. 10 cm to 12 cm
5. 15 m to 9 m
6. 9 ft to 6 ft
7. 25 km to 15 km
8. 18 to 24
9. 63 p to 18 p
10. 360 g to 240 g

11. £84 to £21
12. £60 to £15
13. 20° to 15°
14. 18 gal to 32 gal
15. 21 lb to 14 lb
16. 32 p to 60 p
17. £72 to £15
18. 5 kg to 8 kg
19. 4.2 kg to 3.6 kg
20. 56 mm to 72 mm

21. £2.56 to £5.12
22. 45 p to £2.25
23. £1.44 to 60 p
24. £1.26 to £1.08
25. 2.46 *l* to 2.34 *l*
26. 7.8 cm to 8.2 cm
27. 9.1 km to 7.8 km
28. 65 mm to 3.5 cm
29. 800 m to 2 km
30. 76 p to £3.56

Exercise 7

Write the following as ratios in their simplest form:

1. 12 to 18
2. $1\frac{1}{2}$ to $\frac{3}{4}$
3. $4\frac{1}{2}$ to 3
4. 1.8 to 1.2
5. 5 to $2\frac{1}{2}$
6. $\frac{1}{4}$ to $1\frac{1}{2}$
7. 3.5 to 7
8. 3.5 to 10.5
9. 10.5 to 7
10. 4.8 to 8.4

11. 3.9 to 6.5
12. 3.12 to 1.68
13. $3\frac{1}{8}$ to 5
14. $10\frac{1}{2}$ to $3\frac{3}{4}$
15. 0.12 to 0.4
16. $7\frac{1}{3}$ to $5\frac{1}{2}$
17. $\frac{2}{3}$ to $\frac{6}{5}$
18. $\frac{3}{10}$ to $\frac{1}{2}$
19. 28 mm to 21 mm
20. 3.6 cm to 5.4 cm

21. $4\frac{1}{2}$ km to $6\frac{3}{4}$ km
22. 5.1 cm to 6.8 cm
23. 4.8 cm to 36 mm
24. 7.2 m to 60 cm
25. 5.6 g to 420 mg
26. 57 m to 7600 cm
27. $8\frac{2}{5}$ km to $5\frac{5}{6}$ km
28. $6\frac{1}{2}$ cm to $9\frac{3}{4}$ cm
29. $4\frac{3}{4}$ ℓ to 7 ℓ
30. $1\frac{1}{2}$ m to $1\frac{1}{5}$ m

Exercise 8

A Find the missing values that make the ratios the same:

1. $8 : 6 = 4 : \boxed{?}$
2. $12 : 8 = \boxed{?} : 2$
3. $9 : 15 = \boxed{?} : 5$
4. $10 : \boxed{?} = 5 : 3$
5. $\boxed{?} : 15 = 2 : 3$

6. $3 : 1\frac{1}{2} = 2 : \boxed{?}$
7. $\boxed{?} : 10\frac{1}{2} = 1 : 3$
8. $1.6 : 1.2 = \boxed{?} : 3$
9. $0.9 : \boxed{?} = 3 : 5$
10. $7\frac{1}{2} : 12\frac{1}{2} = \boxed{?} : 5$

B Find the missing quantities that make the ratios correct:

1. 40 p to $\boxed{?}$ = 2 : 3
2. 2 kg to $\boxed{?}$ = 1 : 3
3. $\boxed{?}$ to 10 cm = 3 : 5
4. $\boxed{?}$ to 14 days = 3 : 2
5. 2.4 m to $\boxed{?}$ = 4 : 5

6. $\boxed{?}$ to 3.5 cm = 5 : 7
7. 2 kg to $\boxed{?}$ = 4 : 3
8. $\boxed{?}$ to 36 lb = 5 : 4
9. $\boxed{?}$ to 18 h = 8 : 9
10. 32 pints to $\boxed{?}$ = 4 : 7

Exercise 9

1. In a class there are 16 girls and 12 boys.
   Write in their simplest form:
   (*a*) the ratio of the number of boys to the number of girls,

103

(b) the ratio of the number of girls to the number of boys,

(c) the ratio of the number of boys to the total number of pupils in the class.

2. Two squares have sides of lengths 6 cm and 9 cm.
Find in their simplest form:
(a) the ratio of the lengths of their sides,
(b) the ratio of their areas.

3. A shopkeeper bought six pens for £24 then sold them for £42. What is the ratio of the selling price to the cost price? (Give your answer in its simplest form.)

4.

By measuring the line above, find these ratios (give your answers in their simplest form):
(a) AB : BC   (b) BC : AB   (c) AC : AB   (d) BA : AC

5.

Given that DE = 8 m and DE : EF = 2 : 5, find EF.

6.

If GH : HI = 5 : 3, find the ratio GH : GI.

7. A shopkeeper bought some goods for £108. The goods were sold to make a profit of £36. Find in their simplest form:
(a) the ratio of the profit to the cost price (CP),
(b) the ratio of the profit to the selling price (SP),
(c) the ratio of the SP to the CP.

8. In the following table, the ratio of each top number to the number below it is exactly the same. Copy and complete the table.

4	8		6		36	1	
6		18		42			$4\frac{1}{2}$

Exercise 10

1. Here is a recipe to make 'Chicken à la Queen':

Ingredients

50 g (2 oz) butter
100 g (4 oz) mushrooms, sliced
$\frac{1}{2}$ green pepper, chopped
40 g (1$\frac{1}{2}$ oz) flour
400 ml ($\frac{3}{4}$ pt) milk
225– 350 g (8–12 oz) diced cooked chicken
salt and pepper
paprika or ground nutmeg
15–30 ml (1–2 tbsps) sherry, optional

Melt the butter and fry the mushrooms and pepper until soft. Stir in the flour, cook for 2–3 minutes, remove from the heat and stir in the milk gradually. Bring the sauce to the boil and continue to stir until it thickens. Add the chicken and seasoning, and add the sherry, if you wish. Serve with rice or buttered noodles or as a snack with toast or crisp rolls.

The recipe above is for four people.
(*a*) List the ingredients showing the quantities for two people. (Give both the metric and the imperial measures.)
(*b*) List the quantities for six people.

2. Here are the ingredients for 'Lemon creamed rice with cinnamon'. The quantities on the left are for six people. For how many people are the quantities on the right?

short grain pudding rice	75 g (3 oz)	100 g (4 oz)
milk	900 ml (1$\frac{1}{2}$ pt)	1.2 l (2 pt)
sugar	75 g (3 tbsps)	100 g (4 tbsps)
thinly pared rind of lemon	1	1$\frac{1}{3}$
egg yolks	3	4
cinnamon	a sprinkling	

3. Here are the ingredients for 'Dutch beef stew' to serve five people. Re-write the ingredients for three people.

1 kg chuck steak trimmed of excess fat and cut into 5 cm cubes
30 m*l* malt vinegar
120 m*l* corn oil
50 g lard
5 small onions
25 g flour
300 m*l* brown ale
150 m*l* beef stock
salt and freshly ground black pepper
pinch of sugar
1 bay leaf

Exercise 11

A *e.g.* $66 : 48 = \dfrac{66}{48} : \dfrac{48}{48} = \underline{\underline{1.375 : 1}}$

The ratio 66 : 48 has been written in the form $m : 1$.

Write these ratios in the form $m : 1$

1. 10 : 8	**4.** 35 : 14	**7.** 0.56 : 0.7	**10.** 6230 : 28
2. 6 : 20	**5.** 0.3 : 4	**8.** 0.69 : 1.2	**11.** 11.76 : 0.21
3. 19 : 4	**6.** 0.29 : 8	**9.** 0.0624 : 4.8	**12.** 2223.2 : 3.5

B Write these as ratios in the form $m : 1$

1. £15 to £8	**4.** £2 to 50 p
2. 47.36 m to 20 m	**5.** 4 cm to 8 mm
3. 85.2 *l* to 15 *l*	**6.** 1.2 km to 800 m

C Write these as ratios in the form $1 : n$

1. 8 : 192	**5.** £6 to £42
2. 7 : 119	**6.** £15 to £12
3. 0.04 : 0.94	**7.** 20 cm to 6 m
4. 0.2 : 0.7314	**8.** 250 m*l* to 3 *l*

Exercise 12

1. A car travelled 147 miles in 3 h. Calculate the ratio of the number of miles travelled to the number of hours taken (m.p.h.).

2. A car used 9 gal of petrol in travelling 333 miles. How many miles per gallon did the car travel?

3. A car used 15 *l* of petrol in travelling 240 km. Calculate the ratio of the number of kilometres travelled to the number of litres used. Give your answer in the form $m : 1$.

4. Mrs Gregory saved £48 from her £200 earnings. Mr Wood saved £45 from his earnings of £180.
   (*a*) Who saved the more money?
   (*b*) Calculate their savings to earnings ratios. Give your answers in the form $m : 1$.
   (*c*) Who has the better savings to earnings ratio?

5. A wheel makes 840 full turns (revolutions or revs) in 1 h. Find the number of revs it makes in 1 min (r.p.m.).

Exercise 13

Calculate which is the better value for money:

A 1. 300 g for 60 p or 400 g for 84 p?
   2. 5 m for £2 or 3 m for £1.35?
   3. 3 kg for £2.16 or 2 kg for £1.40?
   4. 5 kg for £2 or 12 kg for £6?
   5. 14 *l* for £2 or 38 *l* for £5?
   6. £5 for 7.5 kg or £8 for 14 kg?
   7. £4.50 for 6 kg or £5.11 for 7 kg?
   8. 24 p for 500 ml or 20 p for 400 ml?

B 1. 320 g for 72 p or 400 g for 88 p?
   2. 2 kg for £2.38 or 1.8 kg for £2.16?
   3. 5 m for £2.85 or 6.5 m for £3.68?
   4. 3.6 m for £3.42 or 4.2 m for £4?
   5. 32 *l* for £13.76 or 34 *l* for £14.45?
   6. £3.48 per litre or 75 c*l* for £2.64?
   7. 2 kg for £5.90 or 400 g for £1.16?
   8. 870 g for £1.40 or 848 g for £1.36?

Exercise 14

1. Copy and complete the table:

Number bought	1	2	3	5		8		15
Cost (in £)		14		35	42		84	

2. Scientists say that density is mass per unit volume (that is, the ratio of mass to volume written in the form $m:1$). Calculate:
  (a) the density of silver, in grams per cubic centimetre, if 7 cm³ have a mass of 73.5 g,
  (b) the density of aluminium, in kilograms per cubic metre, if 4 m³ have a mass of 10 800 kg.

3. Using Ohm's law we can write the resistance (in ohms) in an electrical circuit is the ratio of the voltage to the current (in amperes).
An electric kettle works at 240 V. It carries a current of 8 A. Find its resistance.

4. The ratio of load to effort gives the mechanical advantage of a machine. If an effort of 15 N lifts a load of 75 N, find the mechanical advantage. (N stands for newtons.)

5. The teacher/pupil ratio is calculated for schools. Calculate the ratios in the form $1:n$ for these schools:
  (a) 43 teachers and 774 pupils,
  (b) 979 pupils and 55 teachers.

6. A 60 g bar of chocolate contains about 315 calories. Calculate the number of calories per 100 g for the chocolate.

Exercise 15

1. One rectangle measures 12 cm by 8 cm, while another is 8 cm by 4 cm. Calculate the ratio of:
  (a) their perimeters,   (b) their areas.

2. Brass is an alloy made of copper and zinc. If the ratio of copper to zinc is 3 : 2 and if the copper has a mass of 750 g:

(*a*) what is the mass of the zinc?

(*b*) how heavy is the brass?

3. Jackie got 60 marks out of 80. What should her mark be out of 100?

4. Andrew makes a scale model of a Spitfire. Its length is 11.25 inches. If the ratio of the model's length to the true length is 1 : 32 (that is, its scale is 1 : 32), calculate, in feet, its true length. (12 in = 1 ft.)

5. A map is drawn to a scale of 1 : 50 000 (that is, the ratio of the map distance to the real distance is 1 : 50 000). What is the real distance if the map distance is:

(*a*) 1 cm? (*b*) 6 cm?

(Give your answers in kilometres.)

6. A builder, to do some pointing, used sand and cement in the ratio 2 : 1. If he used 250 kg of sand, how much cement did he use?

7. A photographer diluted her developer with water in the ratio of 1 : 10. If she mixed 330 m*l* of solution:

(*a*) how much developer did she use?

(*b*) how much water did she use?

8. A nurse diluted a drug with water in the ratio 1 : 4. If she used 150 m*l* of the drug, how much solution was made up altogether?

9. An orange drink is diluted with water in the ratio 1 : 4. How much orange is needed to make 3.5 *l* of the drink?

10. A lemon drink is diluted with water in the ratio 1 : 5. If 1.5 *l* of water are used:

(*a*) how many millilitres of lemon are used?

(*b*) how many litres are made up altogether?

11. An orange drink is diluted with water in the ratio 1 : 3. If 500 m*l* of orange are used:

(*a*) how many litres of water are needed?

(*b*) how many litres are made up altogether?

12. In a factory, 500 of the parts being made were faulty out of 20 000 parts. Find the ratio of the number of faulty parts to the total number of parts. Give the answer in the form 1 : *n*.

Geographers calculate the *route factors* for different towns and cities. The route factor is the ratio of the road distance to the direct distance. The smaller the route factor, the more direct is the road distance between the two places.

Road distances in km

London

464	Penzance			
184	658	Norwich		
318	573	294	Manchester	
643	899	606	342	Glasgow
856	1110	797	554	229	Aberdeen

Direct distances in km

London

410	Penzance			
160	550	Norwich		
260	440	250	Manchester	
550	640	510	300	Glasgow
630	810	540	400	190	Aberdeen

Copy and complete the route factors table.
Use the two tables above to help you.

Route factors

London

	Penzance			
		Norwich		
			Manchester	
	1.40			Glasgow
					Aberdeen

e.g. The road distance from Penzance to Glasgow = 899 km
The direct distance from Penzance to Glasgow = 640 km

$$\text{The route factor} = \frac{899}{640} = 1.40$$

Which place tends to have the smallest route factors?

Exercise 17

The amount of heat lost by an animal depends on the surface area of its body. An animal that can keep its body heat for longer periods of time can live in colder regions. So animals with smaller surface areas compared with their body mass (or volume) can live more easily in colder regions. The ratio of surface area to volume depends on the size of the animal. We can see how this ratio changes by calculating surface areas and volumes of cubes.

1. Copy and complete the table:

Edge of cube (cm)	Surface area of cube (cm^3)	Volume of cube (cm^3)	Surface area / Volume
1	6	1	6
2	24		
3	54	27	2
4			1.5
5			
6		216	
7			
8			
10			
12	864		
15			0.4
20	2400		

2. Which size of animal (larger or smaller) is more likely to be found in polar regions?

3. A man weighing 72 kg has a surface area of 1.98 m². Find his surface area to mass ratio in the form $m : 1$.

4. A baby has a mass of 9 kg and a surface area of 0.45 m². Find the surface area to mass ratio in the form $m : 1$.

5. A female white rat has a mass of 0.273 kg and a surface area of 0.071 m². Find the surface area to mass ratio in the form $m : 1$.

6. A one-day old baby rat has a mass of 0.0051 kg and a surface area of 0.0042 m². Find the surface area to mass ratio in the form $m : 1$.

Exercise 18

1. Draw several squares.

2. For each square, measure the length of:
(*a*) its sides,   (*b*) its diagonals.

3. (*a*) For each square, calculate the ratio
    length of diagonal : length of side.
(*b*) What do you notice about the ratios?

4. Find $\sqrt{2}$ on your calculator.

5. Write about your findings.

8 Scales and Scale Drawings

Look at the scale of the map below. Measure each distance between the points marked.

What is the distance, in kilometres, from:

1. Dark Forest to Barracuda Bay?
2. Black Mountains to Skull Island?
3. Barracuda Bay to Ruby River?
4. Smuggler's Cove to Dark Forest?
5. Still Water to Smugglers' Cove?
6. Black Mountains to Barracuda Bay?
7. Ruby River to Skull Island?
8. South-West Point to Black Mountains?
9. South-West Point to Skull Island?
10. Still Water to Lazy River?

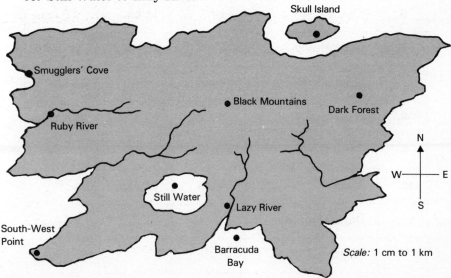

A Trace the map opposite.

On your copy, write the scale of 1 cm to 1 km.

Mark these places on your map.

Use a pair of compasses to help you.

	Place	Distance from		
		North Bay	Hope Island	Dozy River
1.	Blood River	5 km	8 km	—
2.	Old Wreck	9 km	6 km	—
3.	Western Hills	—	6 km	11 km
4.	Palm Grove	4 km	—	3 km
5.	Shark Bay	—	11 km	2.5 km
6.	Long Beach	—	9 km	8 km
7.	Smugglers' Creek	10 km	—	13 km
8.	Wide Straits	8.5 km	—	10 km
9.	Coral Reef	12.5 km	11 km	—
10.	Marsh	6 km	10.5 km	—
11.	Dark Mountain	3.5 km	—	7.5 km
12.	Wreckers' Point	12 km	—	15.5 km

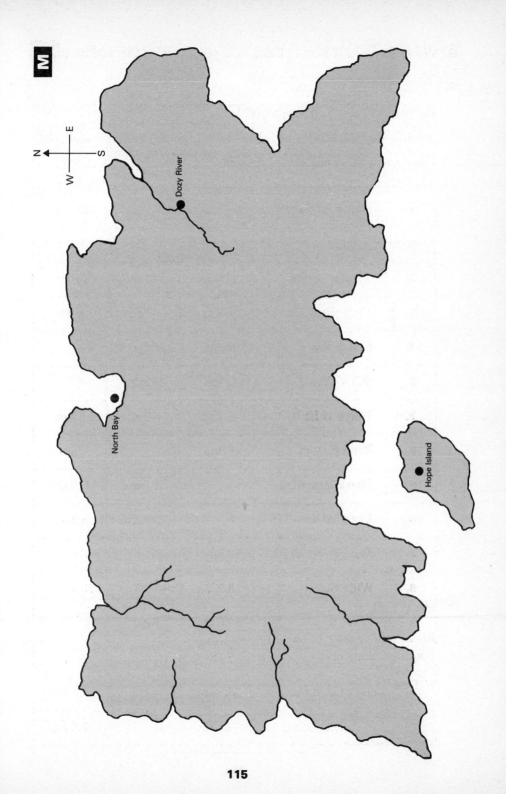

B Write the scale of 1 cm to 2 km on another copy of the map on p. 115.

Mark these places on your map:

	Place	Distance from		
		North Bay	Hope Island	Dozy River
1.	Forest of Fear	14 km	—	22 km
2.	Swamp	—	18 km	22 km
3.	Pirates' Creek	12 km	22 km	—
4.	Cliff View	16 km	—	6 km
5.	South Bay	19 km	6 km	—
6.	West Point	19 km	16 km	—
7.	Black Hills	8 km	—	9 km
8.	Wreck	5 km	—	9 km
9.	Clearwater Lake	—	13 km	17 km
10.	Devil's Cave	—	13.5 km	10 km

Exercise 3

Each line is drawn to the given scale.
Find its true length.

1. 1 cm to 3 m ————————————————————

2. 1 cm to 8 m ——————————————————

3. 1 cm to 4 km ———————————————

4. 1 cm to 2 cm   _____

5. 1 cm to 20 cm   _____

6. 1 cm to 0.5 m   _____

7. 1 cm represents 5 m

_____

8. 1 cm represents 6 km   _____

9. 1 mm to 10 mm   _____

10. 1 mm to 40 mm   _____

11. 1 mm to 5 mm   _____

12. 1 cm to 5 cm   _____

13. 1 mm to 5 cm   _____

14. 1 cm to 5 mm   _____

15. 1 cm represents 8 km   _____

16. 1 mm represents 7 cm   _____

17. $1:10$ _____

18. $1:4$ _____

19. $1:20$ _____

20. $1:100$ _____

21. $1:1000$

_____

22. 1 cm represents 25 km   _____

23. 1 cm to 12 cm   _____

24. $1:40$ _____

25. $1:100\ 000$ _____

1. Here is the ground floor plan of a house.
   It is drawn to a scale of 1 : 100 (1 cm to 1 m).

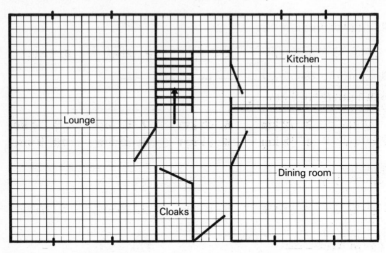

   (a) Give the length and breadth of the lounge?
   (b) Give the length and breadth of the dining room.
   (c) Find the area of the kitchen.

2. Here is a plan of a garden.
   Scale 1 : 500

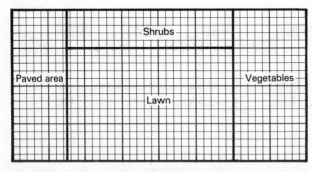

   (a) How long is the vegetable patch?
   (b) Give the length and breadth of the shubbery.
   (c) Give the *dimensions* of the paved area.
   (d) Calculate the area of the paving.
   (e) What is the area of the lawn?
   (f) What is the total area of the garden?

Exercise 5

Using each of the following scales, draw lines representing the given lengths.

A 1 cm represents 2 m

    1. 10 m   **2.** 18 m   **3.** 6 m   **4.** 26 m   **5.** 15 m

B 1 cm represents 6 km

    1. 24 km   **3.** 72 km   **5.** 45 km   **7.** 63 km   **9.** 75 km
    2. 60 km   **4.** 18 km   **6.** 21 km   **8.** 33 km   **10.** 9 km

C 1 cm to 10 m

    1. 90 m   **2.** 120 m   **3.** 30 m   **4.** 25 m   **5.** 85 m

D 1 cm to 8 cm

    1. 56 cm   **2.** 104 cm   **3.** 20 cm   **4.** 92 cm   **5.** 28 cm

E 1 cm represents 4 km

    1. 12 km   **2.** 28 km   **3.** 18 km   **4.** 38 km   **5.** 9 km

F

    1. 35 km   **3.** 25 km   **5.** 50 km   **7.** 27.5 km   **9.** 57.5 km
    2. 40 km   **4.** 15 km   **6.** 42.5 km   **8.** 32.5 km   **10.** 17.5 km

G 1 : 100

    1. 300 cm   **3.** 2 m   **5.** 700 cm   **7.** 8 m   **9.** 650 cm
    2. 900 cm   **4.** 5 m   **6.** 750 cm   **8.** 4.5 m   **10.** 625 cm

H 1 : 400

    1. 800 cm   **2.** 16 m   **3.** 44 m   **4.** 26 m   **5.** 35 m

I 1 cm represents 3 ℓ

1. 12 ℓ **3.** 6 ℓ **5.** 39 ℓ **7.** 22.5 ℓ **9.** 10.5 ℓ
2. 30 ℓ **4.** 27 ℓ **6.** 7.5 ℓ **8.** 33 ℓ **10.** 34.5 ℓ

J 1 cm represents 10 kg

1. 100 kg **2.** 75 kg **3.** 35 kg **4.** 88 kg **5.** 112 kg

Exercise 6 ═══════════════════════════════ M

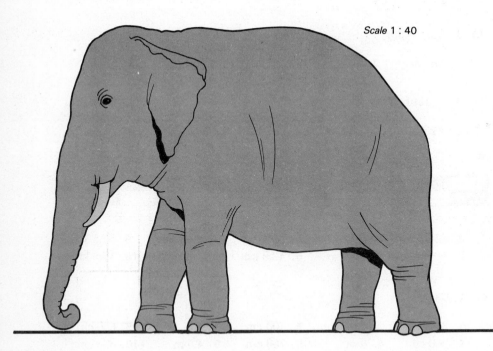

Scale 1 : 40

Trace the elephant.

Next to it, try to draw yourself. (Use the same scale.)

1. A rectangular room measures 4 m by 3 m.
   Make a scale drawing of the room. (Use a scale of 1 cm to 1 m.) How long is a diagonal of this room?

2. X, Y and Z are trees on each side of a river as shown.
   XY = 85 m,   YZ = 100 m   and   XZ = 70 m.
   Find, by scale drawing, the width of the river. (Use a scale of 1 cm to 20 m.)

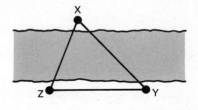

3. Make a scale drawing from the given figure. Use a scale of 1 cm to 10 m. How tall is the tower?

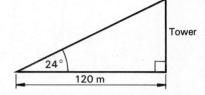

4. The drawing shows a plan of a tennis court. The dimensions are given in feet.
   Draw a plan of the tennis court. (If you have a ruler marked in inches, use a scale of 1 in to 20 ft; otherwise, choose your own scale.)

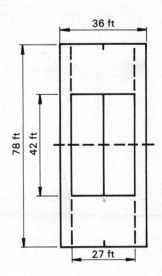

5. The triangle has been drawn to a scale of 1 : 60. Draw it to a scale of 1 : 20.

9 Bases

Copy the sets of crosses. Group them as instructed. Answer the given questions.

e.g.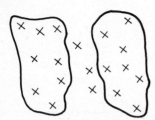

There are 19 crosses.
There are 2 groups of eight.
There are 3 crosses left over.
There are 23_8 crosses.

(Note 23_8 The eight means that we are grouping in eights.)
We say there are 23 crosses in base 8.

1.

(a) How many crosses?
(b) Draw round groups of five.
(c) How many groups of five are there?
(d) How many crosses are left over?
(e) How many crosses are there in base 5?

2.

(a) How many crosses?
(b) Draw round groups of six.
(c) How many groups of six are there?
(d) How many crosses are left over?
(e) How many crosses are there in base 6?

3.

(a) How many crosses?
(b) Draw round groups of three.
(c) How many groups of three are there?
(d) How many crosses are left over?
(e) How many crosses are there in base 3?

4. × × × × × × ×
× × × × × × ×
× × × × × × ×
× × × × × × ×
× × × × × × ×
× × × × × × ×

(a) How many crosses?
(b) Draw round groups of eight.
(c) How many groups of eight are there?
(d) How many crosses are left over?
(e) How many crosses are there in base 8?

5. × × × × × × × × ×
× × × × × × × ×
× × × × × × × ×
× × × × × × × ×
× × × × × × × ×
× × × × × × × ×

(a) How many crosses?
(b) Draw round groups of ten.
(c) How many groups of ten are there?
(d) How many crosses are left over?
(e) How many crosses are there in base ten?

Exercise 2

Copy the following.
Write the correct number in place of each box.

e.g. 1 65_8 = ⬚ eights + ⬚ units = 53_{ten}

e.g. 2 32_5 = ⬚ fives + ⬚ units = 17_{ten}

1. 31_6 = ⬚ sixes + ⬚ units = ⬚ $_{ten}$

2. 14_7 = ⬚ sevens + ⬚ units = ⬚ $_{ten}$

3. 72_9 = ⬚ nines + ⬚ units = ⬚ $_{ten}$

4. 22_4 = ⬚ fours + ⬚ units = ⬚ $_{ten}$

5. 53_9 = ⬚ nines + ⬚ units = ⬚ $_{ten}$

6. 35_7 = ⬚ sevens + ⬚ units = ⬚ $_{ten}$

7. 53_6 = ⬚ sixes + ⬚ units = ⬚ $_{ten}$

8. 40_5 = ⬚ fives + ⬚ units = ⬚ $_{ten}$

Exercise 3

Tins of soup are put into boxes of eight.

1. How many tins are there in 3 boxes?

2. How many tins are there if there are 4 boxes and 2 tins left over?

123

3. How many boxes are needed to hold 48 tins?

4. How many boxes are needed and how many tins will be left over if I have 39 tins?

Exercise 4

Write these base 8 (octal) numbers in base ten (denary):

1. 14_8	**5.** 41_8	**9.** 33_8	**13.** 57_8
2. 16_8	**6.** 53_8	**10.** 60_8	**14.** 45_8
3. 24_8	**7.** 36_8	**11.** 50_8	**15.** 77_8
4. 27_8	**8.** 66_8	**12.** 73_8	

Exercise 5

Change these denary numbers into octal:

1. 26_{ten}	**5.** 10_{ten}	**9.** 25_{ten}	**13.** 52_{ten}
2. 18_{ten}	**6.** 35_{ten}	**10.** 56_{ten}	**14.** 60_{ten}
3. 9_{ten}	**7.** 44_{ten}	**11.** 31_{ten}	**15.** 16_{ten}
4. 8_{ten}	**8.** 13_{ten}	**12.** 49_{ten}	

Exercise 6

Convert the following numbers from their given base into base ten:

1. 35_8	**6.** 15_9	**11.** 52_6	**16.** 40_6	**21.** 31_5
2. 31_4	**7.** 34_6	**12.** 30_5	**17.** 11_2	**22.** 13_4
3. 24_9	**8.** 43_5	**13.** 46_8	**18.** 55_6	**23.** 55_7
4. 24_7	**9.** 11_4	**14.** 58_9	**19.** 66_7	**24.** 86_9
5. 12_3	**10.** 22_3	**15.** 43_7	**20.** 77_9	**25.** 32_6

Exercise 7

Change these from base ten to the given base:

1. 16_{ten} to base 6	**8.** 24_{ten} to base 5	**15.** 72_{ten} to base 9
2. 21_{ten} to base 5	**9.** 45_{ten} to base 7	**16.** 8_{ten} to base 4
3. 46_{ten} to base 8	**10.** 33_{ten} to base 6	**17.** 18_{ten} to base 5
4. 23_{ten} to base 7	**11.** 29_{ten} to base 6	**18.** 39_{ten} to base 7
5. 56_{ten} to base 9	**12.** 57_{ten} to base 8	**19.** 30_{ten} to base 6
6. 7_{ten} to base 3	**13.** 42_{ten} to base 7	**20.** 68_{ten} to base 9
7. 12_{ten} to base 4	**14.** 80_{ten} to base 9	

Exercise 8

Eggs are packed into cartons of 6.
Six cartons of 6 eggs then fill a box.

1. How many eggs does each box hold?

2. How many eggs have I got if I have:
   (*a*) 3 cartons?   (*e*) 2 boxes and 5 eggs?
   (*b*) 2 cartons and 3 eggs?   (*f*) 4 boxes and 2 cartons?
   (*c*) 5 cartons and 5 eggs?   (*g*) 2 boxes, 3 cartons and 1 egg?
   (*d*) 3 boxes?   (*h*) 5 boxes, 1 carton and 4 eggs?

3. Write the number of boxes and cartons that I need, and state
the number of eggs left over if I packed:
   (*a*) 26 eggs   (*c*) 72 eggs   (*e*) 100 eggs   (*g*) 145 eggs
   (*b*) 31 eggs   (*d*) 54 eggs   (*f*) 200 eggs   (*h*) 183 eggs

Exercise 9

Copy the following. Write the correct number in place of each box:

e.g. 1 213_5 = [?] twenty-fives, [?] fives and [?] units = 58_{ten}

1. 123_8 = [?] sixty-four, [?] eights and [?] units = [?]$_{ten}$

2. 203_4 = [?] sixteens, [?] fours and [?] units = [?]$_{ten}$

3. 110_2 = [?] fours, [?] twos and [?] units = [?]$_{ten}$

4. 121_3 = [?] nines, [?] threes and [?] units = [?]$_{ten}$

5. 425_7 = [?] forty-nines, [?] sevens and [?] units = [?]$_{ten}$

6. 432_5 = [?] twenty-fives, [?] fives and [?] units = [?]$_{ten}$

7. 617_9 = [?] eighty-ones, [?] nines and [?] units = [?]$_{ten}$

8. 312_4 = [?] sixteens, [?] fours and [?] units = [?]$_{ten}$

9. 737_8 = [?] sixty-fours, [?] eights and [?] units = [?]$_{ten}$

10. 231_6 = [?] thirty-sixes, [?] sixes and [?] units = [?]$_{ten}$

Exercise 10

46_7 is in base 7. The small number 7 (called the subscript) tells you the base in which each number is written.

For each number, state the value, in base ten, of the underlined digit:

1. $23\underline{1}_5$
2. $1\underline{3}21_4$
3. $54\underline{2}_9$
4. $47\underline{2}_8$
5. $\underline{1}021_3$
6. $1\underline{2}10_3$

7. $221\underline{3}_4$
8. $10\underline{1}10_2$
9. $44\underline{2}3_6$
10. $3\underline{2}40_5$
11. $113\underline{3}2_5$
12. $7\underline{2}6_9$

13. $121\underline{1}2_3$
14. $3\underline{1}21_4$
15. $101\underline{1}001_2$
16. $\underline{2}361_7$
17. $356\underline{2}1_{10}$
18. $\underline{1}0211_3$

19. $2\underline{4}302_6$
20. $1\underline{1}00111_2$
21. $1\underline{3}231_5$
22. $13\underline{2}9_{12}$
23. $2\underline{7}3_{16}$
24. $3\underline{5}8_{16}$

Exercise 11

Change the following numbers from their given base into base ten:

1. 143_5
2. 101_2
3. 213_7
4. 210_3
5. 154_9

6. 175_8
7. 133_4
8. 100_9
9. 100_7
10. 155_6

11. 222_3
12. 213_4
13. 340_5
14. 120_4
15. 362_8

16. 346_7
17. 488_9
18. 333_4
19. 354_6
20. 666_7

21. 546_8
22. 564_7
23. 723_9
24. 1022_3
25. 1203_5

Exercise 12

Convert these from base ten to the given base:

1. 79 to base 8
2. 47 to base 5
3. 63 to base 6
4. 142 to base 9
5. 14 to base 3
6. 44 to base 4
7. 87 to base 7

8. 100 to base 9
9. 100 to base 8
10. 100 to base 7
11. 25 to base 3
12. 121 to base 5
13. 140 to base 8
14. 434 to base 9

15. 155 to base 6
16. 232 to base 7
17. 491 to base 9
18. 11 to base 2
19. 167 to base 5
20. 100 to base 4

Exercise 13

Convert the following numbers from base 2 (binary) to base ten (denary):

1. 10_2
2. 111_2
3. 1010_2
4. 1111_2
5. 1000_2
6. 1101_2
7. 10001_2
8. 10010_2

9. 11110_2 **12.** 100011_2 **15.** 101100_2 **18.** 1001111_2

10. 10110_2 **13.** 101001_2 **16.** 111111_2 **19.** 1110011_2

11. 10100_2 **14.** 111000_2 **17.** 1010100_2 **20.** 1111000_2

Exercise 14

Convert these numbers from denary to binary:

1. 4_{ten} **6.** 19_{ten} **11.** 36_{ten} **16.** 62_{ten}

2. 9_{ten} **7.** 21_{ten} **12.** 43_{ten} **17.** 69_{ten}

3. 12_{ten} **8.** 25_{ten} **13.** 33_{ten} **18.** 81_{ten}

4. 16_{ten} **9.** 31_{ten} **14.** 49_{ten} **19.** 100_{ten}

5. 14_{ten} **10.** 39_{ten} **15.** 55_{ten} **20.** 127_{ten}

Using a Calculator

Exercise 15

e.g. 1   Change 2314_5 from base 5 to base ten.

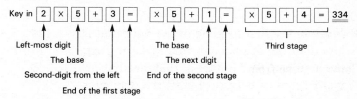

The third stage is a repeat of the second stage but using the next digit from the left.

The second stage is repeated for each digit that remains.

e.g. 2   Convert 120102_3 to base ten.

You could save time by missing out the steps $\boxed{+}\ \boxed{0}$

Now try some of the questions in Exercises 4, 6, 11 and 13 using a calculator.

Exercise 16

A Convert 710_{ten} to base 4.

1. Find and write the base 4 headings. These can be found by keying $\boxed{1} \boxed{\times} \boxed{4} \boxed{\times} \boxed{4} \boxed{\times} \boxed{4} \boxed{\times} \boxed{4}$ and so on. Stop as soon as you reach a number that is bigger than the number in the question (710 in this case). The required headings are   256 64 16 4 1

2. Clear the display.

Display on calculator

3. Key in the given number ($\boxed{7}\boxed{1}\boxed{0}$).   710

4. Subtract the left-most heading
($\boxed{-}\boxed{2}\boxed{5}\boxed{6}\boxed{=}$).   454

Repeat the subtraction until the display is less than the heading (<256).   198

Note how many subtractions were carried out (in this case, 2). That number should be written under the heading that was being subtracted.

   256 64 16 4 1
    2

5. Move to the first heading to the right that is   134
less than the display. (In this case the next,   70
the number, 64.) Subtract that heading as   6
many times as necessary until the display is
smaller than it. The number of subtraction (3
in this case) should be written under the
heading being subtracted:

   256 64 16 4 1
    2   3

6. Repeat step 5 as many times as necessary (-4)
until the display is zero. Zero should be writ-   2
ten under any heading that does not have a (-1)
digit under it (16 in this case).   1

   256 64 16 4 1 (-1)
    2   3   0   1 2   0

B **1.** Test the method on questions in Exercises 5, 7, 12 and 14.

    2. Try to work out a method of your own that uses a calculator.

Copy and complete this table:

	Base ten	Base 2	Base 3	Base 4	Base 5	Base 6	Base 7	Base 8
Odd	1	1	1	1				1
Even	2	10	2	2				
Odd	3	11	10		3		3	
Even	4		11	10		4		
Odd	5	101	12					5
Even	6				11			
Odd	7							
Even	8					12		
Odd	9			21				11
Even	10						13	
Odd	11		102					
Even	12	1100				22		
Odd	13							
Even	14							

2. How would you recognise an even number in:
  (a) base 2? (b) base ten? (c) base 4? (d) base 8? (e) base 6?

3. How would you recognise an even number in:
  (a) base 3?   (b) base 5?   (c) base 7?

Exercise 18

1. If $42_{[?]} = 34_{ten}$, find the missing base.

2. If $152_{[?]} = 68_{ten}$, find the missing base.

3. Which binary number follows 11011_2?

4. Which base 5 number comes immediately before 430_5?

5. Which of these are even numbers:

10110_2, 321_4, 201_3, 465_9, 231_7, 503_8?

6. Write these binary numbers in ascending order of size (*i.e.* from smallest to largest):

10110_2, 11011_2, 1111_2, 110110_2, 101101_2, 10011_2, 111011_2

7. What is the smallest number that ends in a zero in both bases 4 and 5?

8. Which is the largest number, 54_6, 65_7, 72_8, 71_9 or 44_5?

9. Which is the smallest number, 10102_3, 324_5, 234_6, 165_7 or 1133_4?

10. Is it true that $215_6 > 137_8$?

Two-state Systems

Exercise 19   Railway Sidings

The drawing shows some railway sidings.
Every 100 m there is a set of
points at which the line splits
into two lines.

Copy and complete these sentences:

1. At 100 m the line splits into ☐? lines.
2. At 200 m the line splits into ☐? lines.
3. At 300 m the line splits into ☐? lines.
4. At 400 m the line splits into ☐? lines.
5. At 500 m the line splits into ☐? lines.
6. At 600 m the line splits into ☐? lines.

Exercise 20   A Family Tree

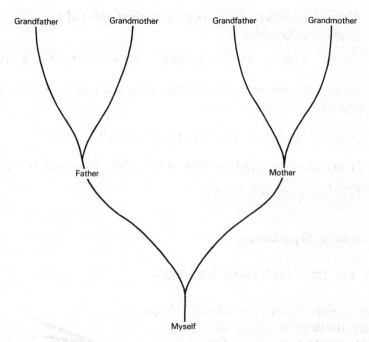

Copy the family tree above and continue it for two more steps (as far as great great grandfathers and great great grandmothers).

Copy and complete these sentences:

1. There are ☐? parents.
2. There are ☐? grandparents.
3. There are ☐? great grandparents.
4. There are ☐? great great grandparents.
5. There are ☐? great great great grandparents.

Exercise 21   Magic Cards

Either use the given set of six magic cards or make your own set.

1	3	5	7	9	11	13	15
17	19	21	23	25	27	29	31
33	35	37	39	41	43	45	47
49	51	53	55	57	59	61	63

A **1.** Ask a friend to think of a number between 1 and 63.

2. Ask that person to show you which cards the number is on.

2	3	6	7	10	11	14	15
18	19	22	23	26	27	30	31
34	35	38	39	42	43	46	47
50	51	54	55	58	59	62	63

3. You can then quickly tell your friend the number he or she thought of.

To do this, add the numbers in the top left-hand corners of the cards your friend shows you.
This total is the required number.

4	5	6	7	12	13	14	15
20	21	22	23	28	29	30	31
36	37	38	39	44	45	46	47
52	53	54	55	60	61	62	63

8	9	10	11	12	13	14	15
24	25	26	27	28	29	30	31
40	41	42	43	44	45	46	47
56	57	58	59	60	61	62	63

16	17	18	19	20	21	22	23
24	25	26	27	28	29	30	31
48	49	50	51	52	53	54	55
56	57	58	59	60	61	62	63

B **1.** Look at the numbers in the top left-hand corner of each card. Which base do the numbers suggest?

2. Try to work out why the method works.

Hint Write down the numbers from 1 to 63 in base 2.

32	33	34	35	36	37	38	39
40	41	42	43	44	45	46	47
48	49	50	51	52	53	54	55
56	57	58	59	60	61	62	63

Exercise 22   Punched Cards ━━━━━━━━

Make a set of 15 cards like the card shown on the left. (The holes should be in the same position on each card.)

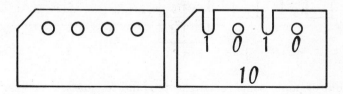

Number the cards from 1 to 15. (Number 10 is shown above.)

Cut out slots on each card using the binary system. A hole stands for 0 and a slot for 1. In the example, 10 is 1010 in binary, so slots are cut out from the left-hand hole and the third from left.

Now shuffle the cards.

Base ten	Base 2
1	0001
2	0010
3	0011
4	0100
5	0101
6	0110
7	0111
8	1000
9	1001
10	1010
11	1011
12	1100
13	1101
14	1110
15	1111

Push a needle through the right-hand holes in the cards. Lift the needle. (The cards with slots in this position will be left behind.) Place the set of cards picked up with the needle at the front of the pack. Now push the needle through the second hole from the right. The cards lifted out should again be placed at the front.

Repeat this for the third hole from the right and then the fourth hole (the left-hand hole).

The cards should now be sorted into order from 1 to 15.

Shopkeepers' Masses

Cut out of paper some rectangles to stand for masses. You can make the three shown above.

To weigh 1 oz, a shopkeeper can use a 1 oz mass.
To weigh 2 oz, a shopkeeper can use a 2 oz mass.
To weigh 3 oz, a 2 oz and a 1 oz mass can be used.
To weigh 4 oz, a 4 oz mass can be used.
For 5 oz, a 4 oz and a 1 oz mass can be used, and so on.

Try to find out what the next three masses must be so that the shopkeeper can weigh up to 63 oz.

Record your answers in a table like this:

Amount to be weighed	Masses needed					
	?	?	?	4 oz	2 oz	1 oz
1 oz	0	0	0	0	0	1
2 oz	0	0	0	0	1	0
3 oz	0	0	0	0	1	1
4 oz	0	0	0	1	0	0
5 oz	0	0	0	1	0	1
6 oz	0	0	0	1	1	0
⋮						
37 oz						
38 oz				1		0
39 oz						
40 oz						

Use a 1 for a mass that is used and 0 for a mass that is not used.
Make out the table to weigh up to 40 oz.

Exercise 24

A Using scales, masses are normally placed all on the same pan. Suppose the masses are placed on either or on both pans, and that we have five masses, 1 oz, 3 oz, 9 oz and two unknown masses:

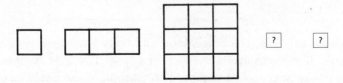

To weigh 11 oz, put the 9 oz mass with the 3 oz mass on one pan (12 oz total).

With 1 oz on the other pan, an 11 oz mass is needed to balance the scales.

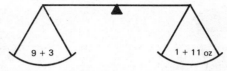

1. Find the two missing masses mentioned above that will allow the heaviest possible mass to be weighed and yet still allow all possible whole numbers of ounces up to that heaviest mass to be weighed.

2. Explain with a diagram how to weigh 47 oz using any of the five masses above and using both pans of a pair of scales.

B 1. Using masses of 1 oz, 4 oz, 7 oz and 17 oz, what mass up to 29 oz cannot be weighed using these four masses, if they can be used on either or on both pans?

2. Which mass up to 33 oz cannot be weighed using the masses 1 oz, 3 oz, 10 oz and 19 oz, if they can be used on either or both pans?

3. Which masses up to 46 oz cannot be weighed using the masses 2 oz, 5 oz, 8 oz and 31 oz, if they can be used on either or both pans?

10 Time, Timetables, and the Calendar

For thousands of years, the Sun, Moon and stars have been used as timekeepers. The Earth orbits the Sun in a year. The time from one new moon to the next gives a month. The rotation of the Earth on its axis shows how the days pass.

The days were divided into hours, and through the ages, many devices were invented to give the time of day. Some of these devices are shown here.

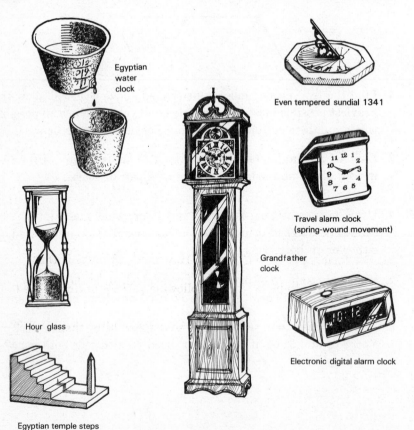

Egyptian water clock

Even tempered sundial 1341

Hour glass

Travel alarm clock (spring-wound movement)

Grandfather clock

Electronic digital alarm clock

Egyptian temple steps

Exercise 1

A   **1.** How many seconds are there in 1 min?

     2. How many minutes are there in 1 h?

     3. How many seconds are there in:
       (*a*) 2 min?   (*b*) 5 min?   (*c*) 7 min?   (*d*) 10 min?

     4. How many minutes are there in:
       (*a*) 2 h?   (*b*) 8 h?   (*c*) 10 h?   (*d*) 12 h?

     5. How many minutes are there in:
       (*a*) 180 s?   (*b*) 480 s?   (*c*) 720 s?

     6. How many hours are there in:
       (*a*) 240 min?   (*b*) 360 min?   (*c*) 420 min?

     7. How many seconds are there in:
       (*a*) 3 min 4 s?   (*b*) 4 min 23 s?   (*c*) 9 min 47 s?

     8. How many minutes are there in:
       (*a*) 1 h 20 min?   (*b*) 2 h 45 min?   (*c*) $3\frac{1}{2}$ h?

     9. How many seconds are there in 1 h?

    10. Change 3 h into seconds?

B   **1.** A runner runs 8 laps of a track at 67 s per lap. How long does that take in minutes and seconds?

     2. A timer needs to be set for $1\frac{1}{2}$ h. How many minutes is that?

     3. A timer needs to be set for the following periods of time. Give the times in minutes.
       (*a*) 1 h 50 min   (*b*) 2 h 15 min   (*c*) 3 h 12 min   (*d*) 2 h 38 min

     4. A 4 × 400 m relay was run. The runners' times were 45.8 s, 46.1 s, 45.6 s and 45 s. Give the time for the relay in minutes and seconds.

     5. A 4 × 800 m relay was run in 8 min 14.6 s. The first three legs were run in 2 min 3.1 s, 2 min 4.7 s and 2 min 3.6 s. How fast was the last leg?

Exercise 2

A How long is a minute?
Try this:
With a friend's help, try to estimate 1 minute. Your friend should use a stopwatch or an ordinary watch that shows seconds. When he or she tells you to start, try to estimate 1 minute. Tell your friend when you think exactly 1 minute has passed. Note the actual time measured. By how many seconds were you wrong?
Now time your friend.

B Use a stopwatch to help you to find the number of beats your pulse makes in 30 s. (It may be easier if a friend helps you.)
How many beats would that be per minute?

C 1. Type the following program into a computer (it should work on most computers):

```
1Ø   REM***TIMING***
2Ø   LET I = Ø
3Ø   PRINT "START"
4Ø   FOR N = 1 TO 1ØØ
5Ø   LET I = I + 1
6Ø   NEXT N
7Ø   PRINT "STOP"
8Ø   END
```

2. Have a stopwatch ready and run the program. When START is printed, start the stopwatch. When STOP is printed, stop the stopwatch. Note the time taken for the program to run.

3. Change line 4Ø of the program as follows then repeat step 2 above:
(a) 4Ø FOR N = 1 TO 5ØØ
(b) 4Ø FOR N = 1 TO 1ØØØ
(c) 4Ø FOR N = 1 TO 5ØØØ
(d) 4Ø FOR N = 1 TO 1ØØØØ
(e) 4Ø FOR N = 1 TO 5ØØØØ

4. What is the program making the computer do after printing START and before printing STOP?

5. Compare the times you have noted.
  - (a) Is the time for 1ØØØØ (in line 4Ø, question 3(d)) double the time for 5ØØØ (in 3(c))?
  - (b) Is the time for 5ØØØØ five times the time for 1ØØØØ?

6. If possible, run the program on different makes of computer. Find out which computer is fastest in running this program.

D A drug manufacturer is not only interested in the product formed by a reaction but also in how fast the reaction is (the *rate of reaction*). A product that is formed quickly is likely to be cheaper to manufacture. You may have carried out this experiment in science:

1. Measure $50 \, cm^3$ of 0.2 M sodium thiosulphate solution into a conical flask.

2. Put $5 \, cm^3$ of 2 M hydrochloric acid into a measuring cylinder.

3. Mark a cross on a piece of filter paper.

4. Place the conical flask over the cross.

5. Pour the acid into the sodium thiosulphate solution, start a stopwatch and shake the flask gently. Put the flask back on top of the cross.

6. Look at the cross on the filter paper through the solution (look from above). Stop the watch when the cross just disappears.

7. Rinse the flask immediately.

8. Note the time taken.

9. Repeat the above steps with $50 \, cm^3$ of diluted solution, using:
  - (a) $40 \, cm^3$ of 0.2 M sodium thiosulphate solution and $10 \, cm^3$ of water,
  - (b) $30 \, cm^3$ of 0.2 M sodium thiosulphate solution and $20 \, cm^3$ of water,
  - (c) $20 \, cm^3$ of 0.2 M sodium thiosulphate solution and $30 \, cm^3$ of water,
  - (d) $10 \, cm^3$ of 0.2 M sodium thiosulphate solution and $40 \, cm^3$ of water.

10. How does the time change as the solution gets weaker?

Exercise 3

1. There are 24 h in 1 day. How many hours are there in 2 days?

2. How many hours are there in:
   (a) 5 days?   (b) 9 days?   (c) 12 days?

3. How many hours are there in:
   (a) 1 week?   (b) a fortnight?   (c) a quarter of a day?

4. How many days are there in:
   (a) 72 h?   (b) 120 h?   (c) 264 h?

5. How many days are there in 8 weeks?

6. How many weeks are there in 42 days?

7. How many weeks are there in 91 days?

8. How many days are there in 52 weeks?

9. How many weeks are there in 182 days?

Exercise 4

A Write these times using the 24-hour clock notation:

1. Twenty minutes past ten in the morning.
2. Half past six in the morning.
3. Quarter past eight in the evening.
4. Five past eleven at night.
5. Twenty-seven minutes past three in the afternoon.
6. Ten minutes to nine in the morning.
7. Quarter to six in the evening.
8. Twenty-five minutes to three in the morning.
9. Five minutes to ten in the evening.
10. Sixteen minutes to twelve at night.
11. Twenty-one minutes to twelve in the morning.
12. Fourteen minutes past twelve in the afternoon.
13. Six minutes past twelve in the morning.
14. Twenty-two minutes to two in the morning.
15. Eight minutes to seven in the evening.

B Write these 24-hour clock times in words:

1. 04.15	**4.** 03.05	**7.** 16.12	**10.** 00.10
2. 07.20	**5.** 22.55	**8.** 09.30	**11.** 19.51
3. 13.45	**6.** 05.40	**9.** 14.37	**12.** 12.04

Do not forget to state whether the time is in the morning, afternoon or evening.

Exercise 5

A Write these times in words:

1. 6.00 a.m.	**4.** 8.45 a.m.	**7.** 12.08 a.m.	**10.** 7.18 p.m.
2. 9.15 p.m.	**5.** 2.50 p.m.	**8.** 4.54 a.m.	**11.** 12.00 a.m.
3. 11.24 p.m.	**6.** 1.32 a.m.	**9.** 10.29 p.m.	**12.** 12.00 p.m.

B Write the times given in Exercise 4A using the 12-hour clock.

C Write these times using the 24-hour clock:

1. 7.15 a.m.	**4.** 10.33 a.m.	**7.** 1.00 a.m.	**10.** 8.48 p.m.
2. 4.25 p.m.	**5.** 2.19 a.m.	**8.** 5.00 p.m.	**11.** 3.57 p.m.
3. 11.46 p.m.	**6.** 6.59 p.m.	**9.** 9.21 a.m.	**12.** 12.03 a.m.

D Write these times using the 12-hour clock:

1. 03.17	**4.** 21.43	**7.** 11.22	**10.** 04.41
2. 14.26	**5.** 13.53	**8.** 06.49	**11.** 12.09
3. 08.07	**6.** 05.34	**9.** 19.36	**12.** 00.58

Exercise 6

1. How many hours are there from 6 o'clock in the morning until 10 o'clock in the evening?

2. How many hours are there from 09.30 to 23.30 on the same day?

3. How many hours are there from 7.15 a.m. to 6.15 p.m. on the same day?

4. How many hours are there from 8 o'clock on Monday evening until 9 o'clock the following morning?

5. How many hours are there from 7 o'clock on Wednesday morning until 6 o'clock in the evening on the Thursday?

6. How many hours are there from 13.00 on Tuesday until 09.00 on the following Thursday?

7. How many hours are there from 18.25 on Friday until 10.25 on the following Monday?

8. How many hours are there from 22.39 on Sunday until 22.39 on the following Sunday?

Exercise 7

A What is the time 15 minutes after these times?

1. 09.45	**3.** 19.05	**5.** 21.12	**7.** 17.37
2. 14.20	**4.** 06.34	**6.** 02.41	**8.** 23.50

B How many minutes are there from these times until the next hour?

1. 08.35	**3.** 16.05	**5.** 10.24	**7.** 03.48
2. 20.40	**4.** 05.52	**6.** 18.34	**8.** 22.19

Exercise 8

1. A TV programme started at 17.55 and finished at 18.40. How long did it last?

2. A programme started at 21.35 and lasted 1 h 40 min. At what time did it finish?

3. A concert finished at ten minutes to ten in the evening. If it started 2 h 35 min earlier, at what time did it start?

4. A turkey needs to be cooked by 19.30. If its cooking time is 20 min per pound, plus an extra 20 min and if the turkey weighs 12 lb, at what time must it be put in the oven?

5. Your train leaves at 10.13. If you need 25 min to walk to the station, what is the latest time at which you should leave the house?

6. It is 15.56. It will take 25 minutes to walk to the bus stop. My bus leaves at 16.53. How many minutes have I to spare?

7. There was a high tide at 10.45 on 16 July. The next high tide was 12 h 17 min later. At what time was that high tide?

8. A film was shown from 13.52 to 16.35. In another cinema a film was shown from 14.33 to 16.48. How many minutes longer was the first film?

9. A timer was set for 1 h 40 min. If the starting time was 17.55, what was the finishing time?

Exercise 9

A Copy and complete the table below:

	Time of departure	Time of arrival	Time taken
1.	09.42	11.51	
2.	15.27		1 h 26 min
3.	10.08		3 h 47 min
4.	20.56	23.19	
5.		12.54	3 h 36 min
6.	22.37	04.35	
7.	21.43		4 h 14 min
8.		19.38	56 min
9.		00.13	1 h 35 min
10.	02.52		3 h 42 min

B Copy and complete the time card below:

Employer: Mint Brothers

Department: Accounts

Name: B.E. Idle

Employee's Ref. No.: 09164

Week ending: 5 May

Day	In	Out	In	Out	Total time	
Mon	08.30	12.00	13.00	17.00	7 h	30 min
Tues	08.45	12.00	13.30	17.00		
Wed	08.32	12.00	13.27	16.30		
Thurs	09.06	12.20	14.03	17.55		
Fri	08.52	11.50	13.15		7 h	18 min
Sat		12.00	13.35	16.20	6 h	14 min
			Total time for the week		h	min

C Some people work *flexitime*.
That means they can vary the times they work each day.

Make out a time card for Mrs S. Sharp.
She needs to work 34 h 15 min during the week.
She does not work on Saturday or Sunday.
She must start in a morning between 08.00 and 09.45.
Lunch can be taken between 11.45 and 14.15.
Work each day can finish at any time between 16.00 and 18.00.

Exercise 10

1. A cinema opens at 13.25 and closes at 22.48. How long is it open throughout that particular day?

2. A coach left Glasgow at 07.29 and arrived in London at 15.54. How long did the journey take?

3. A coach left Plymouth at 17.48 and arrived in Penzance at 21.06. How long did the journey take?

4. I set off for work at 07.46 and arrived at 08.32. For how many minutes was I travelling?

5. I set off on the train at 11.47 and my journey lasts 3 h 28 min. At what time should I arrive at my destination?

6. I arrived at my destination at 14.21 having travelled for 2 h 47 min. At what time did I start?

7. School starts at 08.55 but I arrived at 09.03. How many minutes late was I?

8. My train was 43 minutes late when it arrived in London at 12.26. At what time should it have arrived?

9. I was due to attend a meeting at 15.45 but I was 25 minutes late. At what time did I arrive for the meeting?

10. A train left its station of departure at 10.16. It was already 23 minutes late. Its journey took the same length of time as usual. If the train was due to arrive at its destination at 12.47, at what time did it actually arrive?

11. A train arrived at its destination, 7 minutes late, at 12.03. It had left its point of departure at the scheduled time of 08.42. How long should the journey normally take?

12. A train arrived at its destination at 16.56. The journey should have taken $5\frac{1}{2}$ h, but unfortunately, this train took $\frac{3}{4}$ h longer than usual. At what time had the train set off?

145

Using a Timetable

Cheltenham Spa → Gloucester → Swindon

Mondays to Fridays

Cheltenham Spa	0617	0732	0822	0930	1024		1245	1424	1524	1624	1728	1917	2050	2132
Gloucester	0630	0748	0838	0943	1038		1258	1438	1538	1638	1742	1932	2105	2145
Stonehouse	0642	0800	0850	0955	1050		1310	1450	1550	1650	1754	1944	2117	2157
Stroud	0647	0804	0855	1000	1055		1315	1455	1555	1655	1759	1949	2123	2202
Kemble	0703	0818	0911	1016	1111		1331	1511	1611	1711	1815	2005	2140	2218
Swindon	0720	0834	0928	1033	1128		1348	1528	1628	1730	1832	2022	2157	2235

Saturdays

Cheltenham Spa	0617	0732	0815	0930	1024		1248	1424	1524	1624	1728	1917	2050	2132
Gloucester	0630	0748	0828	0943	1038		1302	1438	1538	1638	1742	1932	2105	2145
Stonehouse	0642	0800	0840	0955	1050		1314	1450	1550	1650	1754	1944	2117	2157
Stroud	0647	0804	0845	1000	1055		1319	1455	1555	1655	1759	1949	2123	2202
Kemble	0703	0818	0903	1016	1111		1335	1511	1611	1711	1815	2005	2140	2218
Swindon	0720	0834	0920	1033	1128		1352	1528	1628	1730	1832	2022	2157	2235

Sundays

Cheltenham Spa	0820		1115	1415	1630	1815	2015	2215
Gloucester	0840		1135	1430	1645	1834	2030	2230
Stonehouse	0900		1155	1442	1657	1848	2042	2242
Stroud	0910		1205	1447	1702	1854	2047	2247
Kemble	0935		1230	1503	1718	1909	2103	2303
Swindon	1005		1300	1522	1735	1926	2120	2320

Swindon → Gloucester → Cheltenham Spa

Mondays to Fridays

Swindon	0730	0848	0942	1042	1142	1300		1542	1642	1740	1837	1942	2102	2248	0050
Kemble	0745	0903	0957	1057	1157	1315		1557	1657	1755	1851	1957	2118	2303	0106
Stroud	0801	0919	1013	1113	1213	1331		1613	1713	1810	1905	2013	2134	2319	0123
Stonehouse	0806	0924	1018	1118	1218	1336		1618	1718	——	1910	2018	2139	2324	0128
Gloucester	0819	0937	1031	1131	1231	1353		1631	1731	1827	1923	2034	2152	2337	0141
Cheltenham Spa	0833	0953	1045	1153	1245	1409		1647	1820	1842	1937	2048	2205	2350	0155

Saturdays

Swindon	0730	0848	0942		1142	1242		1542	1642	1742	1842	1937	2102	0200
Kemble	0745	0903	0957		1157	1257		1557	1657	1757	1857	1951	2118	0230
Stroud	0801	0919	1013		1213	1313		1613	1713	1813	1913	2005	2134	0255
Stonehouse	0806	0924	1018		1218	1318		1618	1718	1818	1918	2010	2139	0305
Gloucester	0819	0937	1031		1231	1331		1631	1731	1832	1931	2023	2155	0325
Cheltenham Spa	0833	0953	1045		1253	1358		1647	1820	1851	1945	2037	2208	0345

Sundays

Swindon	0955		1235	1550	1734	1945	2210
Kemble	1025		1305	1605	1753	2000	2225
Stroud	1050		1330	1621	1808	2016	2241
Stonehouse	1100		1340	1626	1813	2021	2246
Gloucester	1120		1400	1644	1830	2034	2259
Cheltenham Spa	1140		1420	1658	1851	2104	2312

Exercise 11

Answer these using the timetable given:

1. If I leave Cheltenham Spa at 14.24, at what time would I arrive in Swindon?

2. If I leave Kemble on Tuesday at 19.57 at what time would I arrive in Gloucester?

3. If I leave Stroud at 09.19 at what time would I arrive in Cheltenham Spa?

4. Give the time in minutes of the journey from Cheltenham Spa to Kemble on the 20.50 train.

5. Travelling on a Wednesday, if I miss the 21.02 train from Swindon to Stonehouse by just 5 min, how much longer must I wait for the next train?

6. At what time must I have left Stroud to arrive in Gloucester at 23.37?

7. What is the time of the last train on a Saturday from Gloucester to Swindon?

8. If I left Stonehouse at 18.48 to travel to Swindon, on which day must I have travelled?

9. Travelling from Kemble on Friday, I must arrive in Stonehouse before half past two in the afternoon. At what time must I leave Kemble?

10. If I arrived in Gloucester at 13.31 having travelled from Stroud, on which day must I have travelled?

11. How long does the journey take from Gloucester to Swindon if I leave Gloucester at 07.48?

12. I want to travel from Swindon to Stonehouse, leaving Swindon between 5 o'clock and 7 o'clock on a Monday evening. Which train can I catch?

147

Exercise 12

Answer these using the timetable given on p. 146:

1. On a Sunday, travelling to Stroud from Cheltenham Spa, which train must I catch to be in Stroud just after midday (give the time it leaves Cheltenham Spa)?

2. I must be in Gloucester by 12 o'clock (noon) on a Thursday, travelling from Kemble. Which train should I catch?

3. A girl from Stonehouse has an interview in Swindon at quarter past ten on Monday morning. The place where the interview is to be held is 15 min from the station. Which train should the girl catch?

4. A man from Swindon needs to spend $2\frac{1}{4}$ h in Gloucester on business. He needs to be back in Swindon before 2 o'clock in the afternoon. What is the latest time he can set off from Swindon on a Wednesday?

The Calendar

Many different calendars have been used in various parts of the world. Our calendar is based on the Roman calendar. The oldest Roman calendar is probably due to Romulus, the first King of Rome (753–715 BC). The year was 304 days long and was divided into ten months, the first month being Martius (March).

Numa Pompilius, the second king (715–672 BC) is said to have added the two months Januarius and Februarius.

The months were:

(1) Martius	(5) Quintilis	(9) Novembris
(2) Aprilis	(6) Sextilis	(10) Decembris
(3) Maius	(7) Septembris	(11) Januarius
(4) Junius	(8) Octobris	(12) Februarius

When Julius Caesar ruled Rome he decided to make the calendar astronomically correct. He decreed that the year 46 BC would have 445 days, and following that year, each year would have 365 days, with an extra day every fourth year. He decreed that the year should begin with Januarius. Quintilis, the month in which he was born, was changed to Julius. The month of Sextilis was later named after the Emperor Augustus.

The Julian calendar was used until AD 1582 when it was changed slightly by Pope Gregory XIII. It was calculated that a year was not $365\frac{1}{4}$ days long but was 365 days, 5 h, 49 min and 12 s long. In the countries that accepted this new-style calendar, the day after 4 October 1582 became 15 October. The Gregorian calendar was not adopted in Great Britain until 1752 when 11 days were 'lost'.

In the Julian calendar a year is a leap year if it divides exactly by 4 (just divide the last two digits). This is also true of the Gregorian calendar except when the last two digits of a year are both zeros. Then, the first two digits must also divide exactly by 4 (that is, the year must divide by 400). So in the Julian calendar the first year in each new century was a leap year, while in the Gregorian calendar only one in four was a leap year.

e.g. 1 1964 was a leap year (64 divides exactly by 4).

e.g. 2 1938 was not a leap year.

e.g. 3 2200 will not be a leap year (22 does not divide exactly by 4).

Other calendars have since been suggested. In 1931, two schemes were put forward, one was for 13 months of 28 days and the other was as follows:

Jan	31 days	Apr	31 days	July	31 days	Oct	31 days
Feb	30 days	May	30 days	Aug	30 days	Nov	30 days
Mar	30 days	June	30 days	Sept	30 days	Dec	30 days

In both schemes an extra day at the end of each year would be needed. Leap years would be as in the Gregorian calendar. Neither scheme was accepted.

Exercise 13

1. Which of the following years were leap years?
   1946, 1952, 1957, 1960, 1963, 1970, 1972, 1978

2. How many days are there in October?

3. How many days were there in February 1934?

4. How many days were there in May 1972?

5. How many days are there from midnight on 24 April to midnight on 9 May?

6. How many days were there from 05.30 on 17 December 1963 until 05.30 on 6 January 1964?

7. How many days were there from noon on 21 February 1948 until noon on 5 March 1948?

8. Our school summer holidays were from 21 July until 3 September inclusive. How many days was that?

9. I set off on holiday on 4 August and returned on 15 August. How many nights did I spend away?

10. A notice stated that our local cinema would be closed from 23 December until 2 January, inclusive. On how many days would it be closed?

11. A play was due to run for 10 successive nights. If its first night was on 28 April, what would be the date of its final night?

12. How many days are there from 6 August until 6 September, inclusive?

13. How many days are there from 19 November until 19 December, excluding those dates?

14. How many days were there from 3 September 1963 until 5 September 1964, inclusive?

15. Find the number of days from midnight on 19 April 1975 to midnight on 12 July 1978.

16. What is the date 50 days after 1 February 1974?

Exercise 14

1. If 7 January is a Saturday, on what day is 28 January?

2. If 11 January is a Monday, on what day is 29 July?

3. If 6 Aug is a Thursday, on what day is 21 Aug?

4. If 4 April is a Wednesday, on what day is 30 April?

5. It is Friday, 13 April. On what day, of the same year, will 19 May fall?

6. How many hours are there from 11 o'clock in the morning on Tuesday 18 May until 10 o'clock in the morning on 23 May of the same year?

7. If 20 August happens to be a Thursday, what day will 27 September be?

8. If it is 19 March today, what will be the date in exactly 5 weeks' time?

9. 24 September is a Monday. What will be the date of the first Monday in November?

10. 28 July was the date of the last Saturday in that month. What was the date of the first Saturday in March of the same year?

11. How many leap years were there from 1867 to 1979?

12. Peter Kay's grandfather was 53 years old on 16 October, 1982. In which year was he born?

Time Zones

Since the Sun appears to rise in the east, places east of Greenwich have noon before it is noon at Greenwich (noon GMT), while places to the west have their noon later.

In 24 h, the Earth rotates through 360°.
In 1 h, the Earth rotates 15°.

The world is divided into 24 *time zones*. The time zones follow the lines of longitude. (Places to the east are ahead in time by about 1 h for every 15° E. Places to the west are behind by about 1 h for every 15° W.)

Exercise 15   A Holiday in Corfu

You can fly to Corfu from:	Departure Airport and Day	No. of Nights	First Departure	Last Departure	Take-off Time	Home Landing	Flight Code	Sup. (£)
Gatwick 3 h 25 min	GATWICK (Mon)	7/14	2 May	24 Oct/17 Oct	17.45	16.45	5209	18
Luton 3 h 30 min Bristol 3 h 35 min	LUTON (Thu)	7/14	5 May	20 Oct/13 Oct	07.30	00.45 (Fri)	5210	0
Cardiff 3 h 40 min Birmingham 3 h 35 min	BRISTOL (Mon)	7/14	2 May	24 Oct/17 Oct	09.15	01.30 (Tue)	5211	16
East Midlands 3 h 40 min Manchester 3 h 45 min	CARDIFF (Mon)	14	2 May	17 Oct	17.45	16.45	5212*	26
Teesside 3 h 45 min Newcastle 3 h 50 min	BIRMINGHAM (Thu)	7/14	5 May	20 Oct/13 Oct	07.30	15.15	5213	19
Glasgow 3 h 55 min Edinburgh 3 h 55 min	E. MIDLANDS (Mon)	14	9 May	10 Oct	17.45	16.45	5214*	27
The times in Corfu is 2 h ahead of the time in the UK.	MANCHESTER (Mon)	7/14	2 May	24 Oct/17 Oct	08.45	01.45 (Tue)	5215	20
	MANCHESTER (Mon)	10	2 May	17 Oct	08.45	16.45 (Thu)	5215	0
The Sup. column shows the flight supplements.	MANCHESTER (Thu)	7/14	5 May	20 Oct/13 Oct	07.00	16.45	5216	24
	MANCHESTER (Thu)	11	5 May	20 Oct	07.00	01.45 (Tue)	5216	0
	TEESSIDE (Thu)	14	12 May	13 Oct	17.00	15.15	5220*	34
	NEWCASTLE (Thu)	7/14	5 May	20 Oct/13 Oct	08.30	15.15	5217	33
	GLASGOW (Mon)	14	2 May	17 Oct	16.30	01.15 (Tue)	5218*	36
	EDINGBURGH (Thu)	14	5 May	6 Oct	16.45	15.45	5219*	45
Please Quote: Flight Code, Hotel Code and Number of Nights required								
All flights weekly except those marked *fortnightly.								
REMEMBER TO ADD: AIRPORT CHARGES £ 10.30, INSURANCE 7 nts £ 6.50, 10/11 nts £ 7.20, 14 nts £7.80								

Use the information above to help you to answer these questions:

1. Ian and Paula Wilson travelled from Luton to Corfu on 7 July.
    (a) At what time did they take off?
    (b) What was the time in Corfu when they landed?
    (c) What was the time in Corfu when they took off?

2. Ellen and Andrew MacDonald flew from Glasgow to Corfu on 15 August.
    (a) How many nights' holiday did they have?
    (b) On what day did they take off?
    (c) What was the time in Corfu when they landed?
    (d) What was the time in Corfu when they took off?

3. For each departure airport given, work out the time in Corfu when:
    (a) the aeroplane lands in Corfu,
    (b) the aeroplane takes off from Corfu.

Exercise 16   Miscellaneous Questions ━━━━━━

1. How many months are there in 7 years?

2. How many years are there in 108 months?

3. Part of a calendar for May is given. Copy and complete it.

MAY

Sun	Mon	Tues	Wed	Thurs	Fri	Sat
		1	2	3	4	5
6	7	8	9			
		15	16	17		

(a) On which day is 30 May?
(b) What is the date of the last Sunday in May?
(c) How many Tuesdays are there in May?
(d) On which day is 6 June in the same year?
(e) On which day is 23 April in the same year?

4. There was a new moon at 06.39 on 11 January. The next new moon was at 19.23 on 9 February. How many days, hours and minutes were there between the full moons?

5. A baby was born on 2 March last year. How many months old was the baby on 2 October this year?

6. A tropical year is 365.24 days long. Use a calculator to find the length of the year in days, hours and minutes, giving the time to the nearest minute.

7. A sidereal month is 27.32 days long. Change this to days, hours and minutes correct to the nearest minute.

8. The maths lesson times for a second-year class were Mon 35 min, Tues 1 h 10 min, Wed 35 min, Fri 35 min. Calculate the total weekly time for maths.

9. My watch gains 4 s per month. How many minutes and seconds will it gain in 2 years?

10. A tap can fill a bath at a rate of 1 l every 4 s.
(a) How many litres is that per minute?
(b) How long will 56 l take to run into the bath?

11 Area

Rectangular Areas

Exercise 1

Calculate the area of each of these rectangles:

1.
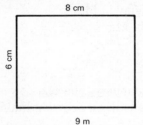

2.
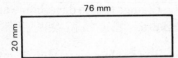

	Length	*Breadth*
3.	7 cm	7 cm
4.	12 cm	6 cm
5.	15 m	7 m
6.	40 mm	18 mm
7.	35 mm	90 mm
8.	24 m	6 m

Exercise 2

Calculate the area of each of these rectangles:

1.
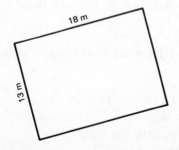

2.

3.
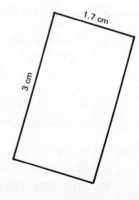

Length	Breadth	Length	Breadth
4. 96 mm	40 mm	**10.** 47.1 cm	34 cm
5. 120 m	90 m	**11.** 1.62 m	2.3 m
6. 52 cm	14 cm	**12.** 5.03 m	1.9 m
7. 84 cm	37 cm	**13.** 6.5 cm	0.8 cm
8. 2.8 m	1.7 m	**14.** 5.6 m	0.31 m
9. 9.3 cm	4.2 cm	**15.** 150 m	78.4 m

Exercise 3

1. A rectangular field measures 150 m by 70 m. Calculate its area.

2. A rectangular lawn is 73 ft long and 52 ft wide. Find its area.

3. A page of a book measures 9 in by 6 in. Find its area.

4. A piece of rectangular card is 45 cm long and 30 cm wide. How many square counters with side 1 cm can be cut from the card?

5. A football pitch is 110 yd long and 75 yd wide. Calculate its area.

6. What is the area of a classroom floor that measures 14 m by 8.4 m?

7. There are two bedrooms in a house. One is 4.3 m square. The other measures 5.1 m by 3.6 m.
   (a) Which is the larger room?
   (b) How much bigger is it?

8. A piece of aluminium foil is 12 in long and 10 in wide. Find the total area of 20 pieces.

9. A rectangular garden, 20 m by 12 m, is to be seeded using grass seed. 80 g of seed cover 1 m^2.
   (a) How many grams of seed are needed?
   (b) If each packet of seed holds 5 kg, how many packets must I buy?

10. A rectangular garden is 18 m long. It is fenced all around except for a 3 m gap. Thirty-eight panels of fencing are used, each 1.5 m wide. Calculate the area of the garden.

If your calculator has the key x^2, then you can quickly find the area of a square when given the length of its side.

If your calculator has the square root key, $\sqrt{}$, then you can easily find the length of each side of a square when given its area.

Exercise 4

A Find the area of the following squares where the lengths of the sides are given. Write your answers to questions 11 onwards correct to 3 significant figures.

e.g. Length of side = 2.9 cm
Key in $\boxed{AC}$ $\boxed{2}$ $\boxed{.}$ $\boxed{9}$ $\boxed{x^2}$
Area of square = $\underline{8.41 \text{ cm}^2}$

Note (1) You may need to use a function key for x^2 to work, e.g. $\boxed{AC}$ $\boxed{2}$ $\boxed{.}$ $\boxed{9}$ $\boxed{F}$ $\boxed{x^2}$

(2) $\boxed{AC}$ is the key that clears the display. It may be a different key on your calculator.

On some calculators this method will work:
Key in $\boxed{AC}$ $\boxed{2}$ $\boxed{.}$ $\boxed{9}$ $\boxed{\times}$ $\boxed{=}$
Try it.

1. 1.7 cm	**5.** 67 cm	**9.** 92 mm	**13.** 198 mm
2. 26 cm	**6.** 4.9 m	**10.** 8.3 cm	**14.** 5.06 m
3. 3.1 m	**7.** 58 mm	**11.** 25.4 m	**15.** 39.2 cm
4. 14 m	**8.** 7.5 cm	**12.** 69.1 cm	**16.** 0.863 m

B Find the lengths of each side of these squares where the area is given. Write your answers to 3 significant figures.

e.g. Area = 6.76 m²
Key in $\boxed{AC}$ $\boxed{6}$ $\boxed{.}$ $\boxed{7}$ $\boxed{6}$ $\boxed{\sqrt{}}$
or if you need a function key
Key in $\boxed{AC}$ $\boxed{6}$ $\boxed{.}$ $\boxed{7}$ $\boxed{6}$ $\boxed{F}$ $\boxed{\sqrt{}}$
Side of square = $\underline{2.6 \text{ m}}$

1. 441 cm²	**5.** 1764 mm²	**9.** 6241 m²	**13.** 1.538 m²
2. 3.24 m²	**6.** 39.69 m²	**10.** 313 600 mm²	**14.** 4.78 cm²
3. 8.41 m²	**7.** 7569 cm²	**11.** 0.1225 cm²	**15.** 8072 cm²
4. 256 m²	**8.** 88.36 cm²	**12.** 0.2116 m²	**16.** 0.7813 m²

C Try to answer the questions in part B without using the square root key. Explain your method.

Exercise 5

1. (a) Write the lengths and breadths of as many different rectangles as possible that have an area of 36 cm². (The lengths and breadths should measure a whole number of centimetres. Note that a length of 36 cm and a breadth of 1 cm is the same as a length of 1 cm and a breadth of 36 cm.)
   (b) Find the perimeter of each rectangle found in part (a).

2. Answer question 1 for these areas:
   (a) 20 cm²   (b) 15 cm²   (c) 13 cm²   (d) 29 cm²   (e) 24 cm²

3. (a) Do all rectangles that have the same area have the same perimeter?
   (b) Do all rectangles that have the same perimeter have the same area?

4. (a) Do all squares that have the same area have the same perimeter?
   (b) Do all squares that have the same perimeter have the same area?

Exercise 6

1. (a) Draw a 6 cm square.   (b) Find the area of a 6 cm square.

2. Draw a rectangle with an area of 6 cm².

3. Is a 6 cm square the same size as 6 cm²?

4. Is a 8 cm square the same size as 8 cm²?

5. Is a 2 cm square the same size as 2 cm²?

6. Is a 1 cm square the same size as 1 cm²?

7. Is it possible to draw a shape that is not a square yet has an area of 9 cm²?

8. Must an area of 16 cm² be a square?

Exercise 7

1. Cut out rectangles of size 5 cm by 5 cm, 3 cm by 2 cm, 1 cm by 3 cm, 4 cm by 2 cm, 2 cm by 1 cm, 6 cm by 2 cm, 2 cm by 3 cm, 5 cm by 2 cm, 2 cm by 4 cm and 1 cm by 1 cm.

2. (a) Can the ten rectangles be placed together to form a square?
   (b) If a square can be made, draw it and give the length of its side.

Exercise 8

1. (a) How many millimetres are there in 1 cm?
   (b) How many square millimetres are there in 1 cm^2?

2. (a) What is the area of the square in fig. 1?
   (Give your answer in square centimetres.)   Fig. 1

   1 cm

   (b) What is the area of the square in fig. 2?
   (Give your answer in square millimetres.)   Fig. 2

   10 mm

   (c) Since both squares are the same size, how many square millimetres are there in 1 cm^2?

3. Draw a sketch of a square with sides of length 1 m. What is the area of this square (give your answer in square metres)?

4. Now draw a sketch of another square with sides that are also 1 m in length, but this time label the length of each side in centimetres. What is the area of this second square (give your answer in square centimetres)?

5. Since the squares in questions 3 and 4 have the same area, how many square centimetres are there in 1 m^2?

6. 12 in = 1 ft.
   How many square inches are there in 1 ft^2?
   (A sketch may help.)

7. How many square feet are there in 1 yd^2? (3 ft = 1 yd.)

8. How many square yards are there in 1 mile^2? (1760 yd = 1 mile.)

Exercise 9

1. Write the following in square millimetres:
   (a) $2\,cm^2$ (b) $9\,cm^2$ (c) $15\,cm^2$ (d) $4.5\,cm^2$ (e) $6.28\,cm^2$

2. Write the following in square centimetres:
   (a) $400\,mm^2$ (c) $1100\,mm^2$ (e) $563\,mm^2$
   (b) $800\,mm^2$ (d) $50\,mm^2$

3. Write the following in square centimetres:
   (a) $2\,m^2$ (b) $7\,m^2$ (c) $27\,m^2$ (d) $8.4\,m^2$ (e) $3\frac{1}{2}\,m^2$

4. Write the following in square metres:
   (a) $60\,000\,cm^2$ (c) $40\,000\,cm^2$ (e) $52\,000\,cm^2$
   (b) $90\,000\,cm^2$ (d) $15\,000\,cm^2$

5. Write the following in square inches:
   (a) $3\,ft^2$ (b) $5\,ft^2$ (c) $8\,ft^2$ (d) $6\,ft^2$ (e) $10\,ft^2$

6. A farmer owns $1\,km^2$ of land. How many square metres is that?

Exercise 10

A 1. A rectangle is 8 cm long and 6 cm wide. How many 2 cm squares will cover it?

2. How many 2 cm squares are needed to cover these rectangles:
   (a) 10 cm by 4 cm?   (b) 18 cm by 12 cm?   (c) 8 cm square?

3. How many 3 cm squares are needed to cover these rectangles:
   (a) 21 cm by 9 cm?   (b) 18 cm by 12 cm?   (c) 15 cm square?

4. What is the biggest number of square counters of side 2 cm that can be cut from a rectangular piece of card measuring:
   (a) 12 cm by 8 cm?   (b) 10 cm by 7 cm?

B To answer the question 'How many 2 cm squares are needed to cover a rectangle measuring 14 cm by 8 cm?', one approach could be:

14 cm

8 cm

1. How many 2 cm squares will fit in a length of 14 cm? (See the diagram.)

159

2. How many rows of 2 cm squares will fit in the breadth of 8 cm?

3. How many 2 cm squares are needed to cover a rectangle measuring 14 cm by 8 cm?

C **1.** How many tiles, 15 cm square, will be needed to tile a bathroom wall measuring 180 cm by 150 cm?

2. (a) If carpet tiles were 1 m square, how many would be needed to carpet a floor measuring 4 m by 3 m?
(b) How many 500 mm square carpet tiles would be needed to carpet the same floor?

3. An area measuring 12 m by 8 m is to be paved using paving stones that are 80 cm square. How many paving stones are needed?

4. (a) A patio measuring 9 m by 6 m is to be paved with paving stones that are 600 mm square. How many paving stones are needed?
(b) If, instead, paving stones that measure 750 mm by 600 mm are used to pave the 9 m by 6 m patio, how many of this size are needed?

5. Planks measure 1.8 m by 15 cm. How many are needed to floor a room that is 3.6 m long and 2.4 m wide?

6. A rectangular garden is 18 m long and 12 m wide. How many pieces of turf, 45 cm by 30 cm, are needed to turf the garden?

7. What is the greatest number of handkerchiefs that are 42 cm square that can be cut from a piece of material measuring:
(a) 2.1 m by 1.68 m?
(b) 2.46 m by 1.05 m?

8. Am I definitely able to cut 40 dusters measuring 60 cm by 40 cm from a piece of material that is 6 m long and 1.6 m wide?

9. Am I definitely able to cut 50 dusters measuring 60 cm by 40 cm from a rectangular piece of material of area 12 m²?

10. Calculate the greatest number of dusters measuring 40 cm by 30 cm that can be cut from a piece of material of length 6 m and breadth 2 m.

Calculate the missing length in each of these rectangles:

1.

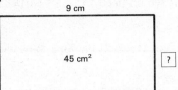

9 cm

45 cm²   ?

3.

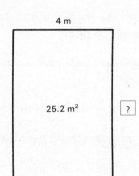

4 m

25.2 m²   ?

2.

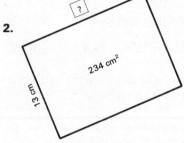

?

234 cm²

13 cm

4.

?

22.31 cm²

2.3 cm

Copy and complete:

M

	Length	Breadth	Area
5.	8 m		56 m²
6.		7 cm	91 cm²
7.		40 mm	2400 mm²
8.	30 cm		750 cm²
9.		14 m	294 m²
10.	42 m		1554 m²
11.	12 mm		102 mm²
12.	2.3 cm		4.37 cm²
13.		3.1 cm	53.32 cm²
14.		6.7 m	107.2 m²
15.	3.5 m		3.57 m²

Exercise 12

1. A rectangle is 5 m long. Its area is 15 m². Find its width.

2. Find the length of a room 4 m wide which need 24 m² of carpet to cover the floor.

3. A piece of paper has an area of 315 cm². If it is 21 cm long, how wide is it?

4. A gym of length 24 m has an area of 408 m². Find its width.

5. A square handkerchief has a perimeter of 164 cm; find its area.

6. A square has an area of 81 cm²; find its perimeter.

7. A rectangle of length 8 m has an area of 52 m²; find its perimeter.

8. A square with side 12 cm has an area twice that of a rectangle with breadth 8 cm. Calculate the length of the rectangle.

Exercise 13 $\boxed{R}$

Calculate the area of these shapes:

1.

23 m

4 m   4 m

10 m   7 m

14 m

2.

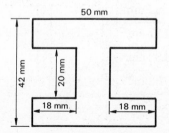

50 mm

42 mm

20 mm

18 mm   18 mm

162

1. Calculate the area of each shaded border:

(a)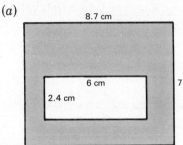

(b)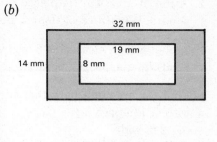

2. A rectangle measures 8 cm by 3 cm. Calculate the area of a border, 2 cm wide, which goes around the outside of this rectangle.

3. Calculate the area of each shaded border:

(a)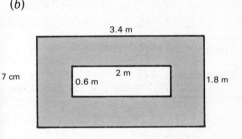

(b)

4. A rectangle measures 7.5 cm by 6 cm. Calculate the area of a border, 1.5 cm wide, which goes around the outside of this rectangle.

Exercise 15

A Calculate the area of each shaded border:

1.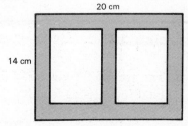

The border is 3 m wide.

2.

The borders are 2 cm wide.

B **1.** A rectangular rug measuring 3 m by 2 m is on the floor of a room 5 m by 4 m. What area of floor is not covered by the rug?

2. A rug of area 8 m² is placed on the floor of a room that is 3.5 m square. What area of floor is not covered by the rug?

3. A photograph measuring 8 cm by 6 cm has a 1 cm border around it. Find the area of the border.

4. Find the area of a path that surrounds a lawn 20 m long and 9 m wide if the path is:
(*a*) 2 m wide   (*b*) $1\frac{1}{2}$ m wide

5. A sheet of tin is 1.5 m long and 0.8 m wide. A strip, 10 cm wide, is cut off all round.
(*a*) Find the area of the tin cut off.
(*b*) What area remains?

6. A photograph of length 24 cm has an area of 408 cm². It is mounted so that it has a border of 20 mm width all round it. Calculate the area of the border.

Exercise 16

1. The diagram shows a net of a cube. Calculate its total surface area if its edges are 4 cm in length.

2. A cuboid is 6 cm long, 5 cm wide and 3 cm high. Calculate its total surface area. (A net may help.)

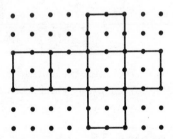

3. A cake tin is 230 mm long, 210 mm wide and 90 mm deep. Calculate the total surface area of the tin without its lid.

Exercise 17

1. The area of the given rectangle is 56 m². Find the missing length.

?

7 m

2. A rectangle has an area of 66 m². If it is 11 m long, find its breadth.

3. The front of a textbook has an area of 330 cm². If its length is 22 cm, calculate its breadth.

4. The length of a rectangle is 9 cm. If it has an area of 60.3 cm², find its breadth.

5. My desk is 1.5 m long. How wide is it if the area of the top is 0.9 m²?

6. A painting has an area of 1.008 m². If its breadth is 0.84 m, find its length.

7. Part of a bathroom wall is tiled using 4 in square tiles. 162 tiles are used. If the wall being tiled is 3 ft wide, how long is it? (12 in = 1 ft.)

8. A kitchen floor is 2.85 m long. It is tiled using 285, 15 cm square tiles. How wide is the floor of the kitchen?

Areas of Parallelograms and Triangles

Exercise 18

1. Draw a parallelogram on a piece of paper. Cut it out.

   Using one straight cut, cut your parallelogram into two pieces so that the two pieces can be moved to form a rectangle.

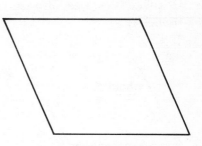

2. Draw a triangle on a piece of paper. Cut it out.

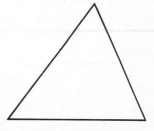

   Using two straight cuts, cut your triangle into three pieces so that the three pieces can be moved to form a rectangle.

Exercise 19

Using the ideas in Exercise 18 and the diagrams in this exercise, try to find formulae for the area of these shapes:

1.

Area of parallelogram = $\boxed{?}$

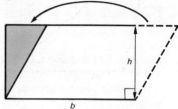

2.

Area of triangle = $\boxed{?}$

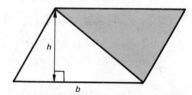

Exercise 20 — $\boxed{R}$

Calculate the area of each of the following parallelograms and triangles:

1.

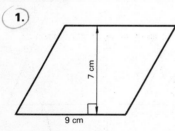

7 cm

9 cm

3.

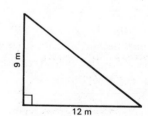

9 m

12 m

2.

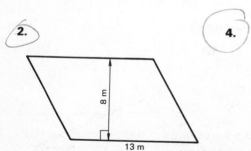

8 m

13 m

4.

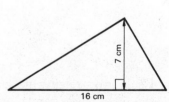

7 cm

16 cm

5.

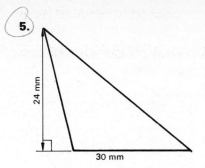

24 mm

30 mm

9.

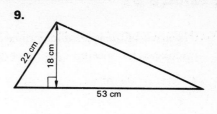

22 cm

18 cm

53 cm

6.

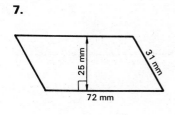

6 m

8.2 m

10.

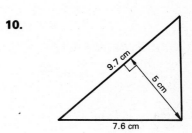

9.7 cm

5 cm

7.6 cm

7.

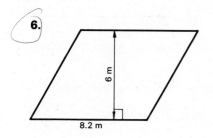

25 mm

31 mm

72 mm

11.

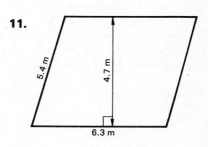

5.4 m

4.7 m

6.3 m

8.

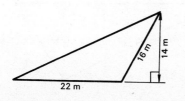

16 m

14 m

22 m

12.

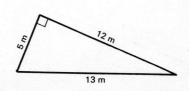

5 m

12 m

13 m

Exercise 21

The areas of these parallelograms and triangles are given. In each case, calculate the missing base or perpendicular height.

1. Area = 96 m²

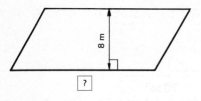

4. Area = 54 m²

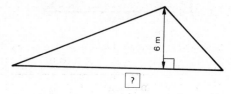

2. Area = 117 cm²

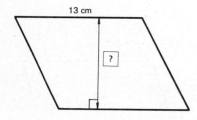

5. Area = 312 mm²

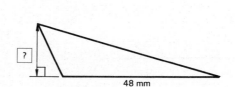

6. Area = 14.7 m²

3. Area = 48 cm²

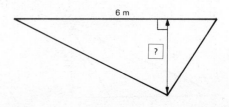

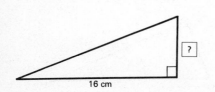

Exercise 22

Copy and complete these tables:

A Parallelograms

	Base	Perpendicular height	Area
1.	8 cm	7 cm	
2.		6 m	66 m^2
3.	9 m		72 m^2
4.	12 cm		72 cm^2
5.		8 m	92 m^2
6.		7 cm	274.4 cm^2
7.	51 mm		1734 mm^2
8.		3.7 m	31.45 m^2

B Triangles

	Base	Perpendicular height	Area
1.	14 m	9 m	
2.	20 cm		80 cm^2
3.		8 cm	52 cm^2
4.	17 m		85 m^2
5.	30 m		322.5 m^2
6.		12 m	49.8 m^2
7.	89 mm		2047 mm^2
8.		5.3 m	36.04 m^2

Exercise 23

1. Do all parallelograms that have the same-size area have the same-size perimeter?

2. Do all parallelograms that have the same-size perimeter have the same-size area?

3. Do all triangles that have the same-size area have the same-size perimeter?

4. Do all triangles that have the same-size perimeter have the same-size area?

Exercise 24

1. Construct $\triangle PQR$ where $QR = 65\,mm$, $\angle PQR = 60°$ and $PQ = 40\,mm$. By measuring a perpendicular height, then by calculating, find the area of the triangle.

2. Construct parallelogram ABCD where $AB = 50\,mm$, $BC = 35\,mm$ and $\angle ABC = 45°$. By measuring, then by calculating, find the area of the parallelogram.

3. A parallelogram has an area of $70\,cm^2$. If its perpendicular height is 5 cm, calculate the length of its base.

4. The base of a triangle measures 24 cm. If the triangle has an area of $132\,cm^2$, calculate its perpendicular height.

5. A parallelogram has an area of $90\,cm^2$ and a perpendicular height of 9 cm. A triangle has the same-size area and the same-size base as the parallelogram. Find the perpendicular height of the triangle.

6. A triangle has an area of $195\,cm^2$ and a base of length 26 cm. A parallelogram with base 21 cm has the same-size perpendicular height as the triangle. Calculate the area of the parallelogram.

7. A triangle and a parallelogram have the same-size base (9.2 cm). They also have the same-size area. The parallelogram has a perpendicular height of 3.8 cm. Find the perpendicular height of the triangle.

8. A triangle has a base of 94 mm and a perpendicular height of 52 mm. A parallelogram having the same-size area as the triangle also has a perpendicular height of 52 mm. Calculate the length of the base of the parallelogram.

Areas of Trapezia, Rhombuses and Kites

Exercise 25

1. Draw a trapezium on a piece of paper.

Cut it out.
Using one straight cut, cut your trapezium into two pieces so that the two pieces can be moved to form a parallelogram.

2. Make two copies of a rhombus on a piece of paper.

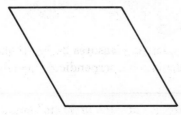

Cut them out.
(*a*) Using one straight cut, cut one rhombus into two pieces so that the two pieces can be moved to form a parallelogram that is not a rectangle nor a rhombus.
(*b*) Using two straight cuts, cut the other rhombus into three pieces so that the pieces can be moved to form a rectangle.

1. (*a*)

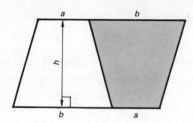

(*b*)

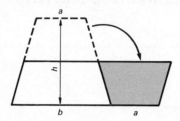

Area of trapezium = ?

2.

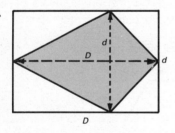

Length of long diagonal = *D* units
Length of short diagonal = *d* units
Area of kite = ?

3.

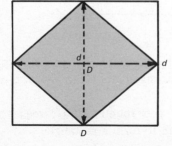

Length of long diagonal = *D* units
Length of short diagonal = *d* units
Area of rhombus = ?

Exercise 27

Calculate the areas of these trapezia:

1.

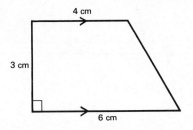

4 cm
3 cm
6 cm

2.

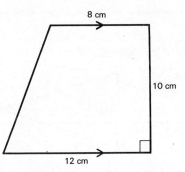

8 cm
10 cm
12 cm

3.

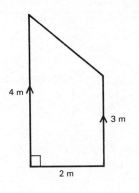

4 m
3 m
2 m

4.

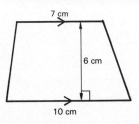

7 cm
6 cm
10 cm

5.

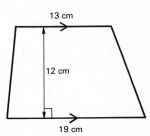

13 cm
12 cm
19 cm

6.

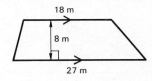

18 m
8 m
27 m

7.

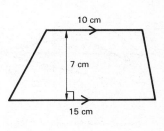

10 cm
7 cm
15 cm

8.

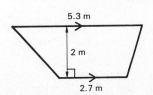

5.3 m
2 m
2.7 m

9.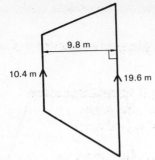

10.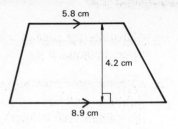

Exercise 28

Calculate the areas of these kites and rhombuses:

1.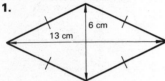

Long diagonal = 13 cm
Short diagonal = 6 cm

4.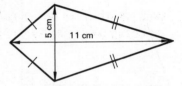

Long diagonal = 11 cm
Short diagonal = 5 cm

2.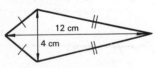

Long diagonal = 12 cm
Short diagonal = 4 cm

5.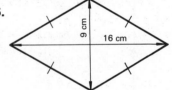

Long diagonal = 16 cm
Short diagonal = 9 cm

3.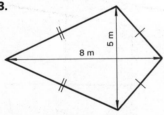

Long diagonal = 8 m
Short diagonal = 5 m

Exercise 29

1. Calculate the area of a kite with long diagonal measuring 9 m and short diagonal 4 m.

2. Calculate the area of a rhombus with diagonals measuring:
   (a) 14 m and 7 m   (c) 7 m and 4.6 m
   (b) 26 mm and 34 mm   (d) 6.7 m and 3.8 m

3. Calculate the area of a kite with diagonals measuring:
   (a) 10 cm and 3 cm   (c) 9.6 m and 4 m
   (b) 42 mm and 15 mm   (d) 7.8 m and 2.6 m

4. A trapezium has parallel sides of lengths 16 m and 9 m. The perpendicular distance between the parallel sides is 8 m. Calculate its area.

5. Calculate the area of a square where each diagonal measures 8 cm.

Exercise 30

Here is a plan showing the plots of land that are being sold for the building of eight houses.
It has been drawn to a scale of 1 : 1000.

1. Calculate the area of each plot.

2. Which is the largest plot?

3. What is the area of the smallest plot?

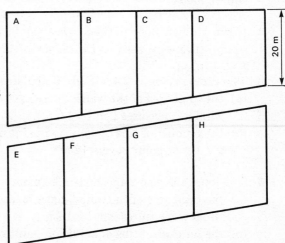

This is a plan of the ground floor of the house built on plot B. The scale is 1 : 200.

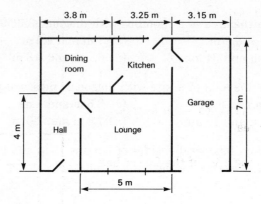

1. Calculate the area of:
   (a) the lounge,
   (b) the garage,
   (c) the dining room,
   (d) the kitchen,
   (e) the hall.

2. Calculate the area of land not covered by the house.

3. Find the cost of carpeting the lounge if carpet costs £16.95 per square metre.

4. If the kitchen floor is tiled, what would the tiles cost if 250 mm square tiles were used and if a pack of 12 tiles cost £5.85?

5. The dining room is 2.4 m high. Calculate:
   (a) the total area of the walls (doors measure 2 m by 0.8 m and the window measures 2 m by 1.2 m),
   (b) the number of tins of emulsion paint needed to paint the walls if 1 tin of paint covers 12 m².

6. The lounge is also 2.4 m high. Calculate:
   (a) the total area of the walls (doors measure 2 m by 0.8 m and the window measures 2 m by 1.2 m),
   (b) the number of tins of emulsion paint needed to paint the walls if 1 tin of paint covers 12 m².

This plan shows the house on plot B. The scale is 1 : 400.

F is a flower bed.
S is a shed.
P is a paved area.

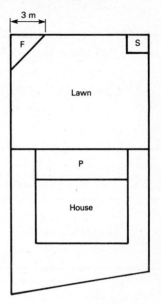

1. The shed measures 2.5 m by 2 m. Find its area.

2. Calculate the area of the flower bed.

3. The paved area is 3 m wide and follows the full length of the house. Calculate the number of 600 mm square paving stones needed. (The house plan in Exercise 31 may help you to find the length of the paved area.)

4. Calculate the area of the lawn.

5. If 35 g of fertiliser are used per square metre of lawn (35 g/m²), how many kilograms of fertiliser are needed for this lawn?

6. Another plan of the lawn is shown, to the same scale. Three possible paths have been marked out. (They have been labelled A, B and C.) Write what you notice about their areas.

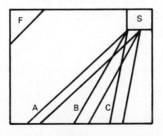

7. Weedkiller is used on exactly half of each plot shown in Exercise 30. If 100 m*l* of weedkiller will treat 30 m^2 of land, calculate, for each plot, the number of litres of weedkiller needed if weedkiller is sold in 100 m*l* bottles.

8. If an area measuring 15 m by 10 m is to be turfed, how many pieces of turf measuring 400 mm by 300 mm are needed?

12 Percentages and Money

Exercise 1

For each square, write what percentage has been shaded:

1.

5.

9.

2.

6.

10.

3.

7.

11.

4.

8.

12.

13.   **14.**   **15.**

Exercise 2   **M**

On squared paper, using a 10 by 10 square as shown for each question, shade the given percentages:

1. 40%	**4.** 65%	**7.** 14%	**10.** 68%
2. 70%	**5.** 95%	**8.** 82%	**11.** 46%
3. 35%	**6.** 53%	**9.** 27%	**12.** 9%

Exercise 3

A Write each percentage as a common fraction:

1. 91%	**5.** 81%	**9.** 59%	**13.** 93%	**17.** 33%
2. 19%	**6.** 47%	**10.** 83%	**14.** 71%	**18.** 69%
3. 67%	**7.** 11%	**11.** 7%	**15.** 63%	**19.** 41%
4. 3%	**8.** 97%	**12.** 31%	**16.** 77%	**20.** 87%

B Write each common fraction as a percentage:

1. $\dfrac{17}{100}$	**4.** $\dfrac{99}{100}$	**7.** $\dfrac{61}{100}$	**10.** $\dfrac{57}{100}$	**13.** $\dfrac{43}{100}$
2. $\dfrac{73}{100}$	**5.** $\dfrac{1}{100}$	**8.** $\dfrac{23}{100}$	**11.** $\dfrac{79}{100}$	**14.** $\dfrac{51}{100}$
3. $\dfrac{21}{100}$	**6.** $\dfrac{13}{100}$	**9.** $\dfrac{49}{100}$	**12.** $\dfrac{31}{100}$	**15.** $\dfrac{89}{100}$

Exercise 4

Try these on a calculator:

Since $48\% = \dfrac{48}{100}$, key in: $\boxed{4}\ \boxed{8}\ \boxed{\div}\ \boxed{1}\ \boxed{0}\ \boxed{0}\ \boxed{=}$

The display shows 48% as a decimal.

Look carefully at your answer.

Now try these on a calculator. Change each percentage to a decimal. (Look carefully at each answer.)

1. 75% **2.** 34% **3.** 4% **4.** 21% **5.** 93%

Now answer the rest of the exercise *without using a calculator*:

6. 31%	**9.** 68%	**12.** 26%	**15.** 18%	**18.** 85%
7. 15%	**10.** 57%	**13.** 94%	**16.** 62%	**19.** 30%
8. 43%	**11.** 89%	**14.** 79%	**17.** 47%	**20.** 9%

Exercise 5

Write each decimal as a percentage:

1. 0.42	**5.** 0.72	**9.** 0.81	**13.** 0.9	**17.** 0.08
2. 0.25	**6.** 0.64	**10.** 0.65	**14.** 0.17	**18.** 0.7
3. 0.53	**7.** 0.12	**11.** 0.96	**15.** 0.06	**19.** 0.49
4. 0.35	**8.** 0.29	**12.** 0.38	**16.** 0.55	**20.** 0.67

Exercise 6

For each square, write what percentage has been shaded:

1.

2.

3.

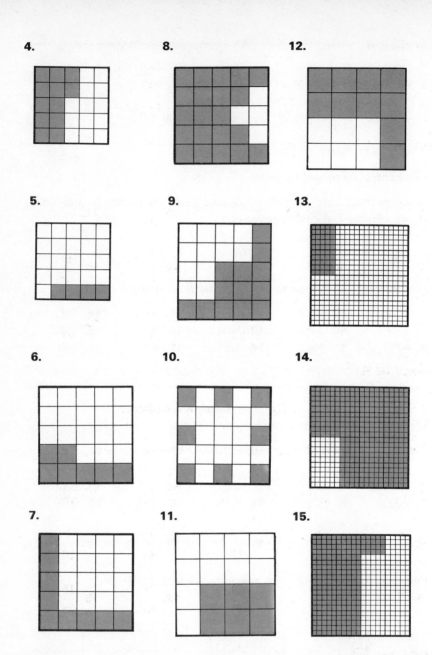

4.

5.

6.

7.

8.

9.

10.

11.

12.

13.

14.

15.

Exercise 7

Write each percentage as a common fraction in its simplest terms:

1. 10%   **2.** 40%   **3.** 50%   **4.** 25%   **5.** 75%

6. 5%	**10.** 42%	**14.** 12%	**18.** 90%	**22.** 15%
7. 35%	**11.** 66%	**15.** 64%	**19.** 72%	**23.** $12\frac{1}{2}\%$
8. 85%	**12.** 80%	**16.** 39%	**20.** 55%	**24.** $2\frac{1}{2}\%$
9. 44%	**13.** 96%	**17.** 8%	**21.** 92%	**25.** $7\frac{1}{2}\%$

Exercise 8

Write as percentages:

1. $\dfrac{3}{10}$	**4.** $\dfrac{3}{5}$	**7.** $\dfrac{9}{20}$	**10.** $\dfrac{3}{8}$	**13.** $\dfrac{11}{25}$
2. $\dfrac{7}{10}$	**5.** $\dfrac{4}{5}$	**8.** $\dfrac{13}{20}$	**11.** $\dfrac{5}{8}$	**14.** $\dfrac{9}{40}$
3. $\dfrac{1}{5}$	**6.** $\dfrac{1}{4}$	**9.** $\dfrac{19}{20}$	**12.** $\dfrac{7}{8}$	**15.** $\dfrac{23}{50}$

Exercise 9

A Check your answers to Exercise 8 with a calculator.

B Use a calculator to change each of these to a percentage:

1. $\dfrac{2}{5}$	**4.** $\dfrac{1}{8}$	**7.** $\dfrac{17}{25}$	**10.** $\dfrac{7}{40}$	**13.** $\dfrac{9}{16}$
2. $\dfrac{9}{10}$	**5.** $\dfrac{19}{25}$	**8.** $\dfrac{13}{25}$	**11.** $\dfrac{39}{40}$	**14.** $\dfrac{7}{16}$
3. $\dfrac{3}{4}$	**6.** $\dfrac{7}{20}$	**9.** $\dfrac{49}{50}$	**12.** $\dfrac{27}{80}$	**15.** $\dfrac{15}{32}$

Exercise 10

A Find:

1. 10% of 30 kg

2. 10% of 100 g

3. 10% of 50 ℓ

4. 10% of 90 m

5. 10% of £40
6. 20% of £40
7. 20% of £60
8. 20% of £600
9. 20% of 30 kg
10. 50% of £6
11. 50% of 70 kg
12. 1% of £200
13. 1% of 400 g
14. 3% of 400 m
15. 8% of 600 people
16. 5% of £300
17. 9% of 200 l

18. 90% of 500 lb
19. 90% of 20 cm
20. 80% of 90 dollars
21. 80% of £700
22. 5% of 800 people
23. 5% of 40 m
24. 40% of 80 kg
25. 40% of £35
26. 70% of 65 marks
27. 50% of 84 kg
28. 25% of 84 kg
29. 25% of £14
30. 75% of £28

B Find:

1. 50% of £18
2. 50% of £13
3. 25% of £7.56
4. 25% of 68 kg
5. 25% of 136 l
6. 70% of 200 m
7. 70% of 1.8 m
8. 75% of £1552
9. 75% of 5.76 m
10. 60% of 47 000 people

11. 45% of 19 380 votes
12. 14% of 1450 tins
13. 56% of 125 marks
14. 30% of 7 l
15. 1% of £623
16. $12\frac{1}{2}$% of £48
17. $2\frac{1}{2}$% of 1000 g
18. $33\frac{1}{3}$% of 75 l
19. $12\frac{1}{2}$% of 51.6 m
20. $7\frac{1}{2}$% of 2.32 kg

e.g. Use a calculator to find 38% of £75.

Here are three methods:

Method 1

Key in | 3 | 8 | ÷ | 1 | 0 | 0 | × | 7 | 5 | = |

or | 7 | 5 | × | 3 | 8 | ÷ | 1 | 0 | 0 | = |

(| 3 | 8 | ÷ | 1 | 0 | 0 | changes 38% into a decimal.)

Method 2

Key in | . | 3 | 8 | × | 7 | 5 | = |

184

To use this second method you need to change a percentage to a decimal in your head. Note that $32\frac{1}{2}\% = 0.325$ and $7\frac{1}{2}\% = 0.075$.

Method 3

This method will only work if you have a $\boxed{\%}$ key.

Key in $\boxed{7}\ \boxed{5}\ \boxed{\times}\ \boxed{3}\ \boxed{8}\ \boxed{\%}$

If this does not work, then you need to experiment or read the instructions for your calculator.

Exercise 11

A Use a calculator to check your answers to Exercise 10.

B Use a calculator to find:

1. 25% of £57
2. 42% of 18 *l*
3. 86% of 60 min
4. 13% of 19 kg
5. 68% of 450 people

6. 79% of 31 m^2
7. 54% of 69 francs
8. 37% of 85 km
9. $22\frac{1}{2}\%$ of 320 days
10. $2\frac{1}{2}\%$ of £76.40

Exercise 12

1. Here are the marks out of 20 for a test. Find the percentage mark for each person. List the names in order from highest percentage to lowest. Write the percentage obtained beside each name.

B. Wise $\dfrac{7}{20}$ A. Pain $\dfrac{10}{20}$ U.B. Jolly $\dfrac{17}{20}$

L. Lowe $\dfrac{3}{20}$ M.T. Case $\dfrac{15}{20}$ E. Venn $\dfrac{14}{20}$

E.B. Close $\dfrac{11}{20}$ O. Kay $\dfrac{9}{20}$ U.R. Last $\dfrac{6}{20}$

2. List these in order from highest percentage to lowest. Write the percentage beside each name. This time, the test is marked out of 25.

C.I. Dee $\dfrac{15}{25}$ R.U. Bright $\dfrac{10}{25}$ U.R. Short $\dfrac{12}{25}$

E.B. Topp $\dfrac{19}{25}$ B. Long $\dfrac{7}{25}$ E.S. Brown $\dfrac{18}{25}$

I.M. Wright $\dfrac{11}{25}$ U. Kay $\dfrac{13}{25}$

3. My bank pays 7% interest. Find 7% of £475.

4. 47% of a population of 7800 are male. How many females are there?

5. I got 25 out of 40 in a test. What percentage was that?

6. In a test, Helen got 70%. What was her mark out of 10?

7. Robert got 80% in an exam. What was his mark out of 20?

8. My percentage mark was 75%. What was my mark out of 16?

9. Our meal cost £40. To this bill 15% VAT was added. What was the total cost of the meal?

10. A pen cost £36 plus 15% VAT. What did the pen cost?

Discount

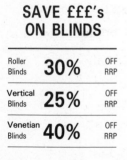

SAVE £££'s ON BLINDS

Roller Blinds	**30%**	OFF RRP
Vertical Blinds	**25%**	OFF RRP
Venetian Blinds	**40%**	OFF RRP

Save up to 20% with our first class offer

LIMITED PERIOD OFFER

The new **Clearview** window range

Economical — Versatile

Exercise 13

1. Mr and Mrs Logan bought some windows from the Clearview window range as advertised on p. 186. The normal price was £300. Find the amount of discount.

2. A bed cost £120 new. If it was sold at a discount of 25%, find the selling price.

3. A record costing £5.40 was sold at a discount of 20%. Find:
   (a) the discount,   (b) the selling price.

4. In a sale, a shop reduced its prices by 10%. Find the discount on goods that cost:
   (a) £15   (b) £62   (c) £114   (d) £2.50   (e) £23.80

5. Another shop reduced its prices by 25%. Find the sale price of goods that cost:
   (a) £62   (b) £19   (c) £3.40   (d) £14.60   (e) £29.52

6. A bicycle was priced at £120. Find its selling price if it was sold at a discount of:
   (a) 20%   (b) 5%   (c) 12%   (d) $17\frac{1}{2}\%$ (e) $33\frac{1}{3}\%$

7. What would venetian blinds cost, as advertised on p. 186, if the recommended retail price (RRP) is £30?

8. A three-piece suite costing £600 was sold at a discount of 12½%. Find (a) the discount, (b) the selling price.

Exercise 14   Miscellaneous Questions

1. A woman earns £80 per week. If she is given a rise of 3%, how much does she now earn per week?

2. A car valued at £4000 last year is now worth 20% less. How much is it now worth?

3. A man has to pay income tax on £2000. If the rate of tax is 30% p.a.*, how much must he pay?

4. Certain goods cost £50 last year. Due to inflation they now cost 7% more. How much do they now cost?

* See the glossary.

5. A watch cost a shopkeeper £15. If it was sold for 10% profit, find the selling price.

6. A credit card company charge 2% interest per month. Find the monthly interest on £74.

7. A firm making light bulbs found that 3% of a certain batch were faulty. How many were faulty out of 2600?

8. Absence from school last Monday was 14%. If 800 pupils normally attend the school, how many were absent on Monday?

Exercise 15

1. VAT at 15% is added to the price of goods costing £38. Find the selling price of the goods.

2. An article costs £78 cash. It can be bought on hire purchase for a deposit of 25% followed by 12 payments of £5.30. Calculate the cost on hire purchase.

3. A salesman gets $7\frac{1}{2}\%$ commission on all sales. How much is that on sales of £684?

4. In measuring a line of length 360 mm, my error was 5%. Find:
(a) the smallest possible length of the line,
(b) the largest possible length of the line.

5. Five years ago, the population of a certain town was 18 500. It has since grown by 17%. What is its population now?

6. A factory made 4376 computers last year. This year, production has increased by $12\frac{1}{2}\%$. Calculate the number made this year.

7. Annie saved 28% of her earnings. How much did she save out of £247?

8. Some solder is made up of 60% lead, 35% tin and 5% bismuth. How much tin is there in 250 g of solder?

Exercise 16

The River Ure in Yorkshire contains approximately:

trout	45%
dace	25%
grayling	15%
tench	10%
roach	5%

Draw a pie chart to show the fish in the River Ure.

Exercise 17

1. Melanie got 13 marks out of 20 while Michael got 16 out of 25. Who got the better mark? (Change both marks to percentages to find out.)

2. Peter was given 54% of a sum of money. Pam was given 48% of a different sum of money. Was Peter given more money than Pam? Explain your answer.

3. Write in order of size: 28%, $\frac{1}{4}$, 0.27. Put the largest first.

4. (a) Find 32% of £8.50.
   (b) Work out 0.32 × £8.50.

5. (a) What is 20% of £10?
   (b) What is 100% of £10?
   (c) Find 100% of £10 + 20% of £10.
   (d) Find 120% of £10.

6. Find 125% of £60.

7. Change 142% to a decimal.

8. Write 175% as a common fraction.

Revision Exercises VII to XII

Revision Exercise VII

1. Enlarge triangle PQR. Make new length PQ twice as long.

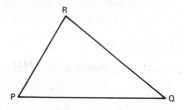

2. How many times as big is the first quantity compared with the second?
   (*a*) 35 km, 7 km   (*b*) 8 cm, 4 mm

3. Write these ratios in their simplest form:
   (*a*) 18 : 12   (*b*) 60 : 75   (*c*) 4.2 : 2.8

4. Write as ratios in their simplest form:
   (*a*) 40 p to 48 p   (*b*) £4.25 to £2.50   (*c*) $5\frac{1}{4}$ to $3\frac{1}{2}$

5. Find the missing values that make the ratios the same:
   (*a*) 12 : 9 = 4 : $\boxed{?}$ (*b*) $\boxed{?}$: 30 = 6 : 5

6. Some goods were bought for £120 and then sold for £144. Find:
   (*a*) the ratio of the selling price to the cost price,
   (b) the ratio of the profit to the cost price.

7.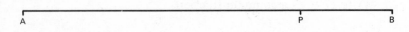

   By measuring the line above, find the ratio AP : PB in its simplest form.

8. Write the ratio 24 : 15 in the form *m* : 1.

9. Write $9 : 126$ in the form $1 : n$.

10. A car used 32 l of petrol in travelling 448 km. Calculate the ratio of the number of kilometres travelled to the number of litres used.

11. Which is the better value for money, 450 g for 92 p or 800 g for £1.64?

12. A drug was diluted with water in the ratio $1 : 3$.
If 250 ml of the drug were used:
(*a*) How much water was used?
(*b*) How much solution was made up altogether?

Revision Exercise VIII

1. _____

The line above has been drawn to a scale of 1 cm to 4 m. What is its true length?

2. Use the scale 1 cm : 5 km to draw a line to represent a length of 30 km.

3. Use the scale 1 : 8 to draw a line to represent 400 mm.

4. Use the scale 1 : 1000 to draw a line to represent 70 m.

5. A map is drawn to a scale of 1 : 300 000. The map distance between two places is 4 cm; calculate the true distance between them.

6. Draw an accurate copy of the given quadrilateral using a scale of 1 cm to 3 m. How long is each diagonal?

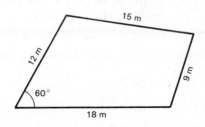

Revision Exercise IX

1. (*a*) Copy the crosses.

(*b*) How many crosses are there?

(*c*) Draw round groups of seven.

(*d*) How many groups of seven are there?

(*e*) How many crosses are left over?

(*f*) How many crosses are there in base 7?

2. $35_5 = \boxed{?}$ fives $+ \boxed{?}$ units $= \boxed{?}_{\text{ten}}$

3. Tins of beans are put into boxes of 12.

(*a*) How many tins are there in 6 boxes?

(*b*) How many tins are there if there are 4 boxes and 3 tins left over?

4. Write in base ten:

(*a*) 26_8 (*b*) 15_6 (*c*) 27_9 (*d*) 33_5 (*e*) 23_4

5. Change these numbers from base ten into the given base:

(*a*) 16_{ten} to base 5   (*b*) 52_{ten} to base 9

6. $212_3 = \boxed{?}$ nines, $\boxed{?}$ threes and $\boxed{?}$ units $= \boxed{?}_{\text{ten}}$

7. In the number $13\underline{4}2_6$ what is the value of the underlined digit?

8. (*a*) Write 231_5 in base ten.

(*b*) Write 1101_2 in base ten.

9. Write these base ten numbers in the given base:

(*a*) 54_{ten} to base 4   (*b*) 143_{ten} to base 8

10. (*a*) Change 10101_2 to base ten.

(*b*) Convert 51_{ten} into binary.

11. Is the number 143_5 odd or even?

12. Which base 4 number comes immediately before 200_4?

Revision Exercise X

1. How many seconds are there in 8 min?

2. How many minutes are there in 7 h?

3. How many minutes are there in 4 h 25 min?

4. A runner runs four laps of a track. The lap times were 62 s, 59 s, 63 s and 61 s. Find the total time in minutes and seconds.

5. There are 24 h in a day. How many hours are there in 6 days?

6. How many days are there in 4 weeks?

7. How many hours are there in 3 weeks?

8. Write these times using the 24-hour clock notation:
   (a) quarter to eight in the evening,
   (b) twenty-five past three in the morning.

9. Write these times using words:
   (a) 16.15   (b) 06.35   (c) 8.20 a.m.   (d) 9.50 p.m.

10. Write these times using the 24-hour clock:
    (a) 7.18 p.m.   (b) 11.47 p.m.   (c) 10.23 a.m.

11. Write these times using the 12-hour clock:
    (a) five minutes to three in the afternoon
    (b) 21.19
    (c) 04.41

12. How many hours are there from 7 o'clock on Monday morning until 6 o'clock on the Tuesday evening?

13. A film lasted 2 h 25 min. If it finished at 21.10, at what time did it start?

14. A turkey weighing 11 lb is put in the oven at 08.45. Cooking time needed is 20 min per pound plus an extra 20 min. At what time will the turkey be cooked?

15. A coach set off at 13.55 and reached its destination at 17.12. How long did the journey take?

16. Use the timetable on p. 146 to help you to answer these:
  (*a*) Find the time of arrival in Kemble of a train that leaves Cheltenham Spa at 17.28.
  (*b*) Which journey is faster and by how many minutes: the Wednesday or the Saturday journey from Swindon to Gloucester travelling on the train that leaves just after half past seven in the evening?

17. Which of these years were leap years?
  1846, 1868, 1884, 1900, 1926, 1966, 1976

18. How many days are there from 23 July until 18 August inclusive?

19. 9 May was a Tuesday. What day was 12 June?

20. 11 January 1971 was a Monday.
  (*a*) What day was 11 January 1972?
  (*b*) What day was 11 January 1973?
  (*c*) What day was 11 January 1983?

Revision Exercise XI

1. A rectangular garden measures 14 m by 9 m. Calculate its area.

2. Calculate the area of a square with side 25 mm.

3. Find the length of the sides of a square having an area of 11.56 m².

4. How many square millimetres are there in 1 cm²?

5. How many square inches are there in 1 ft²?

6. Write 5 m² in square centimetres.

7. How many 15 cm square tiles are needed to cover a wall measuring 2.1 m by 1.8 m?

8. A classroom has an area of 51 m². If it is 6 m wide, how long is it?

9. A rectangular rug measuring 2.5 m by 2 m is placed on the floor of a room 5 m by 4.5 m. What area of floor is not covered by the rug?

10. Calculate the total surface area of a cube where each edge is 7 cm long.

11. Calculate the areas of the parallelogram and the triangle:
(a)   (b)

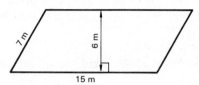 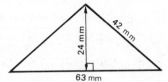

12. A parallelogram with base 9 cm has an area of 47.7 cm². Calculate its perpendicular height.

13. A triangle has an area of 108 m². If its perpendicular height is 12 m, calculate its base.

14. Calculate the area of each of these shapes:
(a) a kite with diagonals of 12 in and 7 in,
(b) a rhombus with diagonals of 54 mm and 32 mm,
(c) a trapezium with parallel sides of 8.2 m and 5.8 m where the perpendicular distance between the parallel sides is 4 m.

Revision Exercise XII

1. Write 45% as a decimal.

2. Write 0.86 as a percentage.

3. Write as common fractions in their simplest form:
(a) 65%   (b) $22\frac{1}{2}\%$

4. Write as percentages:

(a) $\dfrac{3}{10}$ (b) $\dfrac{2}{5}$ (c) $\dfrac{3}{4}$ (d) $\dfrac{17}{25}$ (e) $\dfrac{13}{40}$ (f) $\dfrac{1}{8}$

5. Find:
(a) 20% of £75
(b) 30% of £4.80
(c) 45% of 50 l
(d) $2\frac{1}{2}\%$ of 120 ft

6. Sara got 17 out of 20 in a test. What was her percentage mark?

7. Kevin got 54% in a test. What was his mark out of 25?

8. In a sale, a shop reduced its prices by 20%. Find the sale price of a dress that was priced at £28.50.

9. A woman must pay tax on £1300. If the tax rate is 30% p.a., how much must she pay this year?

10. VAT at 15% is added to the price of goods. Find the selling price of goods that cost £62 before VAT.

11. If a salesman is given 5% commission on sales of £1500, how much does he get?

12. Find 112% of 25 kg.

13 Directed Numbers

Exercise 1 $\boxed{R}$

1. Which temperature is colder, $^-9\,°C$ or $^-4\,°C$?

2. Copy the number line and fill in the missing numbers:

3. (a) Is it true that $^-5 > {}^-2$?
   (b) Is it true that $^-9 < {}^-4$?

4. Copy the following but replace each box with $<$ or $>$ to make each statement correct:
   (a) $^-6$ $\boxed{?}$ 4
   (b) $^-8$ $\boxed{?}$ $^-2$
   (c) $^-1$ $\boxed{?}$ $^-7$
   (d) $^-1$ $\boxed{?}$ 5
   (e) $^-4$ $\boxed{?}$ $^-5$
   (f) $^-9$ $\boxed{?}$ $^-8$

5. Write the numbers $^-8, 0, {}^-2, 5, {}^-10, 1, {}^-1$ in order of size putting the smallest first.

6. A submarine dives from 584 m to a depth of 971 m. How many metres has it dived?

7. Find the value of:
   (a) $^-4 + 9$
   (b) $5 - 11$
   (c) $^-3 - 5$
   (d) $^-9 + 2$
   (e) $^-8 + 5 - 3$
   (f) $2 - 7 + 4$

8. Find the value of:

(a) $^-2 + {}^+4$

(b) $^-5 + {}^-2$

(c) $^+4 + {}^-9$

(d) $^-1 + {}^-6$

(e) $^+8 + {}^-6 + {}^-2$

(f) $9 + {}^-12 + 1$

9. Find the value of:

(a) $(+6) + (-2)$

(b) $(-6) + (+2)$

(c) $(-6) + (-2)$

(d) $(-9) + (-1)$

(e) $(-3) + (-8) + 4$

(f) $12 + (-5) + 2$

10. For each question, find the missing number that makes each statement true:

(a) $\boxed{?} + {}^-7 = {}^-3$

(b) $^-3 + \boxed{?} = {}^-1$

Exercise 2   M

Copy and complete:

	Previous temperature	New temperature	Change in temperature	Calculation
1.	$^+2\ °C$	$^+9\ °C$		$9 - 2\quad=$
2.	$^+19\ °C$	$^+25\ °C$	$^+6°C$	$25 - 19\quad=$
3.	$^+45\ °C$	$^+60\ °C$		$60 - 45\quad=$
4.	$^+\ 8\ °C$	$^+12\ °C$		$12 - 8\quad= 4$
5.	$0\ °C$	$^+28\ °C$		$28 - 0\quad=$
6.	$^-6\ °C$	$^+3\ °C$	$^+9°C$	$3 + 6\quad=$
7.	$^-14\ °C$	$^+8\ °C$		$8 + 14\quad=$
8.	$^-7\ °C$	$^+12\ °C$		$12 + 7\quad=$
9.	$^+9\ °C$	$^+6\ °C$	$^-3°C$	$6 - 9\quad=$

	Previous temperature	New temperature	Change in temperature	Calculation
10.	$^+23\,°C$	$^+15\,°C$		$15 - 23\ =$
11.	$^+8\,°C$	$^+1\,°C$		$1 - 8\ \ =$
12.	$^+6\,°C$	$0\,°C$		$0 - 6\ \ =$
13.	$^-5\,°C$	$^+4\,°C$		$4 + 5\ \ =$
14.	$^-10\,°C$	$^-3\,°C$	$^+7°C$	$^-3 + 10\ =$
15.	$^-15\,°C$	$^-9\,°C$		$^-9 + 15\ \ =$
16.	$^-12\,°C$	$^-19\,°C$		$^-19 + 12\ \ =$
17.	$^-2\,°C$	$^-14\,°C$		$^-14 + 2\ \ =$
18.	$^+62\,°C$	$^+23\,°C$		$23 - 62\ \ =$
19.	$^-12\,°C$	$^+6\,°C$		$6 + 12\ \ =$
20.	$^-5\,°C$	$^+7\,°C$		$7 - {}^-5\ \ =$
21.	$^-8\,°C$	$^+3\,°C$		$3 - {}^-8\ \ =$
22.	$^-7\,°C$	$^+6\,°C$		$6 + 7\ \ =$
23.	$^-19\,°C$	$^-11\,°C$		$^-11 + 19\ \ =$
24.	$^-13\,°C$	$^-7\,°C$		$^-7 - {}^-13\ =$
25.	$^-18\,°C$	$^-24\,°C$		$^-24 + 18\ \ =$
26.	$^+7\,°C$	$^-12\,°C$		$^-12 - 7\ \ =$
27.	$^-18\,°C$	$14\,°C$		$14 + 18\ \ =$
28.	$^+26\,°C$	$^-9\,°C$		$^-9 - 26\ \ =$

Exercise 3

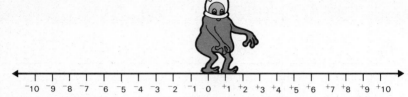

$$\begin{array}{ccccccccccccccccccccc} & {}^{-}10 & {}^{-}9 & {}^{-}8 & {}^{-}7 & {}^{-}6 & {}^{-}5 & {}^{-}4 & {}^{-}3 & {}^{-}2 & {}^{-}1 & 0 & {}^{+}1 & {}^{+}2 & {}^{+}3 & {}^{+}4 & {}^{+}5 & {}^{+}6 & {}^{+}7 & {}^{+}8 & {}^{+}9 & {}^{+}10 \end{array}$$

A In the drawing above, each step taken by the Martian is one position on the number line.

Answer the following questions. (Show steps backwards with a negative sign, e.g. $^{-}7$ means 7 steps backwards.)

How many steps does the Martian take in walking from:

1. (a) $^{+}3$ to $^{+}8$?   (b) $^{+}8 - {}^{+}3$ =   (c) $8 - 3$ =
2. (a) $^{+}6$ to $^{+}10$?   (b) $^{+}10 - {}^{+}6$ =   (c) $10 - 6$ =
3. (a) $^{+}4$ to $^{+}5$?   (b) $^{+}5 - {}^{+}4$ =   (c) $5 - 4$ =
4. (a) $^{-}2$ to $^{+}4$?   (b) $^{+}4 - {}^{-}2$ =   (c) $4 + 2$ =
5. (a) $^{-}7$ to $^{+}2$?   (b) $^{+}2 - {}^{-}7$ =   (c) $2 + 7$ =
6. (a) $^{-}10$ to $^{+}10$?   (b) $^{+}10 - {}^{-}10$ =   (c) $10 + 10$ =
7. (a) $^{-}10$ to $^{-}4$?   (b) $^{-}4 - {}^{-}10$ =   (c) $^{-}4 + 10$ =
8. (a) $^{-}6$ to 0 ?   (b) $0 - {}^{-}6$ =   (c) $0 + 6$ =
9. (a) $^{+}7$ to $^{+}2$?   (b) $^{+}2 - {}^{+}7$ =   (c) $2 - 7$ =
10. (a) $^{+}9$ to $^{+}4$?   (b) $^{+}4 - {}^{+}9$ =   (c) $4 - 9$ =
11. (a) $^{+}5$ to $^{-}3$?   (b) $^{-}3 - {}^{+}5$ =   (c) $^{-}3 - 5$ =
12. (a) $^{+}8$ to $^{-}5$?   (b) $^{-}5 - {}^{+}8$ =   (c) $^{-}5 - 8$ =
13. (a) $^{-}9$ to $^{-}1$?   (b) $^{-}1 - {}^{-}9$ =   (c) $^{-}1 + 9$ =
14. (a) $^{-}4$ to $^{-}1$?   (b) $^{-}1 - {}^{-}4$ =   (c) $^{-}1 + 4$ =
15. (a) $^{-}6$ to $^{+}2$?   (b) $^{+}2 - {}^{-}6$ =   (c) $2 + 6$ =

B Calculate:

1. $6 - {}^{-}2$
2. $14 - {}^{-}9$
3. $^{-}4 - {}^{-}7$
4. $^{-}12 - {}^{-}5$
5. $0 - {}^{-}13$
6. $^{-}8 - {}^{-}11$

Exercise 4

Six villages, P, Q, R, S, T and U, lie on a hillside.

Their altitudes are shown in the diagram opposite.

Three of the villages, P, Q and R, are above sea-level while three villages, S, T and U are below sea-level.

Note that the altitude of Q is $^{+}35$ m while the altitude of T is $^{-}25$ m (25 m below sea-level).

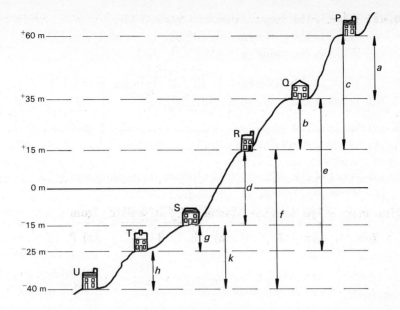

1. (a) What is the vertical distance marked *a*?
   (b) What is the difference in altitude between villages P and Q?
   (c) What is the value of 60 − 35?

2. (a) What is the vertical distance marked *b*?
   (b) What is the difference in altitude between villages Q and R?
   (c) What is the value of 35 − (+15)?

3. (a) What is the vertical distance marked *c*?
   (b) What is the difference in altitude between P and R?
   (c) What is the value of (+60) − (+15)?

4. (a) What is the vertical distance marked *d*?
   (b) What is the difference in altitude between R and S?
   (c) What is the value of (+15) − (−15)?

5. (a) What is the difference in altitude between Q and T?
   (b) What is the value of (+35) − (−25)?

6. (a) What is the difference in altitude between R and U?
   (b) What is the value of (+15) − (−40)?

7. (a) What is the vertical distance marked *g*?
   (b) What is the difference in altitude between S and T?
   (c) What is the value of (−15) − (−25)?

8. (a) What is the vertical distance marked h?
   (b) What is the difference in altitude between T and U?
   (c) What is the value of $(-25) - (-40)$?

9. (a) What is the difference in altitude between S and U?
   (b) What is the value of $(-15) - (-40)$?

10. (a) What is the difference in altitude between P and T?
    (b) What is the value of $(+60) - (-25)$?

11. (a) What is the difference in altitude between Q and U?
    (b) What is the value of $(+35) - (-40)$?

12. (a) What is the difference in altitude between R and T?
    (b) What is the value of $(+15) - (-25)$?

Exercise 5

A Copy these. By finding a pattern, fill in the missing answers.

1. $^+4 - {}^+3 = {}^+1$	**2.** $^+4 - {}^-3 = {}^+7$	**3.** $^-4 - {}^+4 = {}^-8$
$^+4 - {}^+2 = {}^+2$	$^+4 - {}^-2 = \boxed{?}$	$^-4 - {}^+3 = {}^-7$
$^+4 - {}^+1 = \boxed{?}$	$^+4 - {}^-1 = \boxed{?}$	$^-4 - {}^+2 = \boxed{?}$
$^+4 - \ 0 = {}^+4$	$^+4 - \ 0 = {}^+4$	$^-4 - {}^+1 = \boxed{?}$
$^+4 - {}^-1 = \boxed{?}$	$^+4 - {}^+1 = \boxed{?}$	$^-4 - \ 0 = {}^-4$
$^+4 - {}^-2 = \boxed{?}$	$^+4 - {}^+2 = {}^+2$	$^-4 - {}^-1 = \boxed{?}$
$^+4 - {}^-3 = \boxed{?}$	$^+4 - {}^+3 = {}^+1$	$^-4 - {}^-2 = \boxed{?}$
$^+4 - {}^-4 = \boxed{?}$	$^+4 - {}^+4 = \boxed{?}$	$^-4 - {}^-3 = \boxed{?}$
$^+4 - {}^-5 = \boxed{?}$	$^+4 - {}^+5 = \boxed{?}$	$^-4 - {}^-4 = \boxed{?}$
$^+4 - {}^-6 = \boxed{?}$	$^+4 - {}^+6 = \boxed{?}$	$^-4 - {}^-5 = \boxed{?}$
$^+4 - {}^-7 = \boxed{?}$	$^+4 - {}^+7 = \boxed{?}$	$^-4 - {}^-6 = \boxed{?}$
$^+4 - {}^-8 = \boxed{?}$	$^+4 - {}^+8 = \boxed{?}$	$^-4 - {}^-7 = \boxed{?}$

B Now answer these:

1. $^+8 - {}^+2$	**5.** $7 - {}^-2$	**9.** $4 - 13$	**13.** $^-6 - {}^-4$
2. $9 - {}^+3$	**6.** $^+4 - {}^+9$	**10.** $^-4 - {}^+7$	**14.** $^-6 - {}^-8$
3. $12 - 5$	**7.** $5 - {}^+12$	**11.** $^-4 - 9$	**15.** $^-6 - {}^-12$
4. $^+9 - {}^-4$	**8.** $^+3 - 7$	**12.** $^-6 - 3$	**16.** $^-9 - {}^-15$

Exercise 6

A Use a ruler on this nomogram to help you to answer these questions:

1. $1 + 5$	**7.** $-6 + 8$
2. $7 + 3$	**8.** $4 + {}^-1$
3. $2 + 0$	**9.** $5 + {}^-9$
4. $3 + {}^-3$	**10.** ${}^-8 + 6$
5. $6 + {}^-4$	**11.** ${}^-10 + 3$
6. $5 + {}^-1$	**12.** ${}^-5 + {}^-9$

B The nomogram can also be used for subtraction. Use it to help you to answer these:

1. $10 - 3$	**11.** ${}^-6 - 0$
2. $6 - 2$	**12.** ${}^-6 - {}^-2$
3. $8 - 0$	**13.** $0 - {}^-5$
4. $4 - {}^-2$	**14.** $12 - 8$
5. $2 - {}^-3$	**15.** ${}^-5 - {}^-8$
6. $1 - {}^-6$	**16.** ${}^-5 - 3$
7. $0 - {}^-8$	**17.** ${}^-14 - {}^-6$
8. ${}^-2 - 1$	**18.** ${}^-12 - {}^-9$
9. ${}^-4 - 3$	**19.** ${}^-8 - {}^-9$
10. ${}^-6 - 2$	**20.** ${}^-2 - {}^-7$

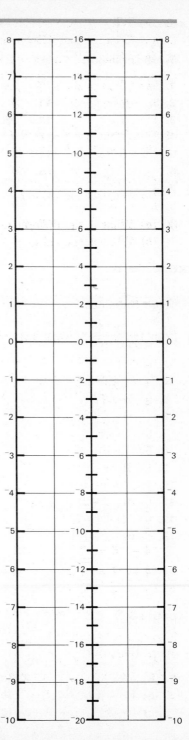

203

Exercise 7

Work these out:

1. $14 - 8$
2. $9 - {}^+5$
3. $4 - 7$
4. $3 - {}^+12$
5. ${}^-2 - 6$
6. ${}^-4 - {}^+3$
7. $8 - {}^-2$
8. $4 - {}^-5$
9. ${}^-3 - {}^-7$
10. ${}^-2 - {}^-13$
11. ${}^-9 - {}^-4$
12. ${}^-12 - {}^-1$
13. ${}^-5 - {}^-5$
14. ${}^-3 - {}^-13$
15. ${}^-9 - {}^+7$
16. ${}^-9 - {}^-7$
17. ${}^+9 - {}^+7$
18. $9 - {}^-7$
19. $4 - {}^-12$
20. ${}^-4 - {}^-12$
21. ${}^-12 - {}^-4$
22. $5 - {}^-2 - {}^+4$
23. ${}^-9 - {}^-6 - {}^+8 - {}^-11$
24. ${}^-10 - 18 - {}^-12 - {}^+3$
25. ${}^+6 - {}^+9 - {}^-12 - {}^+4$

Exercise 8

Work these out:

1. $17 - 9$
2. $8 - (+3)$
3. $6 - 11$
4. $4 - (+9)$
5. $(-5) - 12$
6. $(-7) - (+4)$
7. $9 - (-5)$
8. $6 - (-10)$
9. $(-3) - (-8)$
10. $(-1) - (-10)$
11. $(-8) - (-3)$
12. $(-14) - (-7)$
13. $(-6) - (-15)$
14. $(-9) - (-9)$
15. $(-8) - (+5)$
16. $(-8) - (-5)$
17. $(+8) - (+5)$
18. $8 - (-5)$
19. $3 - (-9)$
20. $(-3) - (-9)$
21. $(-9) - 3$
22. $(+7) - (-4) - (+7)$
23. $(-3) - 14 - (-5) - (+11)$
24. $(-12) - (-3) - (+5) - (-15)$
25. $14 - (+10) - (-8) - (-1)$

Exercise 9

Work these out:

1. (a) $5 + {}^-3$
   (b) $5 - {}^+3$
   (c) $5 - 3$
2. (a) $8 + {}^-2$
   (b) $8 - {}^+2$
   (c) $8 - 2$
3. (a) $12 + {}^-5$
   (b) $12 - {}^+5$
   (c) $12 - 5$

4. (a) $13 + {}^-8$
   (b) $13 - {}^+8$
   (c) $13 - 8$

5. (a) $7 + (-4)$
   (b) $7 - (+4)$
   (c) $7 - 4$

6. (a) $9 + (-6)$
   (b) $9 - (+6)$
   (c) $9 - 6$

7. (a) $14 + (-3)$
   (b) $14 - (+3)$
   (c) $14 - 3$

8. (a) $17 + (-8)$
   (b) $17 - (+8)$
   (c) $17 - 8$

9. (a) $8 - {}^-5$
   (b) $8 + {}^+5$
   (c) $8 + 5$

10. (a) $10 - {}^-4$
    (b) $10 + {}^+4$
    (c) $10 + 4$

11. (a) $17 - {}^-8$
    (b) $17 + {}^+8$
    (c) $17 + 8$

12. (a) $11 - {}^-1$
    (b) $11 + {}^+1$
    (c) $11 + 1$

13. (a) $6 - (-2)$
    (b) $6 + (+2)$
    (c) $6 + 2$

14. (a) $12 - (-6)$
    (b) $12 + (+6)$
    (c) $12 + 6$

15. (a) $19 - (-4)$
    (b) $19 + (+4)$
    (c) $19 + 4$

16. (a) $16 - (-8)$
    (b) $16 + (+8)$
    (c) $16 + 8$

Exercise 10

Find the missing numbers that will make each statement correct:

1. $\boxed{?} - {}^+4 = {}^+5$
2. $\boxed{?} - {}^+7 = 6$
3. $12 - \boxed{?} = 10$
4. $\boxed{?} + {}^+5 = 9$
5. $\boxed{?} + {}^-5 = 9$
6. $7 + \boxed{?} = 10$
7. $7 + \boxed{?} = 3$
8. $\boxed{?} - {}^+8 = 4$
9. $\boxed{?} - {}^-8 = 15$
10. $19 - \boxed{?} = 8$
11. $13 - \boxed{?} = 17$
12. $\boxed{?} + {}^+9 = 13$
13. $\boxed{?} + {}^+9 = 6$
14. $\boxed{?} + {}^+2 = {}^-4$
15. $\boxed{?} + {}^-8 = 3$

16. $\boxed{?} + {}^-8 = 0$
17. $\boxed{?} + {}^-8 = {}^-5$
18. $\boxed{?} + {}^-8 = {}^-14$
19. $5 + \boxed{?} = {}^-3$
20. $6 + \boxed{?} = 4$
21. $4 + \boxed{?} = 1$
22. $9 + \boxed{?} = {}^-3$
23. $\boxed{?} - {}^-3 = 7$
24. $\boxed{?} - {}^-5 = 2$
25. $5 - \boxed{?} = 8$
26. $7 - \boxed{?} = {}^-8$
27. $\boxed{?} - {}^-8 = {}^-4$
28. ${}^-6 - \boxed{?} = {}^-3$
29. ${}^-2 + \boxed{?} = {}^-9$
30. ${}^-4 - \boxed{?} = 12$

205

Exercise 11

Find the value of:

1. (a) $3 + 6 - 2 + 4$
   (b) $3 + 6 + 4 - 2$

2. (a) $9 - 3 - 5 + 4$
   (b) $9 + 4 - 3 - 5$

3. (a) $6 - 8 + 6 - 1$
   (b) $6 + 6 - 8 - 1$

4. (a) $3 - 9 - 2 + 7 + 5$
   (b) $3 + 7 + 5 - 9 - 2$

5. (a) $2 - 4 - 8 + 1 + 3$
   (b) $2 + 1 + 3 - 4 - 8$

6. (a) $5 - 10 + 2 - 9 + 4$
   (b) $5 + 2 + 4 - 10 - 9$

7. (a) $^-2 + 4 - 7 + 9 - 1$
   (b) $4 + 9 - 2 - 7 - 1$

8. (a) $^-6 + 8 - 5 - 4 + 7$
   (b) $8 + 7 - 6 - 5 - 4$

9. (a) $^-4 - 9 - 3 + 8 + 5$
   (b) $8 + 5 - 4 - 9 - 3$

10. (a) $^-5 + 6 + 5 - 6 + 7$
    (b) $5 - 5 + 6 - 6 + 7$

11. (a) $14 - 9 - 12 + 3 - 7$
    (b) $14 + 3 - 9 - 7 - 12$

12. (a) $^-8 - 10 + 10 - 4 + 8 - 5$
    (b) $10 - 10 + 8 - 8 - 5 - 4$

Exercise 12   Like Terms

Write the following in a shorter form. If no shorter form is possible, write 'NO SHORTER FORM'.

1. $x + x + x + x$
2. $2d + 5d + d$
3. $3s + 8s - 4s$
4. $5m - m + 3m - 2m$
5. $6p + 4p - 4p - 6p$
6. $x + x + y + x + y$
7. $4t + 3u + 8t - 2u - 5t$
8. $3k + 12l - 5l - 2k + 6l$
9. $16h - 4h + 10f - 5h - 9f$
10. $4v + 7j - 2v - 4j - 2v$
11. $7e + 5 - 2e + 3$
12. $15g + 6w - 6w + g$
13. $6t + 4h - 2t + 3n$
14. $7z + 3i + 6f + 2$
15. $5k - 6k + 3k + 4k$
16. $2b + 5 - b - 3 + 3b - 1$

17. $p - 2p + 4p - p + 7p$
18. $3f - 5n + 2n - 2f + 3n$
19. $4l + 7 - l - 12 - 3l + 6$
20. $9u - 7z + u + 2z - 3u + 6z$
21. $3i + 8h - 7i - 2h - 4i + 8i$
22. $2e - 6q + 5e + 12q - 4e$
23. $3c + 5d + 4e$
24. $7v - 9 + 2b - 4v + 6 + 3b$
25. $9 + 3y - 2x + 4w$
26. $5j + 7k - 4l + 2j - l - k$
27. $2p - 3q - 2q + p + s$
28. $3t - 5k - 2t + 3k - t + 2k$
29. $s - 5 - t - 2s + t + 4s + 1$
30. $5y - 6z - y + 4n - z$
31. $12h - 7w + 2e - a$
32. $k - v - 2c - 4 + 3v + 1 - k$

Multiplication and Division

Exercise 13

Copy these. By finding a pattern, fill in the missing answers.

1. $^+4 \times {}^+3 = {}^+12$
   $^+4 \times {}^+2 = {}^+8$
   $^+4 \times {}^+1 = \boxed{?}$
   $^+4 \times 0 = 0$
   $^+4 \times {}^-1 = \boxed{?}$
   $^+4 \times {}^-2 = \boxed{?}$
   $^+4 \times {}^-3 = \boxed{?}$
   $^+4 \times {}^-4 = \boxed{?}$

2. $^-4 \times {}^+4 = {}^-16$
   $^-4 \times {}^+3 = \boxed{?}$
   $^-4 \times {}^+2 = \boxed{?}$
   $^-4 \times {}^+1 = \boxed{?}$
   $^-4 \times 0 = 0$
   $^-4 \times {}^-1 = \boxed{?}$
   $^-4 \times {}^-2 = \boxed{?}$
   $^-4 \times {}^-3 = \boxed{?}$

3. Work these out:

   (a) $^+5 \times {}^-3$ (d) $^-6 \times 7$ (g) $5 \times {}^-6$
   (b) $7 \times {}^-2$ (e) $^-2 \times {}^-8$ (h) $^-6 \times 0$
   (c) $^-3 \times {}^+4$ (f) $^-9 \times {}^-4$

The line $\underset{0 \qquad\quad +3}{\longmapsto}$ can stand for $^+3$ (that is, 3).

$\underset{0 \qquad\qquad\qquad +6}{\longmapsto}$ then stands for $2 \times {}^+3$. This new line is twice as long, so $2 \times {}^+3 = {}^+6$.

If $\underset{-4 \qquad\qquad 0}{\longmapsto}$ stands for $^-4$ then $\underset{-8 \qquad\qquad\qquad\qquad\qquad 0}{\longmapsto}$ stands for $2 \times {}^-4$. Once again the new line is twice as long. This time, since the number $^-4$ is negative, the line showing $^-4$ points to the left. The new line is twice as long and also points to the left, so $2 \times {}^-4 = {}^-8$.

Exercise 14

For each question, draw lines to show (a) the given number and (b) the answer to the given calculation:

1. (a) Show $^+4$ (b) Show $2 \times {}^+4$

2. (*a*) Show ⁻2   (*b*) Show 5 × ⁻2

3. (*a*) Show ⁻3   (*b*) Show 6 × ⁻3

4. (*a*) Show ⁻6   (*b*) Show ⁺4 × ⁻6

5. (*a*) Show 5   (*b*) Show ⁺3 × 5

6. (*a*) Show ⁻7   (*b*) Show 2 × ⁻7

Now if multiplication by ⁻1 causes a rotation through 180° and since ⊢——┴——┴——⊣ stands for ⁺4, then ⊢——┴——┴——⊣ stands for
0   ⁺4   ⁻4   0

⁻1 × ⁺4. This can be more easily seen on one diagram:

The diagram shows that ⁻1 × ⁺4 = ⁻4.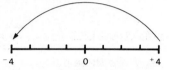

Remember   Multiplying by ⁻1 causes a rotation through 180°.

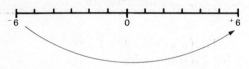

shows that ⁻1 × ⁻6 = ⁺6

Exercise 15

Work these out. You may draw a line to help you.

1. ⁻1 × ⁺5	**5.** ⁻1 × ⁻3	**9.** ⁻1 × ⁻7
2. ⁻1 × ⁺10	**6.** ⁻1 × ⁺2	**10.** ⁻1 × ⁺12
3. ⁻1 × ⁻2	**7.** ⁻1 × ⁺1	**11.** ⁻1 × ⁻12
4. ⁻1 × ⁻8	**8.** ⁻1 × ⁻1	**12.** ⁻1 × ⁻25

The ideas used in Exercises 14 and 15 can now be used to help us to work out calculations such as ⁻4 × ⁻6.

Since ⁻4 = 4 × ⁻1, ⁻6 must be multiplied by both ⁻1 and 4. Multiplying ⁻6 by ⁻1 rotates a line that stands for ⁻6, so that it becomes ⁺6. Multiplying by 4 enlarges the ⁺6 line 4 times so that it becomes ⁺24,

so   ⁻4 × ⁻6 = ⁺24

Exercise 16

Work these out:

A
1. $4 \times \ ^-3$
2. $5 \times \ ^-7$
3. $7 \times \ ^-4$
4. $^+6 \times \ ^-2$
5. $^+3 \times \ ^-3$
6. $^-2 \times 8$
7. $^-9 \times \ ^+6$
8. $^-3 \times \ ^+9$
9. $^-8 \times \ ^+7$
10. $^-2 \times \ ^-9$
11. $^-7 \times \ ^-4$
12. $^+6 \times \ ^-11$
13. $^+4 \times \ ^+3$
14. $^-12 \times \ ^-6$
15. $^+6 \times \ ^-9$
16. $^+6 \times \ ^+9$
17. $^-6 \times \ ^+9$
18. $^-6 \times \ ^-9$
19. $^-2 \times \ ^+4 \times \ ^-3$
20. $^-4 \times \ ^-5 \times \ ^-9$
21. $^+6 \times \ ^-3 \times \ ^+2$
22. $^-7 \times \ ^-4 \times \ ^+3$
23. $^+5 \times \ ^-1 \times 0$
24. $^+2 \times \ ^-9 \times \ ^-4$
25. $^+6 \times \ ^+8 \times \ ^-3$

B
1. $7 \times (-9)$
2. $4 \times (-8)$
3. $(+10) \times (+2)$
4. $(+5) \ \times (-3)$
5. $(-6) \ \times (+4)$
6. $(-11) \times (+2)$
7. $(-7) \ \times (-1)$
8. $(-10) \times (+9)$
9. $(+5) \ \times (-7)$
10. $(-2) \times (-12)$
11. $(-3) \ \times (+8)$
12. $(+7) \ \times (-8)$
13. $(+5) \times 0$
14. $(-4) \ \times (-4)$
15. $(-8) \times (-4)$
16. $8 \times (-4)$
17. $(-8) \times (+4)$
18. $(+8) \times (+4)$
19. $(-4) \times (-1) \times (+8)$
20. $(+7) \times (-3) \times (-3)$
21. $(-6) \times (+2) \times (-9)$
22. $(+2) \times (-9) \times (+5)$
23. $(-5) \times (-6) \times (-7)$
24. $(-8) \times (-5) \times 9$
25. $(+3) \times (-1) \times 12$

Exercise 17

A Copy these and fill in the missing numbers:

1. (a) $7 \times \ \ 4 = $? (b) $28 \div \ \ 7 = $?
2. (a) $5 \times \ \ 3 = $? (b) $15 \div \ \ 5 = $?
3. (a) $^+4 \times \ ^-6 = $? (b) $^-24 \div \ ^+4 = $?
4. (a) $^+3 \times \ ^-7 = $? (b) $^-21 \div \ ^+3 = $?
5. (a) $^-5 \times \ ^-4 = $? (b) $^+20 \div \ ^-5 = $?

6. (a) $^-6 \times {}^-8 = \boxed{?}$ (b) $^+48 \div {}^-6 = \boxed{?}$

7. (a) $^-6 \times {}^+3 = \boxed{?}$ (b) $^-18 \div {}^-6 = \boxed{?}$

8. (a) $^-2 \times {}^+9 = \boxed{?}$ (b) $^-18 \div {}^-2 = \boxed{?}$

B Work these out:

1. $^+8 \div {}^+4$

2. $^-12 \div 3$

3. $\dfrac{^-18}{6}$

4. $28 \div {}^-7$

5. $^-42 \div {}^-6$

6. $^+63 \div {}^-9$

7. $^-54 \div {}^-6$

8. $\dfrac{40}{^-8}$

9. $\dfrac{^-72}{^-12}$

10. $^-49 \div {}^+7$

11. $16 \div {}^-4$

12. $\dfrac{^-60}{^-5}$

13. $\dfrac{^-40}{8}$

14. $\dfrac{^+45}{^-9}$

15. $\dfrac{^-32}{^+4}$

C Work these out:

1. $\dfrac{(+12)}{(+2)}$

2. $(-42) \div (+6)$

3. $\dfrac{(-18)}{(+3)}$

4. $\dfrac{(+72)}{(-9)}$

5. $\dfrac{(-40)}{(-5)}$

6. $\dfrac{(+56)}{(-7)}$

7. $(+36) \div (-4)$

8. $(-96) \div (+8)$

9. $\dfrac{(-88)}{(+11)}$

10. $(-36) \div (-3)$

11. $(+90) \div (+10)$

12. $\dfrac{(-54)}{(+6)}$

13. $(-16) \div (-2)$

14. $\dfrac{(+56)}{(-8)}$

15. $\dfrac{(-81)}{(-9)}$

Exercise 18

For each question, find the missing number that will make the statement correct:

1. $\boxed{?} \times {}^+3 = 21$ **3.** $\boxed{?} \times {}^-5 = {}^-35$ **5.** $^-2 \times \boxed{?} = {}^-24$

2. $\boxed{?} \times {}^+4 = {}^-32$ **4.** $\boxed{?} \times {}^-9 = 36$ **6.** $^-8 \times \boxed{?} = {}^+24$

7. $12 \div \boxed{?} = 6$ **14.** $\boxed{?} \times {}^-2 = {}^-18$ **21.** $\dfrac{\boxed{?}}{{}^+5} = {}^+45$

8. ${}^-36 \div \boxed{?} = {}^-6$ **15.** $\boxed{?} \times {}^-3 = 0$

9. $\boxed{?} \div 3 = {}^-11$ **16.** $\boxed{?} \div {}^-8 = 0$ **22.** ${}^-49 \div \boxed{?} = {}^+7$

10. $\dfrac{{}^-72}{\boxed{?}} = {}^-8$ **17.** $\dfrac{\boxed{?}}{{}^-9} = {}^-9$ **23.** ${}^-12 \times \boxed{?} = {}^+96$

11. $\dfrac{{}^-42}{\boxed{?}} = {}^+6$ **18.** ${}^-7 \times \boxed{?} = {}^-56$ **24.** $\dfrac{{}^-108}{\boxed{?}} = {}^-36$

19. $\boxed{?} \times {}^+7 = {}^-7$

12. $24 \div \boxed{?} = {}^-8$

13. $8 \times \boxed{?} = {}^-40$ **20.** $\dfrac{48}{\boxed{?}} = {}^-8$ **25.** $\boxed{?} \times {}^-9 = {}^-63$

Using a Calculator

Most calculators have a $\boxed{{}^+/_-}$ key on them which allows negative numbers to be used. To use such a key you may need to press a function key first.

For instance, to key in ${}^-6$ you will probably need to key in $\boxed{6}\ \boxed{F}\ \boxed{{}^+/_-}$ if a function key is needed, or just $\boxed{6}\ \boxed{{}^+/_-}$ if the function key is not needed. You normally need to key in the number before using the $\boxed{{}^+/_-}$ key.

Exercise 19

Key in some negative numbers on your calculator. (If you do this correctly, the calculator's display should show the negative sign in front of the number itself.)

In the following examples I have not used the function key. If the function key is needed for the $\boxed{{}^+/_-}$ key to work, then it must be pressed immediately before the $\boxed{{}^+/_-}$ key.

e.g. 1 ${}^-5 - {}^-2 = \boxed{?}$

     Key in: $\boxed{5}\ \boxed{{}^+/_-}\ \boxed{-}\ \boxed{2}\ \boxed{{}^+/_-}\ \boxed{=}$

     ${}^-5 - {}^-2 = \underline{\underline{{}^-3}}$

$e.g. 2$ $^-3 \times {}^+8 =$ $\boxed{?}$

Key in $\boxed{3}$ $\boxed{{}^+/_-}$ $\boxed{\times}$ $\boxed{8}$ $\boxed{=}$

$^-3 \times {}^+8 = \underline{\underline{{}^-24}}$

Exercise 20

Use a calculator to check your answers to Exercises 7, 8, 9, 16 and 17.

Exercise 21

Work these out *without* using a calculator:

1. $8 - 15$

2. $3 - {}^-9$

3. $7 + {}^-6$

4. $^-16 + 7$

5. $^-8 - 19$

6. $^-13 + 7$

7. $^-6 - {}^-8$

8. $^-15 - {}^-7$

9. $^-23 + {}^-12$

10. $^-18 + 17$

11. $17 - (-8)$

12. $(-25) - (-17)$

13. $(-32) + 17$

14. $13 + (-9)$

15. $(-16) + (-15)$

16. $3 \times {}^-7$

17. $^-8 \times {}^-4$

18. $(-6) \times 7$

19. $(-3) \times (-9)$

20. $^-12 \times {}^-7$

21. $\dfrac{(-18)}{(-3)}$

22. $\dfrac{{}^-24}{6}$

23. $\dfrac{35}{{}^-7}$

24. $\dfrac{72}{(-6)}$

25. $\dfrac{{}^-36}{{}^-9}$

Exercise 22

In a game, cards were given for points won or lost. The card $\boxed{{}^+3}$ was for 3 points won, while $\boxed{{}^-4}$ was for 4 points lost.

1. Jim was given the following cards: $\boxed{{}^+2}$, $\boxed{{}^-6}$, $\boxed{{}^+4}$ and $\boxed{{}^+3}$.
How many points did he have?

2. Tim was given five identical cards. They were $\boxed{{}^-3}$.
How many points had he lost?

3. Sumitra had won the card $^+8$ while Brenda was given $^-7$. What is the difference in points on these two cards?

4. Three people played as a team and shared the points. Their final points came to $^-18$. If these points were shared equally, what did each person get?

5. Carol got three $^-2$ cards and four $^+6$ cards. What did her points total?

Exercise 23   Magic Squares   M

Copy and complete the magic squares. The sum of the numbers in each row, column or diagonal should always be the same.

1.

	$^-3$	2
	3	
		$^-2$

5.

5		3
	2	
1		

9.

	$^-9$		5
		$^-1$	$^-6$
1		$^-5$	$^-2$
	3		$^-7$

2.

	1	$^-4$
	$^-3$	
$^-2$		

6.

	$^-4$	1
	0	
	4	

10.

7		$^-5$	$^-2$
$^-4$			
6		$^-6$	$^-1$
$^-7$			4

3.

$^-2$		
$^-7$	$^-5$	$^-3$

7.

	7		9
			6
5	$^-2$	11	0
	1	4	

11.

0			$^-3$
		$^-6$	$^-8$
$^-7$	$^-9$	$^-10$	$^-4$
		$^-1$	

4.

		2
$^-4$	1	0

8.

$^-6$			6
	$^-1$		
7	0	4	
$^-3$		$^-2$	9

12.

7			$^-5$
		1	8
	4	0	
10	$^-1$		$^-2$

13.

9	16		0	7
15	-3		6	
2	4	11	13	-5
	10		-6	1

14.

-6	-13			
		-5	1	-11
-10	8	-4	-16	2
3	-9		-3	-15
			5	

Exercise 24 Algebraic Substitution

A If $c = {}^-7$, find the value of:

1. $3c$

2. $5c$

3. $2c$

4. $8c$

5. $7c$

6. $9c$

7. $4c$

8. $6c$

9. $c + 8$

10. $c - 9$

11. $c + 4$

12. $8 + c$

13. $10 - c$

14. $4c + 5$

15. $6c - 9$

16. $7 - 3c$

B **1.** $y = 2x - 7$. Find the value of y if x equals:

(a) 4   (b) 1   (c) ${}^-2$ (d) ${}^-8$ (e) 0

2. Given that $y = 3x + 2$, find the value of y if x equals:

(a) 5   (b) 0   (c) ${}^-1$ (d) ${}^-4$ (e) ${}^-7$

3. If $s = 30t$, find s when t equals:

(a) 4   (b) 0   (c) ${}^-1$ (d) ${}^-3$ (e) ${}^-5$

4. If $y = 10 - x$, find the value of y when x equals:

(a) 6   (b) 10   (c) 12   (d) ${}^-2$ (e) ${}^-10$

5. If $x + y = 8$, find the value of y when x equals:

(a) 4   (b) 0   (c) 10   (d) ${}^-3$ (e) ${}^-6$

6. If $R = l + m$, find the value of R when:

(a) $l = 7$ and $m = {}^-4$ (b) $l = {}^-2$ and $m = {}^-9$

C If $z = {}^-4$ and $x = {}^-9$, find the value of m if:

1. $m = z + 7$
2. $m = x - 3$
3. $m = x + z$
4. $m = z - x$
5. $m = 4x$
6. $m = 6z$
7. $m = 7x$

8. $m = 5x + 3$
9. $m = 4z - 7$
10. $m = 3z + x$
11. $m = 2z + x$
12. $m = 6x - z$
13. $m = 8 + 3x$
14. $m = 12 - 9z$

15. $m = 2x + 7z$
16. $m = 8z + 2x$
17. $m = 5z - 9x$
18. $m = 4(3x - 7z)$
19. $m = x - (2z - 6)$
20. $m = (x + 4x) \div 4$

Exercise 25

A Which number lies exactly halfway between the given numbers?

1.

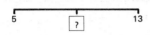

4.

2.

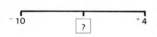

5.

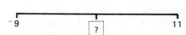

3.

6.

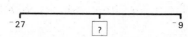

B Which number lies exactly halfway between the given pairs of numbers?

1. 6 and 14
2. 3 and 21
3. ${}^-7$ and ${}^+5$
4. ${}^-9$ and ${}^-1$
5. ${}^-8$ and ${}^+14$

6. ${}^-1$ and 13
7. ${}^-13$ and ${}^+1$
8. ${}^-8$ and ${}^+8$
9. ${}^-18$ and ${}^-10$
10. 49 and 85

11. ${}^-23$ and ${}^+51$
12. ${}^-76$ and ${}^-4$
13. ${}^-62$ and ${}^+28$
14. ${}^-18$ and 64
15. ${}^-96$ and ${}^+22$

215

Exercise 26

1. Write the following numbers in order of size, largest first:

   $^-3$, 8, 5, $^-6$, 0, $^+1$, $^-1$, $^-3\frac{1}{2}$, $^-4.5$

2. Write four pairs of numbers whose sum is zero.

3. Using only the numbers $^-5$, $^-2$ and 4, where each number is used once only in each question, and using only the operations $+$, $-$, $\times$ and $\div$, write as many questions as you can that give a negative answer.

4. Using all the numbers $^-4$, $^-6$, $^-2$ and 5, and any of the operations $+$, $-$, $\times$ and $\div$ (the operations may be used several times but the numbers must each be used only once), write a question that gives the largest possible answer. What is this largest possible answer?

Exercise 27

A Give the next three terms of each of these sequences:

1. 8, 6, 4, 2, 0, $^-2$, $\boxed{?}$, $\boxed{?}$, $\boxed{?}$
2. $^+5$, $^+3$, $^+1$, $\boxed{?}$, $\boxed{?}$, $\boxed{?}$
3. $^+5$, $^+4$, $^+2$, $^-1$, $\boxed{?}$, $\boxed{?}$, $\boxed{?}$
4. $^-8$, $^-5$, $^-2$, $^+1$, $\boxed{?}$, $\boxed{?}$, $\boxed{?}$
5. $^+1$, $^-3$, $^+5$, $^-7$, $^+9$, $\boxed{?}$, $\boxed{?}$, $\boxed{?}$
6. $^-12$, $^-10$, $^-6$, 0, 8, $\boxed{?}$, $\boxed{?}$, $\boxed{?}$
7. 5, 3, $^-1$, $^-7$, $\boxed{?}$, $\boxed{?}$, $\boxed{?}$
8. $^-2$, $^-4$, $^-6$, $^-8$, $\boxed{?}$, $\boxed{?}$, $\boxed{?}$

B Copy these sequences. Fill in the missing numbers.

1. $^+10$, $^+7$, $\boxed{?}$, $^+1$, $\boxed{?}$, $\boxed{?}$, $^-8$, ...
2. $^-3$, $^+6$, $^-9$, $\boxed{?}$, $^-15$, $\boxed{?}$, $\boxed{?}$, ...
3. $^-2$, $^-8$, $\boxed{?}$, $^-20$, $\boxed{?}$, $^-32$, $\boxed{?}$, ...
4. 19, 8, $\boxed{?}$, $\boxed{?}$, $^-25$, $\boxed{?}$, $^-47$, ...
5. $^-8$, 2, $^-6$, 6, $^-4$, 10, $\boxed{?}$, 14, $\boxed{?}$, $\boxed{?}$, ...

Exercise 28

Using the following table, plot a graph to convert °C (Celsius) to °F (Fahrenheit). Use a scale of 20 mm to 20 °C on the horizontal axis and use 20 mm to 40 °F on the vertical axis.

°C	⁻60	⁻40	⁻20	0	20	40	60	80	100
°F	⁻76	⁻40	⁻4	32	68	104	140	176	212

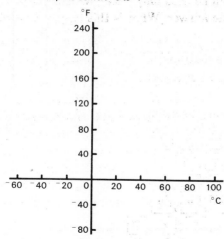

Graph to Convert °C to °F

Now use your graph to help you to change the given temperatures into the other system:

1. 30 °C
2. 90 °C
3. 158 °F

4. 10 °C
5. 122 °F
6. 95 °F

7. 85 °C
8. 14 °F
9. ⁻30 °C

10. ⁻40 °F
11. ⁻50 °C
12. ⁻49 °F

Relations Between Two Sets

Consider the set of pupils and the set of shoe sizes.

The relationship between the two sets can be shown on a *relation diagram* (sometimes called an arrow diagram or a mapping diagram).

A *relation* is when we have two sets (which may be equal) and a statement that links any member or members of one set with any member or members of the other set in a given order. (*Note* Not all members of a set need to be used.)

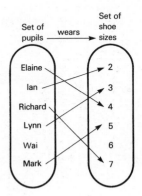

Exercise 1 M

Copy and complete each diagram to show the given relation for the two sets:

1.

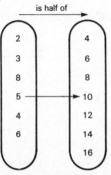

is half of

2.

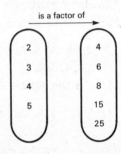

is a factor of

3.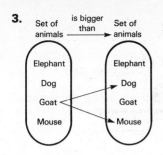

5.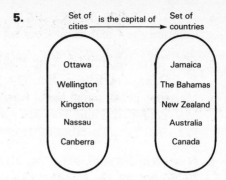

4.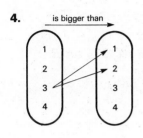

6.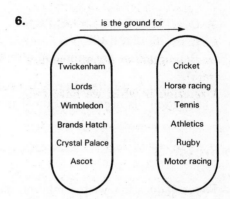

Exercise 2

For each question, two sets are given, together with a rule which relates them. (Sometimes other necessary information is given.) Show each relation on a diagram.

1. $B = \{$Golden Gate bridge, Tagus bridge, Firth of Forth bridge, Severn bridge$\}$
$L = \{$England, Portugal, Scotland, United States$\}$
Relation: 'can be found in' from set B to L.

2. $S = \{25, 4, 16, 36, 9, 1, 49\}$
$N = \{1, 2, 3, 4, 5, 6, 7\}$
Relation: 'is the square of' from set S to N.

3. $M = \{4, 5, 6, 7, 8, 9, 10, 11\}$
$N = \{1, 2, 3, 4, 5, 6, 7\}$
Relation: 'is 3 more than' from set M to N.

4. $N = \{1, 2, 3, 4, 5, 6, 7, 8, 9, 10\}$
Relation: 'is 4 less than' from set N to N.

5. $M = \{$Mrs North, Mrs West, Mrs Old, Mrs Young$\}$
$C = \{$Margaret, Eileen, Jim, Tom$\}$
Margaret is the daughter of Mrs North, Eileen is the daughter of Mrs Young, Jim and Tom are sons of Mrs West.
Relation: 'is the mother of' from set M to set C.

6. $N = \{265, 389, 496, 508, 6134, 7012, 73\,460\}$
Relation: 'has the same remainder when divided by 9 as' from set N to N.

7. $Q = \{2.8 \times 6.1, 3.4 \times 6.8, 7.6 \times 2.1, 37.2 \times 4.2\}$
$R = \{16, 18, 21, 160\}$
Relation: 'has an estimated answer of' from set Q to set R.

8. $P = \{$Mars, Jupiter, Earth, Venus, Saturn, Pluto$\}$
Relation: 'is nearer the Sun than' from set P to P.

Exercise 3

For each question, write a relation that is true for all pairs of numbers that are linked in each arrow diagram:

1.

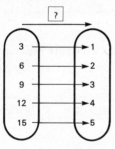

3.

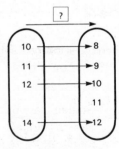

2.

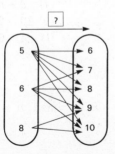

4.

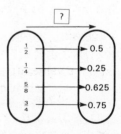

Exercise 4

1. (a) Copy and complete the mapping* diagram so that each solid *maps to* its number of edges.
   (b) Which solid maps to 9?
   (c) Which solid maps to 8?

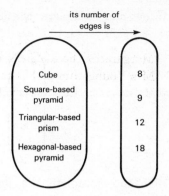

2. (a) Copy and complete the mapping diagram so that each common fraction or decimal maps to the percentage having the same value.
   (b) Which number maps to 40%?
   (c) Which number maps to 75%?
   (d) What does $\frac{1}{8}$ map to?

* See the glossary.

Exercise 5

1. If $n = 4$, find the value of:
   (a) $n + 3$ (d) $2n$ (g) $2n + 5$ (j) $9 - n$
   (b) $n + 6$ (e) $3n$ (h) $4n - 1$ (k) $10 - 2n$
   (c) $n - 2$ (f) $7n$ (i) $6n - 7$ (l) $24 - 6n$

2. Find the value of:
   (a) $3c$ when $c = 6$ (e) $2d - 7$ when $d = 8$
   (b) $8x$ when $x = 7$ (f) $5m + 6$ when $m = 7$
   (c) $p + 8$ when $p = 9$ (g) $46 - 3d$ when $d = 10$
   (d) $12 - k$ when $k = 9$ (h) $100 - 4y$ when $y = 16$

1. Copy and complete the mapping diagram for the mapping $x \to x + 9$:

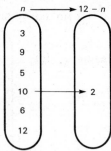

2. Copy and complete the mapping diagram for the mapping $n \to 12 - n$:

3. Draw a mapping diagram to show $x \to 4x$ where x is a member of the set $\{1, 2, 4, 9, 10, 15\}$.

4. Show the mapping $n \to 3n - 2$ on a diagram where the first set (called the *domain**) is $\{1, 3, 5, 8, 10, 18\}$.

5. Using the domain $\{2, 4, 6, 8, 10\}$, draw a diagram to show the mapping $m \to 20 - 2m$.

6. Use the set $\{\frac{1}{2}, 1, 2, 3, 4, 6, 12\}$ as the domain. Draw a diagram to show the mapping $c \to \dfrac{12}{c}$.

7. Using the set $\{1, 2, 3, 4, 5, 6, 7\}$ as the domain, draw diagrams to show the mappings:
   (a) $x \to 2x + 4$
   (b) $x \to 40 - 3x$

* See the glossary.

1. For the mapping $n \to n + 6$:
   (a) what does 3 map to?   (b) what number maps to 11?

2. For the mapping $x \to x - 7$:
   (a) what does 25 map to?   (b) what number maps to 9?

3. The rule for a mapping is 'double then subtract 3'. Draw a mapping diagram using the domain $\{4, 5, 6, 7, 8, 9, 10\}$.

4. Use the rule 'multiply by 10 then add 6'. Draw a mapping diagram using the domain $\{1, 2, 3, 4, 5, 6, 7, 8\}$.

5. Copy and complete the mapping diagram in each question so that the pairs of elements that are linked by arrows are linked by the same rule:

(a)

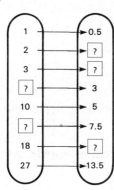

(c)

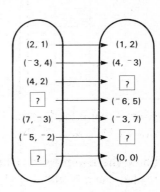

(b)

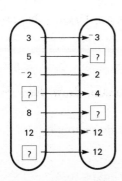

(d)

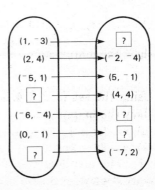

Copy and complete each diagram to show the given mapping for the two sets:

1.

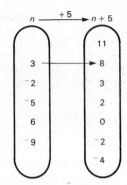

2.

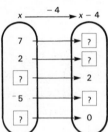

3.

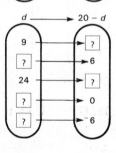

4.

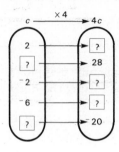

5.

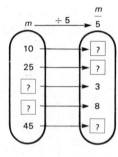

6.

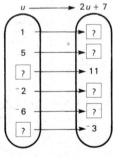

Exercise 9

1. Use the set $\{^-5, ^-3, ^-2, 0, 2, 4\}$ as the domain. Draw a mapping diagram to show $n \to 3n + 1$.

2. For the mapping $x \to x - 6$:
   (a) what does $^-2$ map to?   (b) what maps to 0?

3. For the mapping $v \to 10 - 2v$:
   (a) what does 8 map to?   (b) what maps to 8?

15 Co-ordinates and Graphs

Exercise 1

Draw a pair of axes as shown. (Use 1 cm to represent 1 unit on both axes.) (x ranges from 0 to 14 while y ranges from 0 to 18.)

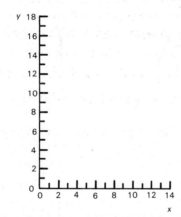

Now plot and label the following points:

A (9, 15)	F (12, 5)	K (10, 0)	P (13, 17)	U (3, 18)
B (0, 14)	G (3, 9)	L (4, 2)	Q (11, 13)	V (1, 16)
C (2, 4)	H (5, 12)	M (7, 17)	R (8, 8)	W (5, 7)
D (14, 2)	I (6, 1)	N (9, 6)	S (10, 3)	X (6, 3)
E (14, 12)	J (10, 10)	O (0, 0)	T (5, 11)	Y (14, 9)

Measure and write the length of each of the following straight lines:

1. AH
2. CJ
3. MF
4. BR
5. LS
6. EN
7. KT
8. GP
9. OW
10. UD
11. IV
12. QX
13. AC
14. PY
15. LP

225

Exercise 2

Draw a pair of axes as shown. Use a scale of 1 cm to 1 unit on both axes.
Label the x-axis from ⁻8 to 8. Label the y-axis from 0 to 20.
Answer all questions on the same piece of graph paper using the same pair of axes.

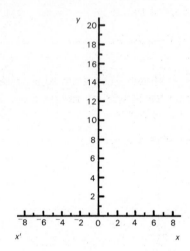

For each question, plot the points and join them in the given order.

Draw the axis (or axes) of symmetry on each shape.

1. $(8, 8)$ $(8, 14)$ $(4, 14)$ $(4, 8)$ $(8, 8)$

2. $(0, 15)$ $(4, 15)$ $(4, 19)$ $(0, 19)$ $(0, 15)$

3. $(2, 10)$ $(2, 14)$ $(⁻4, 12)$ $(2, 10)$

4. $(⁻8, 10)$ $(⁻2, 10)$ $(⁻3, 7)$ $(⁻7, 7)$ $(⁻8, 10)$

5. $(⁻8, 2)$ $(⁻6, 4)$ $(⁻4, 4)$ $(⁻2, 2)$ $(⁻4, 0)$ $(⁻6, 0)$ $(⁻8, 2)$

6. $(2, 8)$ $(⁻2, 6)$ $(2, 4)$ $(6, 6)$ $(2, 8)$

7. $(2, 2)$ $(8, 0)$ $(6, 4)$ $(2, 2)$

8. $(⁻6, 16)$ $(⁻4, 18)$ $(⁻6, 20)$ $(⁻8, 18)$ $(⁻6, 16)$

9. $(⁻2, 16)$ $(⁻2, 14)$ $(⁻6, 12)$ $(⁻4, 16)$ $(⁻2, 16)$

10. $(2, 1)$ $(1, 4)$ $(⁻2, 5)$ $(⁻1, 2)$ $(2, 1)$

Exercise 3

Draw a pair of axes as shown.

Use a scale of 2 cm to 1 unit on both axes.

Label the x-axis from $^-5$ to 3.
Label the y-axis from $^-4$ to 6.

Answer all the questions on the same piece of graph paper, using the same pair of axes.

For each question, plot the points and join them in the given order.

You will have drawn half a symmetrical shape.

Complete each shape.

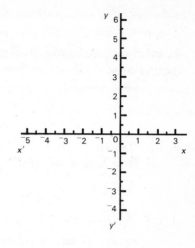

1. $(^-3, 0)$ $(^-4, 0)$ $(^-4, ^-2)$ $(^-3, ^-2)$. A square.
2. $(^-1, 5)$ $(^-2, 6)$ $(^-5, 5)$. A kite.
3. $(^-1, ^-2)$ $(0, 1)$ $(^-1, 1)$. An isosceles triangle.
4. $(1, ^-2)$ $(0, ^-3)$ $(1, ^-4)$ $(2, ^-3)$. A rectangle.
5. $(0, 4)$ $(1, 5)$ $(3, 3)$ $(2, 2)$. A square.
6. $(^-1, 2)$ $(^-3, 1)$ $(^-5, 2)$. A rhombus.

Exercise 4

Draw a pair of axes as shown.
Let $^-7 \leqslant x \leqslant 7$
and $^-8 \leqslant y \leqslant 10$

Use a scale of 1 cm to 1 unit on both axes.

Answer all the questions on the same piece of graph paper and use the same pair of axes.

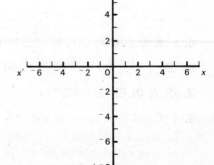

1. (*a*) Join ($^-2, 10$) to ($2, 8$) to ($0, 6$) to ($^-2, 10$) using straight lines.
(*b*) What is the name of the triangle you have drawn?

2. (*a*) Join ($^-7, 9$) to ($^-1, 5$) with a straight line.
(*b*) What are the co-ordinates of the mid-point of this line that you have drawn?

3. (*a*) Join ($1, {}^-8$) to ($^-3, {}^-5$) with a straight line.
(*b*) How long is this line?

4. (*a*) The straight line joining ($^-4, 5$) to ($^-4, 1$) is a diagonal of a square. Draw the square.
(*b*) What are the co-ordinates of the other two vertices?

5. (*a*) Join ($3, 4$) to ($6, 10$) using a straight line.
(*b*) Draw a perpendicular from the point ($7, 7$) to this line.
(*c*) Give the co-ordinates of the point where the perpendicular meets the line.

6. Find the co-ordinates of the point of intersection of the line joining ($^-7, {}^-4$) to ($^-4, {}^-8$) and the line joining ($^-6, {}^-7$) to ($^-4, {}^-3$).

7. (*a*) The short diagonal of a rhombus joins ($1, 3$) to ($3, {}^-1$). If the long diagonal is twice as long as the short diagonal, draw the rhombus.
(*b*) What are the co-ordinates of the end-points of the long diagonal?

8. ($2, {}^-3$), ($2, {}^-6$) and ($6, {}^-5$) are three vertices of a parallelogram. If these vertices can be joined in any order, find three possible positions for the fourth vertex.

Exercise 5

1. (*a*) On graph paper, draw a pair of axes as shown, using a scale of 10 mm to 1 unit.

$$^-8 \leqslant x \leqslant 8$$
and $^-10 \leqslant y \leqslant 10$.

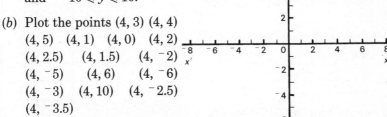

(*b*) Plot the points $(4, 3)$ $(4, 4)$ $(4, 5)$ $(4, 1)$ $(4, 0)$ $(4, 2)$ $(4, 2.5)$ $(4, 1.5)$ $(4, ^-2)$ $(4, ^-5)$ $(4, 6)$ $(4, ^-6)$ $(4, ^-3)$ $(4, 10)$ $(4, ^-2.5)$ $(4, ^-3.5)$

(*c*) What do you notice about all these points you have plotted on your graph paper?

(*d*) Join the points to form a straight line. (Use a ruler.)

(*e*) Look at the pairs of co-ordinates given in part (*b*) above. In each case, the first number is always 4. If the ordered pairs (or pairs of co-ordinates) are written as (x, y), then the x-value is always 4, that is, $x = 4$.
The *equation of this line* is therefore $x = 4$.
Label your line '$x = 4$'.

2. On the same piece of graph paper and using the same pair of axes, draw these lines:
(*a*) $x = 3$ (*b*) $x = 1$ (*c*) $x = 5\frac{1}{2}$ (*d*) $x = {}^-5$

3. Using the same pair of axes, draw:
(*a*) $y = 3$ (*b*) $y = 6$ (*c*) $y = 7\frac{1}{2}$ (*d*) $y = {}^-4$

4. Using the same pair of axes draw:
(*a*) $x = 0$ (*b*) $y = 0$

5. What is special about the lines drawn in question 4?

6. What is the equation of the straight line that joins these points?
$(^-7, ^-2)$ $(^-7, 4)$ $(^-7, 9)$ $(^-7, ^-6.5)$

229

7. What is the equation of the straight line that joins these points?
($^{-}1, 5$) ($3, 5$) ($2, 5$) ($6, 5$) ($^{-}5, 5$) ($2.5, 5$) ($^{-}7, 5$)

Exercise 6

1. Consider the relation 'is 3 less than' for the set of real numbers*.

Copy and complete the mapping diagram.

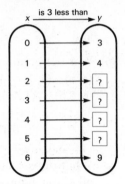

2. The relation can be shown using ordered pairs. Copy these ordered pairs and fill in the missing y-values.

($0, 3$)
($1, 4$)
($2, ?$)
($3, ?$)
($4, ?$)
($5, ?$)
($6, 9$)

3. The same relation can be shown in a table:

x	0	1	2	3	4	5	6
y	3	4					9

Copy and complete the table above.

4. (a) Plot the points to form a graph. Use a scale of 20 mm to 1 unit on both axes. Your x-values should range from 0 to 6 ($0 \leqslant x \leqslant 6$) while the y-values should range from 0 to 9 ($0 \leqslant y \leqslant 9$).

(b) Join the points with a straight line. (Since a straight line is obtained, the graph is called a *linear graph*.)

* See the glossary.

5. For this relation, the x-value 'is 3 less than' the y-value. So the y-value must be '3 more than' the x-value. Copy and complete the statements in parts (a) and (b):

(a) The y-value = the x-value + $\boxed{?}$.

(b) That is, $y = x + \boxed{?}$. (This is called the equation of the graph.)

(c) Write the equation of the graph along your graph.

Exercise 7

A **1.** Draw a mapping diagram to show the relation 'is 2 less than'.

2. Show the relation as a set of ordered pairs.

3. For each of the ordered pairs, what must be added to the first number to obtain the second number?

4. Copy and complete these statements for the ordered pairs that satisfy the relation 'is 2 less than':

(a) The y-value = the x-value + $\boxed{?}$

(b) that is, $y = x + \boxed{?}$

5. Plot a graph to show this relation. Draw a pair of axes where $0 \leqslant x \leqslant 14$ and $0 \leqslant y \leqslant 20$. Use a scale of 10 mm to 1 unit on both axes.

6. Label your graph with its equation.

B **1.** Find equations that are true for the given sets of ordered pairs:

(a) $\{(0, 6), (1, 7), (2, 8), (4, 10), (7, 13), (10, 16), (12, 18), (14, 20)\}$

(b) $\{(0, 4), (1, 5), (3, 7), (6, 10), (8, 12), (11, 15), (13, 17), (14, 18)\}$

2. Draw graphs of the equations in question 1. Use the same pair of axes as in part A.

C Using the same pair of axes as used above, draw graphs of:

1. the relation 'is 1 less than'

2. $y = x$

3. $y = x + 5$

If you have not already labelled each graph you have drawn, then write the equation of each graph on each line.

Exercise 8

1. Copy and complete the mapping diagram for the relation 'is 3 less than'.

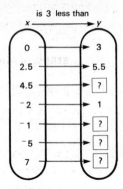

2. Since the equation for this relation is $y = x + 3$, find the value of y when $x = {}^-4$.

3. $({}^-6, \boxed{?})$, $({}^-3, \boxed{?})$ and $(1.5, \boxed{?})$ are ordered pairs that satisfy this relation. Find the missing numbers and write the three pairs of co-ordinates.

4. Draw a pair of axes where x ranges from $^-6$ to $^+8$ $({}^-6 \leqslant x \leqslant {}^+8)$ and y from $^-10$ to $^+10$ $({}^-10 \leqslant y \leqslant {}^+10)$. Use a scale of 10 mm to 1 unit on both axes.

5. Plot the points given by the relation. Label the graph $y = x + 3$.

Exercise 9

Throughout this exercise, draw every graph using the same pair of axes as drawn in question 4 of Exercise 8.

1. Copy and complete the mapping diagram for the relation 'is 2 more than'.

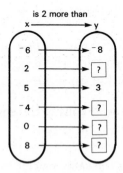

2. Since x is 2 more than y then y is 2 less than x.
the y-value = the x-value $- 2$
that is, $y = x - 2$.
Find the value of y when:
(a) $x = 6$ (b) $x = {}^-3$

3. $(7, \boxed{?})$, $(3, \boxed{?})$, $(1, \boxed{?})$, $({}^-2, \boxed{?})$ and $({}^-2.5, \boxed{?})$ are ordered pairs that satisfy the equation $y = x - 2$. Find the missing numbers and write the five ordered pairs.

232

4. Draw the graph of $y = x - 2$. Label your graph.

5. Draw the graph of $y = x - 4$. Label it.

6. Draw and label the graph of $y = x$.

7. Draw the graph of the relation 'is 3 more than'.

8. Draw the graph of the relation 'is 1 more than'.

Exercise 10

Draw a pair of axes where the x-values range from $^-2$ to $^+6$ (use a scale of 20 mm to 1 unit) and where the y-values range from $^-10$ to $^+30$ (use a scale of 20 mm to 5 units).
Use the pair of axes you have just drawn for all the following graphs:

1. Draw the graph of the relations:
    (a) 'is half of',   (b) 'is one-quarter of'.

2. Draw graphs of:
    (a) $y = x$ (b) $y = 5x$ (c) $y = 3x$ (d) $y = \frac{1}{2}x$

Exercise 11

Give (a) the relation for, and (b) the equation of each of the following graphs:

1.

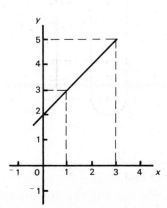

2.

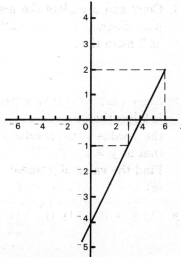

233

3.

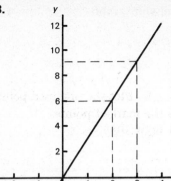

5.

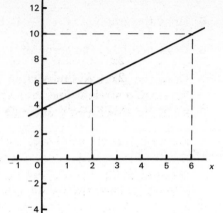

4.

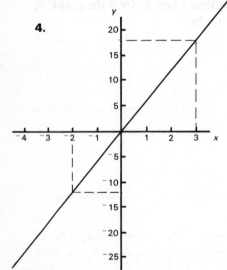

6.

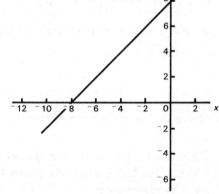

Exercise 12

Draw a pair of axes where $^-8 \leqslant x \leqslant ^+8$ (use a scale of 1 cm to 1 unit on the x-axis) and $^-20 \leqslant y \leqslant 25$ (use a scale of 2 cm to 5 units on the y-axis).

Use this pair of axes for all the graphs throughout this exercise.

1. (a) If $\qquad$ $y = 2x + 3$
when $x = 2$, $\quad y = 4 + 3 = 7$
This gives the point (2, 7). Plot the point (2, 7).

(b) If $y = 2x + 3$, find y when $x = 6$. Plot the obtained point.
(c) If $y = 2x + 3$, find y when $x = 0$. Plot the obtained point.
(d) If $y = 2x + 3$, find y when $x = 8$. Plot the obtained point.
(e) If $y = 2x + 3$, find y when $x = {}^-2$. Plot the obtained point.
(f) If $y = 2x + 3$, find y when $x = {}^-6$. Plot the obtained point.
(g) If $y = 2x + 3$, find y when $x = {}^-8$. Plot the obtained point.
(h) Draw a straight line through all the marked points.
(i) Label this linear graph with the equation $y = 2x + 3$.

2. For each part of question 2, use the equation $y = 2x + 5$. In each case, use the given value of x to find the y-value, then plot the obtained point. Finally, draw a straight line through the plotted points and label the graph with its equation, $y = 2x + 5$.

(a) $x = 4$ (b) $x = 8$ (c) $x = 0$ (d) $x = {}^-2$ (e) $x = {}^-8$

3. Using the same method as in questions 1 and 2, draw the graph of $y = 2x - 1$. Work out some points first.

4. Now draw the graph of $y = 2x - 4$.

5. Draw the graph of $y = 2x$.

6. What do you notice about all the graphs you have drawn in this exercise?

Exercise 13

Draw a pair of axes where x ranges from $^-7$ to $^+7$ and y ranges from $^-25$ to $^+25$. Use a scale of 1 cm to 1 unit on the x-axis and 2 cm to 5 units on the y-axis.

Use this pair of axes for all the graphs in this exercise.

A Draw graphs of:

1. $y = 3x$ 4. $y = 3x - 2$
2. $y = 3x + 4$ 5. $y = 3x - 1$
3. $y = 3x + 2$ 6. $y = 3x - 4$

B 1. Write what you notice about all the graphs you drew in part A.

2. Where would the graph of $y = 3x + 5$ cross the y-axis?

235

Exercise 14

Draw a pair of axes where x ranges from $^-8$ to $^+8$ and y ranges from $^-50$ to $^+50$. Use a scale of 10 mm to 1 unit on the x-axis and 10 mm to 5 units on the y-axis.

A Now plot these graphs using the pair of axes you have drawn:

1. $y = x$ **5.** $y = 5x$

2. $y = 2x$ **6.** $y = 6x$

3. $y = 3x$ **7.** $y = \frac{1}{2}x$

4. $y = 4x$ **8.** $y = \frac{5}{2}x$

B **1.** Write what you notice about all the graphs you drew in part A.

    2. List the graphs in order of steepness, giving the steepest first.

Exercise 15

1. Does the point $(3, 4)$ lie on the line $y = 3x - 5$?

2. The point $(2, \boxed{?})$ lies on the line $y = 2x + 4$.

3. The point $(3, \boxed{?})$ lies on the line $y = x - 7$.

4. The point $(\boxed{?}, 9)$ lies on the line $y = 3x - 6$.

5. The point $(2, \boxed{?})$ lies on the line $y = 5$.

6. Does $(^-2, 4)$ lie on the line $y = x + 2$?

7. Does $(1, ^-2)$ lie on the line $y = x - 3$?

8. On which line does the point $(^-3, ^-2)$ lie, on $y = 2x + 4$ or on $y = 2x - 4$?

9. A point with x-co-ordinate of 6 lies on the line $y = 2x - 8$. Find the y-co-ordinate.

10. A point with y-co-ordinate of 3 lies on the line $y = 2x - 11$. Find the x-co-ordinate.

Exercise 16

A On a journey I travelled at a steady 60 kilometres per hour. The table below shows how far I travelled every hour.

Time taken, t (h)	0	1	2	3	4	5	6
Distance travelled, s (km)	0	60	120	180	240	300	360

1. Use the table to help you to plot a graph of distance against time. Draw your axes as shown. Use a scale of 2 cm to 1 h on the time axis and 1 cm to 20 km on the distance axis.

2. Use your graph to help you to answer these questions:
   (a) How far had I travelled in $1\frac{1}{2}$ h?
   (b) How long did it take me to travel 270 km?
   (c) How far had I travelled in 5 h 24 min?
   (d) How long did it take me to travel 168 km?

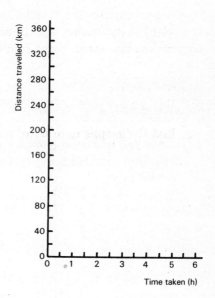

B

Load (N)	10	20	30	40	50	60
Length (cm)	33	36	39		45	

The table above gives the length of a stretched spring when different loads hang from it.

1. Draw a graph. Use a scale of 1 cm to 5 N for the load and 2 cm to 5 cm for the length.

2. Copy the table. Use your graph to help you to complete it.

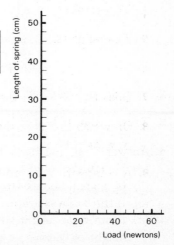

237

3. Use your graph to help you to answer these questions:
   (a) How long is the unstretched spring?
   (b) How long is the spring when a load of 35 N hangs from it?
   (c) What load is needed to stretch the spring to 43.5 cm?

C In experiments, the points plotted often do not lie in a line, but almost give a line. In such cases we draw what is called '*the line of best fit*'. This is the line that fits the points best.

In a science experiment, a ball was dropped several times. Each time, the height from which it was dropped was noted and the height of its bounce was measured. Some results are given in this table:

Height of drop (cm)	40	60	80	100	120	140	160	180	200
Height of bounce (cm)	13	20	30	35	44	51	56	65	72

1. Draw a pair of axes as shown. Use a scale of 10 mm to 10 cm on the 'horizontal axis' for the height of drop and 10 mm to 5 cm on the 'vertical axis'.

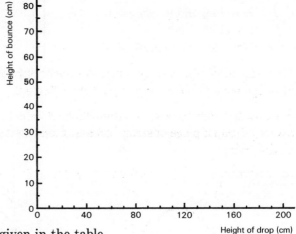

2. Plot the points given in the table.

3. Draw a 'line of best fit'.

4. Answer these questions using your graph:
   (a) How high would the ball bounce if dropped from 50 cm?
   (b) If the ball bounces to 54 cm, from what height was it dropped?
   (c) If the ball was dropped from 92 cm, how high would it bounce?
   (d) From what height should the ball be dropped to bounce to a height of 68 cm?

16 Circumference of a Circle

3.141 592 653 589 793 238 462 643 383 279 502 884 197 169 399 375 . . .

Exercise 1

For this exercise you need several cylindrical objects such as jars, tins, coins and so on. They should be different sizes.

Find the diameter and the circumference of each circular base (or cross-section) of each object you have collected.

To find the circumference either wrap a tape measure around the object or wrap a piece of string around it and then measure the length of the string.

Show your results in a table as follows:

Object	Circumference, C	Diameter, d	$\dfrac{C}{d}$

Complete the last column by dividing the circumference by the diameter. Write what you notice.

From Exercise 1 you probably found that the circumference is slightly more than 3 times the diameter. In the Bible, when King Solomon was building his temple, the circumference was thought to be three times the diameter. In 1 Kings, chapter 7, verse 23, it says 'And he made a molten sea, ten cubits from the one brim to the other: it was round all about, and his height was five cubits: and a line of thirty cubits did compass it round about.' (See also 2 Chronicles, chapter 4, verse 2.) The molten sea was a very large bowl that contained over 500 barrels of water for the priests' use in washing themselves and the sacrifices. They also used the water for keeping the courts of the temple clean.

Exercise 2

Find the circumference of each circle.

Use: Circumference, $C \approx 3d$.

e.g. 1 Diameter, d = 6 cm

Circumference, $C \approx 3d$

$= 3 \times 6$

$\therefore$ the circumference = 18 cm

240

e.g. 2

Radius, r = 2.4 m

∴ diameter, d = 4.8 m

Circumference, $C \approx 3d$

$= 3 \times 4.8$

∴ the circumference = 14.4 m

1.

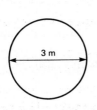

5 m

5.

60 mm

9.

3.07 m

2.

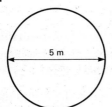

3 m

6.

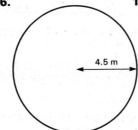

4.5 m

10.

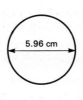

5.96 cm

3.

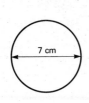

7 cm

7.

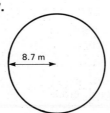

8.7 m

11.

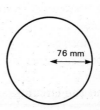

76 mm

4.

2 cm

8.

12.9 cm

12.

7.28 m

Exercise 3 π (pi)

The circumference of a circle happens to be slightly more than 3 times the diameter.

The Greek letter π (pi) is used as a symbol for the ratio of the circumference to the diameter of any circle, so $\pi = \dfrac{C}{d}$, but we often re-write this as: Circumference of a circle, $C = \pi d$.

π has not got an exact value. It is non-terminating and non-recurring when written as a decimal. For thousands of years, mathematicians have tried to calculate more and more accurate values of pi.

(The value of pi to 48 decimal places has been given at the beginning of this chapter.)

A About 1580 BC, in the Rhind Papyrus, a method for calculating the area of a circle was given by Ahmes, the scribe. From this method, pi was found to be $\dfrac{256}{81}$. Use a calculator to change this to a decimal.

Compare its accuracy with the decimal value given on p. 239.

B Over 2000 years ago, Archimedes (287–212 BC), a Greek mathematician, showed that the value of pi lies between $3\frac{10}{71}$ and $3\frac{1}{7}$. Use a calculator to change these two values of pi into decimals. Compare their accuracy using the decimal value given on p. 239. (Note that $3\frac{1}{7}$ is still used as a suitable approximation to π.)

C About AD 150, Ptolemy, another Greek, found pi to have the value of $3°8'30''$. This is $3\frac{17}{120}$ or $\frac{377}{120}$.

Change $\dfrac{377}{120}$ to a decimal and compare it with the decimal value given on p. 239.

D In China, about AD 480, Tsu Ch'ung-Chih found quite an accurate value of pi. He gave the value $\frac{355}{113}$.

Change $\frac{355}{113}$ to a decimal. Compare it with the decimal value given on p. 239.

Note that this value together with $\frac{22}{7}$ can be used to find Ptolemy's value for pi:
$$\frac{355 + 22}{113 + 7} = \frac{377}{120}$$

E About AD 1430, the Persian mathematician, Jemshid Al-Kashi, gave pi to 16 decimal places.

F Ludolf van Ceulen (1540–1610), a German, found pi to 35 decimal places. He had worked on the problem for most of his life.

G About 1655, John Wallis gave pi as a *series*. This series can be written as:
$$\text{pi} = 2 \times \frac{2}{1} \times \frac{2}{3} \times \frac{4}{3} \times \frac{4}{5} \times \frac{6}{5} \times \frac{6}{7} \times \frac{8}{7} \times \frac{8}{9} \times \frac{10}{9} \times \ldots$$

The numbers follow a pattern and continue for ever.
The more numbers that are used, the more accurate is the value of pi. It takes a long time to find a reasonable approximation for pi using this series. Try it for yourself on a calculator.

There have been a number of different series used to find π over the years:

(1) William Shanks (1853) used a series to find π to 707 decimal places. However, the last 180 digits were incorrect. It took him about 20 years of calculating!

(2) In 1949, the ENIAC computer calculated π to 2035 decimal places in 80 h of machine time.

(3) In 1958, G. E. Felton used a Ferranti Pegasus computer to find π to 10 021 places in 33 machine hours. (This would have taken about 100 years to work out on a calculator!)

243

(4) Dr Daniel Shanks and Dr John W. Wrench Jr in New York in 1961, used an IBM 7090 computer to calculate π to 100 265 places in 8 h 43 min.

(5) In 1981, Dr Kazunori Miyoshi of the University of Tsukuba in Japan worked out π to two million decimal places in 137 h on a FACOM M200 computer.

(6) In 1983, two other Japanese mathematicians, Yoshiaki Tamura and Yasumasa Kanada succeeded in working out π to eight million decimal places in 7 h using a HITAC M280H computer.

(7) The world record for memorising π is held by Rajan Mahadevan of India who memorised 31 811 decimal places.

(8) The British record of memorising 20 013 decimal places of π is held by Creighton Carvello of Redcar.

(9) The first person to use the symbol π to stand for the ratio $\dfrac{C}{d}$, was probably an English writer called William Jones. He used π in 1706.

Exercise 4

In Exercise 3, several ratios were given for π.
Here are some more. Use a calculator to change these to decimals. In each case, state the number of decimal places that are correct, by comparing with the value given on p. 239:

1. $\dfrac{333}{106}$ 5. $\dfrac{487}{155}$ 9. $\dfrac{776}{247}$ 13. $\dfrac{1021}{325}$

2. $\dfrac{421}{134}$ 6. $\dfrac{531}{169}$ 10. $\dfrac{820}{261}$ 14. $\dfrac{1043}{332}$

3. $\dfrac{443}{141}$ 7. $\dfrac{688}{219}$ 11. $\dfrac{864}{275}$ 15. $\dfrac{1354}{431}$

4. $\dfrac{465}{148}$ 8. $\dfrac{732}{233}$ 12. $\dfrac{908}{289}$ 16. $\dfrac{1376}{438}$

Exercise 5

In Exercise 3 and 4 there are a number of different ratios that give good approximations for π.

Try to find some ratios of your own that give approximations for π.

Note that ratios such as $\frac{44}{14}$ are not allowed ($\frac{44}{14}$ can simplify to a ratio that has already been given, namely $\frac{22}{7}$.)

Exercise 6

In Exercise 3, part D, two ratios were used to give another ratio:

$$\frac{355 + 22}{113 + 7} = \frac{377}{120}$$

Look at the ratios in Exercise 4, starting with question 2:

$$\left(\text{Note that } \frac{44}{14} = \frac{22}{7}. \right)$$

Investigate other ratios for π in this way.
Write about your findings.

Two mnemonics for π given in the magazine *Mathematical Pie* are:

How I like a cuddle
3 . 1 4 1 6

and How I wish I could recollect pi easily today
3 . 1 4 1 5 9 2 6 5

(Count the number of letters in each word.)

Exercise 7

Find the circumference of the following circles.
Use the formula: Circumference of a circle, $C = \pi d$ and use $\pi = \frac{22}{7}$.
As a check, estimate each answer using $\pi = 3$.

1.

14 cm

7.

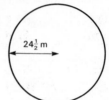

$24\frac{1}{2}$ m

2.

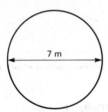

7 m

8.

$3\frac{1}{2}$ cm

3.

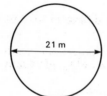

21 m

9.

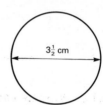

$\frac{7}{8}$ m

4.

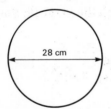

28 cm

10.

$4\frac{3}{8}$ m

5.

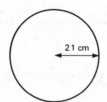

21 cm

11.

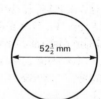

$52\frac{1}{2}$ mm

6.

35 cm

12.

$1\frac{3}{11}$ m

246

Exercise 8

Calculate the circumference of the following circles, where d = diameter and r = radius. Use $\pi = 3.14$. As a check, estimate each answer using $\pi = 3$.

1. $d = 8$ cm
2. $r = 2.5$ cm
3. $d = 9$ m
4. $d = 40$ mm
5. $r = 30$ cm

6. $r = 12$ m
7. $d = 29$ mm
8. $d = 7.3$ cm
9. $r = 27$ mm
10. $d = 6.2$ m

11. $d = 78$ mm
12. $r = 8.6$ cm
13. $r = 2.18$ m
14. $d = 34.2$ m
15. $d = 693$ m

Exercise 9

Do not forget to estimate each answer first, using $\pi = 3$.

1. Find the circumference of a circle with a diameter of 3 m. (Use $\pi = 3.14$.)

2. Calculate the circumference of a circle with a radius of 24 mm. (Use $\pi = 3.14$.)

3. Calculate the circumference of a circle with diameter $10\frac{1}{2}$ cm. (Use $\pi = \frac{22}{7}$.)

4. The diameter of a bicycle wheel is 490 mm.
   Calculate its circumference in metres. (Use $\pi = \frac{22}{7}$.)

5. The 'straights' of a running track are 120 m long. If the distance between the straights is 51 m, find the distance around the track. (Give your answer to the nearest metre. Use $\pi = 3.14$.)

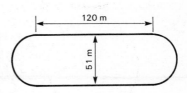

6. If the radius of the Earth is 6370 km, calculate the distance around the Earth at the equator. (Use $\pi = 3\frac{1}{7}$.)

7. A circular cycle track has a diameter of 160 m.
   Calculate the distance around the track. (Use $\pi = 3.14$.)

8. A pedal bin has a circular rim of diameter 245 mm.
How long is the piece of plastic strip that goes around this rim? (Use $\pi = \frac{22}{7}$.)

Exercise 10

1. A cyclist travels 40 laps of a circular track that has a radius of 75 m. How far does the cyclist travel altogether?
Use $\pi = 3.14$ and give your answer in kilometres.

2. The diagram shows a running track with 'straights' of 120 m. The distance between the straights is 49 m. Find the distance, in metres, run in 8 laps. (Use $\pi = \frac{22}{7}$.)

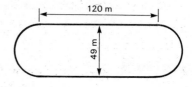

3. The diameter of the roller on my lawn mower is 210 mm. If it makes 50 revs when I mow one length of my lawn, how long is the lawn? (Use $\pi = 3\frac{1}{7}$.)

4. A coffee jar has a diameter of 85 mm. Calculate the length of the label that goes round the jar if it overlaps itself by 10 mm. (Use $\pi = 3.14$.)

5. A dart-board is edged with a metal strip. If the dart-board has a diameter of 430 mm, find the length of the metal strip to the nearest millimetre. (Use $\pi = 3.142$.)

6. Six pieces of wire are fixed to a dart-board to form concentric circles. If the diameters of the circles formed by the pieces of wire are 17 mm, 35 mm, 190 mm, 210 mm, 316 mm and 336 mm, calculate the length of each piece to the nearest millimetre. (Use $\pi = 3.142$.)

7. Labels are made to a length of 231 mm. They must go round soup tins of diameter 75 mm and overlap themselves by 10 mm. How much longer should the labels be? (Use π = 3.14.)

8. Calculate the distance around the circle of latitude 52 °N, if its radius is about 2450 miles. (Use π = 3.14.)

Exercise 11

1. The wheels of a car have a diameter of 581 mm. On a journey the wheels make 15 000 revs. Find the length of the journey in kilometres giving your answer correct to the nearest tenth of a kilometre. (Use π = 3.142.)

2. A 3ℓ tin of paint has a diameter of 155 mm. In making the tin, an extra 15 mm of metal must be allowed to form a seam which must be leakproof.

(a) Calculate the length of the piece of metal needed to make the curved face of the tin. (Use π = 3.142 and do not forget to allow 15 mm extra for the seam.)

(b) The wired edge at the top rim of the can is made from wire that is 3 mm thick (diameter = 3 mm). Calculate the length of wire needed. (Find the distance around the wired edge following the centre of the wire all the way round. (Use π = 3.142.)

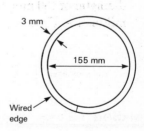

3. (a) A bicycle wheel has a diameter of 26 in. How many yards would the bicycle travel if the wheels turned 900 times? (Use π = 3.14. Note that 12 in = 1 ft and 3 ft = 1 yd.)

(b) How far would the bicycle have travelled if the diameter of the wheels were half the size (that is, 13 in)?

4. A protractor, as shown, is in the shape of a semi-circle with base diameter of 4 in together with an extra piece of plastic measuring 4 in by $\frac{1}{4}$ in. Calculate the perimeter of this protractor. (Use $\pi = 3.14$.)

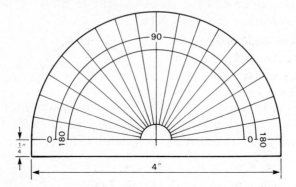

In fig. 1, angle APB is the angle *subtended** at P by the line AB.

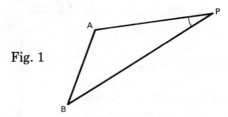

Fig. 1

In fig. 2, arc XY subtends an angle θ at the centre of the circle.

Fig. 2

* See the glossary.

Exercise 12

A What fraction of the circumference is each given arc?

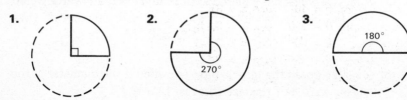

1. **2.** 270° **3.** 180°

4.

5.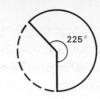

B In each question, the angle sub-tended at the centre of a circle by an arc is given (angle θ in the diagram). What fraction of the circumference is each arc?

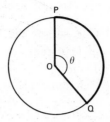

1. 240°	**5.** 210°	**9.** 72°
2. 60°	**6.** 30°	**10.** 108°
3. 45°	**7.** 150°	**11.** 75°
4. 135°	**8.** 36°	**12.** 105°

Exercise 13

A Find the length of each arc. (Use $\pi = \frac{22}{7}$.)

1.
7 cm

2.
120°
14 m

3.
$3\frac{1}{2}$ m
45°

4.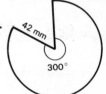
42 mm
300°

B In each question, the radius of a circle is given, together with the angle subtended at the centre of the circle by an arc and a value of π. Calculate the length of each arc.

1. $r = 12$ m, $\theta = 60°$ (use $\pi = 3.14$)
2. $r = 8$ cm, $\theta = 90°$ (use $\pi = 3.14$)
3. $r = 20$ m, $\theta = 135°$ (use $\pi = 3$)
4. $r = 4.8$ cm, $\theta = 40°$ (use $\pi = 3$)
5. $r = 72$ mm, $\theta = 150°$ (use $\pi = 3.142$)
6. $r = 3$ m, $\theta = 30°$ (use $\pi = 3.14$)
7. $r = 3.2$ m, $\theta = 225°$ (use $\pi = 3.14$)
8. $r = 56$ mm, $\theta = 63°$ (use $\pi = 3.142$)

Exercise 14

1. Draw a pair of axes as shown. Use a scale of 1 cm to 1 cm for the diameter and 2 cm to 5 cm for the circumference.

2. (a) Choose any diameter that is less than or equal to 15 cm.
   (b) Calculate the circumference of the circle using $\pi = 3.14$.
   (c) On your graph paper, plot a point to show the circumference and the diameter.

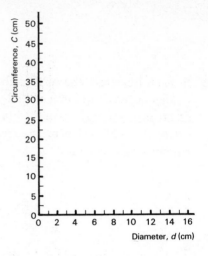

3. Repeat question 2 using other sizes of diameter that are less than 15 cm.

4. Write what you notice about the points you have plotted.

Exercise 15

1. Draw another pair of axes as in Exercise 14.

2. Use the measurements that you took in Exercise 1. For each cylindrical object that you used, plot the measured circumference against the measured diameter. (If the diameter was more than 15 cm, just ignore that measurement — otherwise you would have to draw another pair of axes with larger diameters and circumferences marked on them.) Continue until you have plotted a point for each object that was measured.

3. This time, the points probably do not give a straight line. They are probably scattered about as shown in the diagram opposite. The points should suggest a straight line. Draw 'the line of best fit' as in Chapter 15, Exercise 16C on p. 238.

4. Choose any diameter (10 cm has been chosen on this diagram).

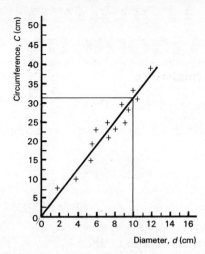

Draw a straight line, as shown, up to the graph, then draw a line across to the circumference axis. Read the value of the circumference.

Divide this value of the circumference by the diameter.

5. What do you notice about the answer obtained in question 4? If you do not notice anything, repeat question 4 using a different size of diameter.

17 Transformation Geometry

We live in a world where many things move. It can be useful to study how they move.

A train travelling on straight railway tracks

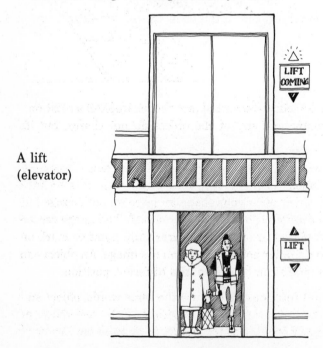

A lift
(elevator)

People on an
escalator

The movements shown in all these drawings are alike in some way. All three drawings show movement in a straight line. We call movement in a straight line a *translation*. The movement may be in any direction but must be in a straight line for it to be a translation. The object being moved must not turn. The shape and size of the object do not change but its position does.

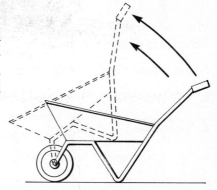

A wheelbarrow being tipped shows a different type of movement. It turns about a point. This type of movement is called a *rotation*.

The handle on a tap needs to be turned (another example of a rotation). Once again, the shape and size of the object do not change but its position does.

If you look in an ordinary mirror you will see a *reflection* of yourself. Although you yourself do not move, your *image* can be seen in a different position. Once again your shape and size do not change but your image is in a different position from yourself. The image can be seen of any object placed in front of a mirror. Any point or mark on the object maps to a similar point or mark on the image. An object can be drawn, and its image can be drawn in a different position.

For translations and rotations we can use the same words, *object* and *image*. Consider the train: the original position can be referred to as the object and the new position as the image. Each point on the object maps to a similar point on the image (as for reflections). Also for the wheelbarrow, each point on the wheelbarrow in its original position (the object) maps to a similar point on the wheelbarrow in its new position (the image).

With translations, reflections and rotations, changes have happened — each point on the object has been mapped to a new position (the image position).

Translations, reflections and rotations are called *transformations*. A transformation is the relation between each point on an object and its image point.

Exercise 1

e.g. The movement of a snooker cue during a game is a translation.

A Write the type of transformation: translation, reflection or rotation, for each of these movements:

1. An aeroplane as it taxis along a runway.

2. The movement of a tennis racket when the player is serving.

3. The closing of a door with a hinge.

4. The opening of a sliding window.

5. The opening of a book.

6. The turning of a key in a lock.

7. Opening a drawer.

8. The movement of the drum in a washing machine.

B 1. Write two other examples of a translation.

2. Write two other examples of a rotation.

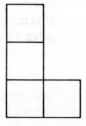

Make a copy of this L-shape.
Cut out your copy. (It may be better made out of card.)
Use your L-shape in the following exercises.

Translations

Exercise 2

1. On a piece of 1 cm squared paper, trace around your L-shape as suggested by the sketch. Translate the L-shape 6 cm to the right then draw round it again. (This second drawing is the image of the first.)

2. Draw another copy of your L-shape on a different part of your piece of squared paper. Translate this L-shape 4 cm downwards.

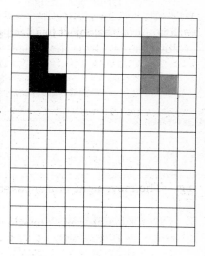

3. Translate another copy of your L-shape 3 cm upwards.

4. Translate another copy of your L-shape 8 cm to the left.

5. Draw your L-shape again. This time, translate the L-shape in any direction you wish except straight up, down, to the left or to the right. Carefully draw this image position.

Exercise 3

1. Draw your L-shape on another piece of 1 cm squared paper as shown. Translate it 4 cm to the right, followed by a translation of 3 cm upwards. Draw this new position. (On the given sketch, this image position has been shaded.)

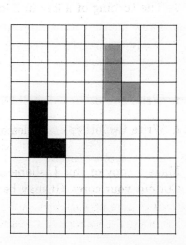

2. Draw your L-shape again then translate it 6 cm to the right then 2 cm downwards. Draw this image position.

3. Translate another copy of your L-shape 5 cm to the left then 1 cm upwards. Draw the image.

4. Translate another copy of your L-shape 2 cm to the left then 2 cm downwards. Draw the image.

Reflections | ƨnoitɔɘlʃɘЯ

Exercise 4 ━━━━━━━━━━━━━━━━━━━━━━━ **M**

A 1. Place your L-shape on top of the black L below.
   Reflect your L in the mirror line. (A mirror or a piece of coloured perspex may help.)

2. Copy the given L and the mirror line on to squared paper. Draw the image on your paper.

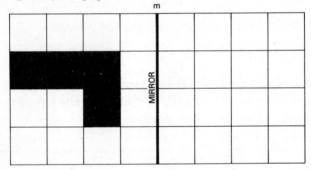

3. Draw another L, as shown below, on a different part of your piece of squared paper. Draw the mirror, m. Reflect the L in the mirror. Draw its image.

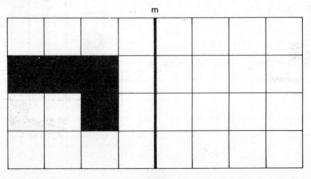

B On a piece of squared paper, draw the L-shapes and the mirrors in the positions suggested by the drawings. For each one, reflect the L-shape in the given mirror and draw the image. (Note that the squares on each of these drawings represent 1 cm squares. Also, a shape can be reflected in either side of the mirror.) Use the L-shape you made to help you.

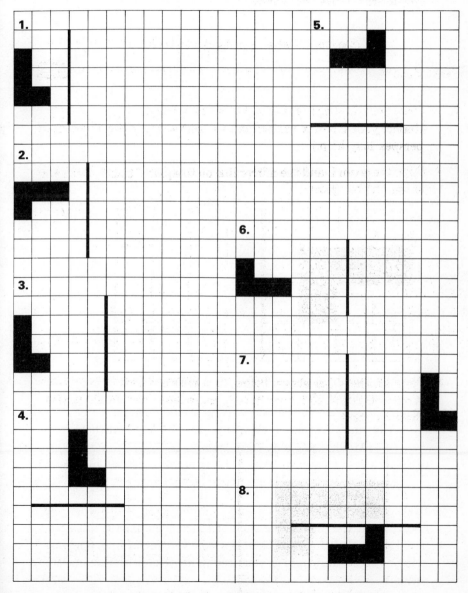

Exercise 5

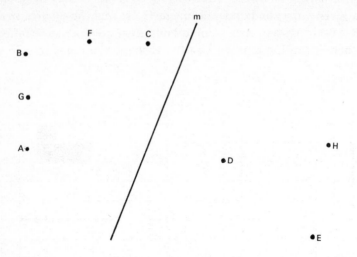

Trace the mirror line and the 8 points given above on to tracing paper. By folding the tracing paper along the mirror line, find the images of the 8 points from a reflection in the mirror line, m. Label each image (the image of A is A′, B′ is the image of B, C′ of C, and so on).

Exercise 6

Draw a mirror line on another piece of tracing paper. Carry out these investigations. Draw points on the tracing paper and fold the paper along the mirror line to help you.

1. (a) Mark any point (the object) and find its image when reflected in the mirror line.
   (b) Join the object to the image using a straight line.
   (c) Write what you notice about the straight line and the mirror line? (At what angle do they cross?)
   (d) Check your answer to (c) by drawing more points and by joining each of these objects to its image using a straight line.

2. Draw any point as the object and find its image. Write what you notice about the distance of the object from the mirror line compared with the distance of its image from the mirror line. (Draw as many objects and images as you need to help you with this investigation.)

3. Plot any point as the object and find its image.

    (*a*) What happens to the image when the object is moved further away from the mirror line?

    (*b*) What happens to the image when the object is moved closer to the mirror line?

4. Plot any point as the object and find its image.

Label the object A and its image A′.

Now reflect A′ in the same mirror line.

Write what you notice. (Draw as many objects and images as you need to help you with this.)

5. Write what you notice about points that lie on a mirror line and their images from a reflection in that mirror line.

Exercise 7   **M**

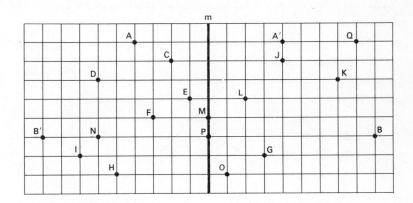

A′ is the image of A when A is reflected in the two-sided mirror, m.
B′ is the image of B.

Copy the mirror line and points on to squared paper.

Mark and label the image of each given point. (C′ is the image of C, D′ the image of D, and so on).

The given points are from C to Q.

Which two points are the images of themselves?
(They do not move when reflected.)

261

Exercise 8

On *plain* paper, draw any mirror line.

Mark any 5 points as objects.

Draw the images of these objects when reflected in the mirror line.

Exercise 9 M

Copy these mirror lines and points on to squared paper. Draw and label the image of each object point when reflected in the mirror line.

1.

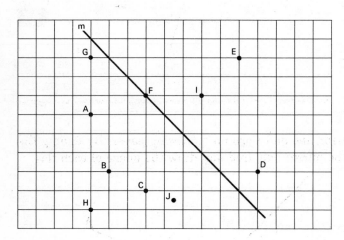

2.

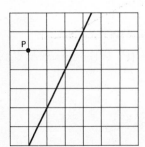

3.

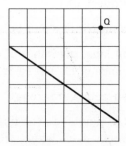

Copy this mirror line and the given points (use tracing paper).

Draw and label the image under reflection of each object point.

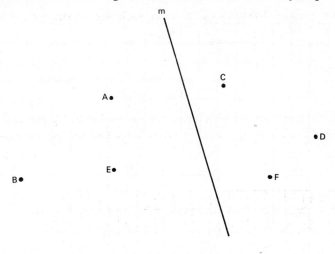

Exercise 11 ━━━━━━━━━━━━━━━━━━━━━━━━━

Trace the mirror line and flags on to tracing paper. By folding the paper along the mirror line, find and draw the image of each flag.

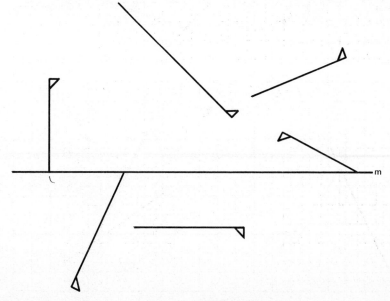

Copy the flags and mirror lines on to squared paper.
Draw the image of each flag after it has been reflected in the given mirror line.

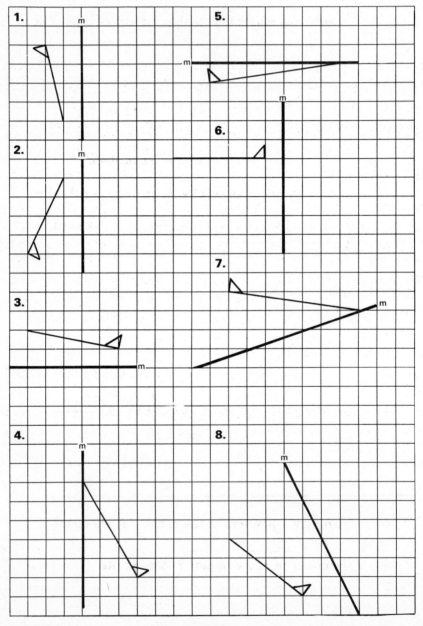

Exercise 13

1. On tracing paper, draw any mirror line.

2. Draw any flag on the tracing paper (this is the object).

3. By folding along the mirror line, find and draw the image flag.

4. (a) How long is the object flag?
   (b) How long is the image flag?

5. Write what you notice about the length of the image compared with the length of the object.

6. Answer questions 2 to 5 using several different flags.

7. A line is 75 mm long. How long is its image under a reflection?

8. An image is a line of 42 mm long. How long is the object line?

Exercise 14

1. Trace the 2 points on to tracing paper. (A′ is the image of A after a reflection in a mirror line.)

A′
•

A
•

2. By folding the tracing paper, find the mirror line.

3. How many different positions of the mirror line are there?

4. Answer the questions above for any 2 other points.

5. Write what you discover.

Exercise 15

Copy these flags and mirror lines (use tracing paper).

Draw the image of each flag after it has been reflected in the given mirror line.

1.

3.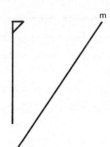

2.

Exercise 16

Use tracing paper throughout this exercise. Trace the given shapes and mirror lines. By folding along each mirror line, find and draw each image.

1.

2.

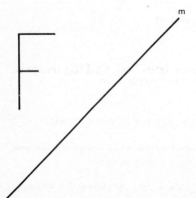

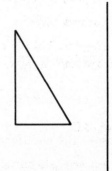

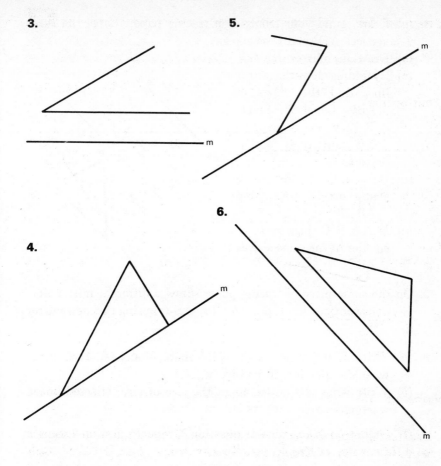

3.

5.

4.

6.

Exercise 17

Draw any shape on a piece of tracing paper.

Draw a mirror line.

Ask a friend to fold the paper along the mirror line, find the image of your shape and draw it.

Exercise 18

Make any triangle out of card (a suggested size is with sides that lie between 20 mm and 50 mm).

A **1.** (*a*) Draw round your triangle on tracing paper. Label the three vertices A, B and C as shown.

(*b*) Draw any mirror line.

(*c*) By folding along the mirror line, find the image of △ABC. Label the image A′B′C′ where A maps to A′, B maps to B′ and C maps to C′.

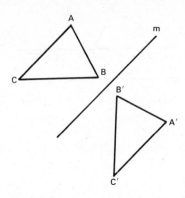

(*d*) Is △A′B′C′ the same shape or different from △ABC?

(*e*) Is △A′B′C′ bigger, smaller or the same size as △ABC?

2. On the same piece of tracing paper, draw a different mirror line. Now answer question 1, parts (*c*), (*d*) and (*e*) using this new mirror line.

3. (*a*) Write what you notice about the shape of any reflected image when compared with its object.

(*b*) Write what you notice about the size of any reflected image when compared with its object.

(If you are unable to answer question 3, repeat question 2 using a different mirror line.)

B **1.** Draw round your triangle on another piece of tracing paper. Label the tracing LMN.

2. Draw any mirror line.

3. By folding, reflect △LMN in the mirror line and draw and label its image L′M′N′ as in question A1(c).

4. Is the object labelled clockwise or anticlockwise?

5. Is the image labelled clockwise or anticlockwise?

6. Repeat questions 1 to 5 above.

7. Write about your findings.

c

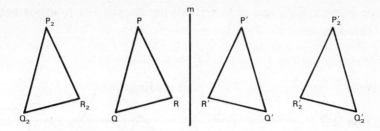

1. Draw round your triangle on another piece of tracing paper. Label it PQR.

2. Draw a mirror line and by folding, find and draw the image of △ PQR. Label it P′Q′R′.

3. Use your cardboard triangle to 'move' △ PQR further away from the mirror line (vertices P, Q and R should all move the same distance). Label the new position $P_2Q_2R_2$ as shown above.

4. Using the same mirror line as in question 2, find the image of △ $P_2Q_2R_2$. Label it $P_2′Q_2′R_2′$.

5. (a) How far has vertex P moved in moving to position P_2?
   (b) How far has vertex Q moved in moving to position Q_2?
       (It should have moved the same distance as vertex P.)
   (c) How far has △ PQR moved in moving to position $P_2Q_2R_2$?

6. How far has the image P′Q′R′ moved in moving to the new image position $P_2′Q_2′R_2′$?

Exercise 19

1. Using tracing paper, draw any angle XYZ, as shown, and any mirror line.

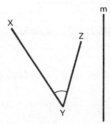

2. By folding along your mirror line, find and draw the image of XYZ. Label it X′Y′Z′.

3. Measure $\angle$ XYZ and $\angle$ X'Y'Z'. What do you notice about both these angles?

4. Repeat questions 1 to 3 for different-sized angles.

5. Write what you notice about your findings.

Exercise 20 M

Trace these mirror lines and shapes on to plain paper or into your exercise book. Sketch the image of each shape after reflection in the given mirror line.

1.

3.

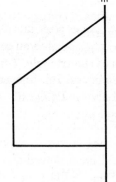

2.

4.

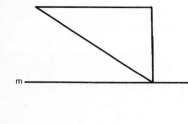

Exercise 21

A Make a right-angled triangle ABC out of card where AB = 15 mm, BC = 30 mm and $\angle$ ABC = 90°.

When △ABC is reflected in a mirror line where side BC lies on the mirror line, the object and image make an isosceles triangle, as shown.

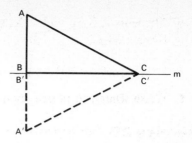

1. What shape do the object and image make if the triangle is reflected in a line on which the side AB lies?

2. What shape do the object and image make if the triangle is reflected in a line on which the side AC lies?

B Experiment with other sizes and types of triangle. (Make them out of card.) Reflect each triangle you make in a mirror line that lies along one of the sides of the triangle. Try to make the following shapes with a triangle and its image. If it is possible to obtain a certain shape, show, as in the example and diagram given above, how you obtained it; otherwise write 'impossible'.

1. a square
2. a rectangle
3. a parallelogram
4. a rhombus
5. a trapezium

6. an equilateral triangle
7. a right-angled isosceles triangle
8. a right-angled triangle that is not isosceles

Exercise 22

Trace each of these shapes.
By folding your paper and then by tracing, try to complete each shape.

1. Square

2. Rectangle

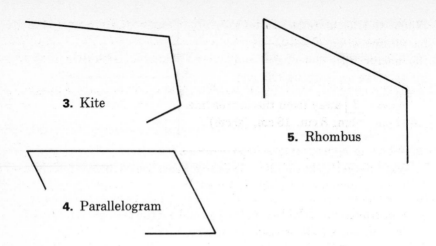

3. Kite

5. Rhombus

4. Parallelogram

Exercise 23

Copy and complete each sentence by making the correct choice from answers given in brackets:

1. The straight line that joins a point to its image from a reflection in a mirror line, crosses that mirror line at ? °.
(45°, 90°, 180°)

2. The distance of an object from a mirror line ? the distance of its image from the same mirror line.
(is less than, equals, is greater than)

3. When an object is moved further away from a mirror line its image moves ? the same mirror line.
(closer to, further away from)

4. If A′ is the image of A in a mirror line, then ? is the image of A′ in the same mirror line.
(A, A′, B′)

5. A point that lies ? a mirror line is an image of itself when reflected in that same mirror line.
(to the left of, on, to the right of)

6. When a straight line is reflected in a mirror line, its image is ? the object line itself.
(shorter than, the same length as, longer than)

272

7. When a triangle is reflected in a mirror line, its image has ⬚?⬚ the original object triangle.
(a smaller area than, the same area as, a larger area than)

8. When an object is moved 4 cm away from a mirror line, its image moves ⬚?⬚ away from the mirror line.
(2 cm, 4 cm, 8 cm, 16 cm, 20 cm)

9. When an angle is reflected in a mirror line, it ⬚?⬚ .
(gets bigger, gets smaller, stays the same size)

10. If a shape is labelled clockwise, then its image when reflected in a mirror line is labelled ⬚?⬚ .
(clockwise, anticlockwise)

Rotations

Each of these diagrams shows a rotation about a point.
In the first diagram, a point is being rotated, in the second, a straight line and in the third, a triangle.

e.g. 1

e.g. 2

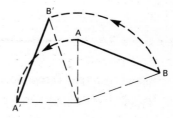

e.g. 3

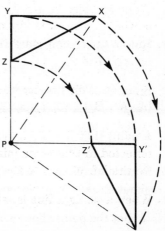

The rotation can be clockwise or anticlockwise. The amount of turning can vary. In the examples, the rotation is 'a quarter turn'.

273

The curved lines need not be drawn to show the actual turning. In fact, only the shapes themselves need be drawn. The two diagrams below show the triangle in e.g. 3 again being rotated through a quarter turn clockwise.

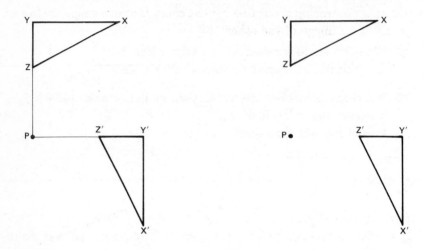

Exercise 24

Use tracing paper throughout this exercise.

A 1. Trace △XYZ and point P (use one of the diagrams above).

2. Keep your tracing in position and place a pencil point at position P.

3. Rotate the tracing clockwise about point P until △XYZ fits on top of △X'Y'Z'.

4. Since △XYZ fits exactly on top of △X'Y'Z', △X'Y'Z' is the image of △XYZ. (△XYZ is the object, as it is in reflections and translations.)
   X' is the image of X. Which point is the image of point Z?

5. What sort of curve did point Y follow as the triangle was rotated about P until Y fitted on top of point Y'?

Note that the point about which a shape rotates is called the *centre of rotation*.

B Using the same method as in part A, trace line AB on p. 273 and check that A'B' is the image of AB when AB is rotated anticlockwise through a quarter turn.

C By tracing each object and each centre of rotation labelled C, then by rotating the tracing about that centre, check that one shape (or line or point) is an image of the other:

1.
  T •   C •

  T' •

4.
  C•
  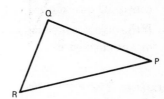
  P ——————— Q

  Q'|
  P'|

2.
  C •
  F •

  F' •

3.
  P ——————— Q   C•
  Q'|
  |
  P'|

5.
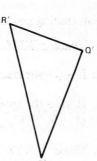

Exercise 25

Draw any triangle in your exercise book and mark any centre of rotation. Label the centre of rotation C.

Trace your triangle and the centre on to tracing paper.

Keep the tracing paper in position and place a pencil point at C to hold the tracing paper in place. Now rotate the tracing paper about C to any new position. Copy your triangle into your exercise book in this new position.

Repeat the process above until you have at least three image positions of the triangle in your exercise book.

Now use your drawings to help you to answer these equations:

1. Are all the images the same size or of different sizes?

2. Are the images smaller than, bigger than, or the same size as the object?

3. When a shape is rotated, does its shape change?

4. Measure the distances of certain points on the object from C. Measure the distances of the images of these same points from C. Write what you notice about object and image distances from the centre of rotation.

5. If the object is labelled clockwise, will its image be labelled clockwise or anticlockwise?

Exercise 26

To rotate a shape through 90°, 180°, 270° or 360° (using tracing paper and a set square)

1. Copy the shape and the centre of rotation into your exercise book.

2. Join the centre of rotation to any point on the object shape, using a straight line (CR in the diagram).

3. Trace the object, the centre of rotation and the straight line joining the centre of rotation to a point on the object (line CR).
   (All the lines mentioned so far are shown as full lines on the given diagram).

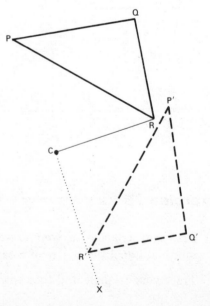

4. In your exercise book and using a set square, draw a perpendicular to the straight line (line CR) at point C (given as CX on the diagram).

5. Place your tracing of the object over the object drawn in your exercise book (the tracing of point C should lie on point C). With your pencil at C, rotate the tracing paper until the line CR on the tracing lies on top of line CX in your exercise book.

6. Copy the new position (the image position) into your exercise book. (The easiest way is probably to use a pin to prick through the tracing on to your page. In the example, a pin was used to mark the image positions P', Q' and R'.)

7. The object should have been rotated through 90°.
A similar approach can be used for angles of 270°.

Exercise 27 ═══════════════════════════════════ **M**

Trace these shapes into your book. Rotate each one as instructed about the given centre of rotation, C. (Use tracing paper and a set square to help you.)

1. A rotation of 90° anticlockwise:

C
•

P
•

2. A rotation of 180° clockwise:

X ————————— Y

•
C

3. A quarter turn clockwise:

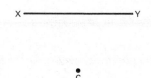
P————————• C

4. A rotation of 360° anticlockwise:

P————————————Q   • C

Write what you notice about rotations through 360°.

5. A rotation of 180° clockwise:

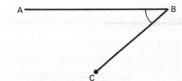

Write what you notice about ∠ ABC when compared with the image of ∠ ABC.

277

6. A rotation of 180° anticlockwise.

8. A rotation of 90° clockwise:

Write what you notice about ∠LCM when compared with the image of ∠LCM.

7. A rotation of 270° clockwise:

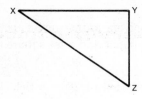

C

What anticlockwise rotation gives the same image?

Exercise 28

In each drawing an object and its image is given. In each case, is the point P the centre of rotation?

1.

A
•

A′
•

•
P

2.

•B

P•

•B′

278

3.

X'
•

P
•

X
•

5.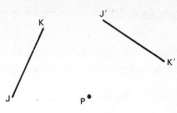

K

J'

K'

J

P
•

4.

M

L

P
•

L'

M'

Exercise 29

If each drawing shows a rotation of 90°, explain why **Q** is not the centre of rotation:

1.

X
•

Q
•

X'•

3.

Q
•

D

D'   E'

E

2.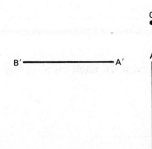

Q
•

B'————————A'

A

B

4.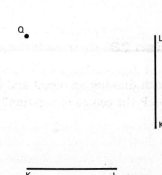

Q
•

L'

K'

K   L

A

B

Copy each point, line and triangle on to squared paper.
Rotate each one about the given centre of rotation, C.

1. 90° clockwise:

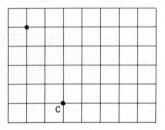

3. A three-quarter turn anticlockwise:

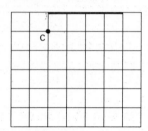

2. A quarter turn anticlockwise:

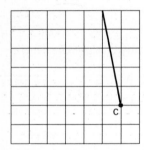

4. A half turn clockwise:

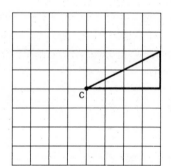

Rotations and Quadrilaterals

Exercise 31

e.g. A scalene triangle can be rotated through 180° about
the mid-point of one of its
sides. The diagram shows
how the object and image
together give a parallelogram.

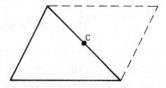

Answer these questions. (You may use tracing paper to help you.) In each question, the rotation is a half turn about the mid-point of one of the sides. (For each triangle, use all three sides.)

What types of quadrilateral can be made by rotating:

1. a scalene triangle?
2. an isosceles triangle?
3. an equilateral triangle?
4. a right-angled triangle? (Try also a right-angled isosceles triangle.)

Exercise 32

A bottle top is rotated when it is used. The centre of rotation lies on the top itself.

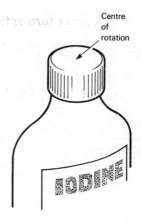

Centre
of
rotation

1. (a) Trace the equilateral triangle and also the centre of rotation, C.

(b) Copy the triangle and centre of rotation into your exercise book.

(c) Place your tracing over your copy of the triangle and holding a pencil at C, rotate the tracing until the traced triangle fits exactly on top of the drawn triangle again. (It should make one full turn.)

2. (*a*) Trace this equilateral triangle and its centre of rotation, C.

(*b*) Copy the triangle and centre of rotation into your exercise book.

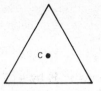

(*c*) Place your tracing on top of the drawn triangle. Hold a pencil at C and rotate the tracing until the traced triangle fits exactly on top of the drawn triangle again.

(*d*) Through what fraction of a turn does the tracing turn this time? (It is not a full turn.)

(*e*) How many times will the tracing fit exactly on top of the drawing during a rotation through one full turn? (Count each position only once.)

Note that in this instance the centre of rotation is in the same position as the centre of rotational symmetry.

3. Repeat question 2 using a square. (Use the centre of rotational symmetry as the centre of rotation.)

Exercise 33

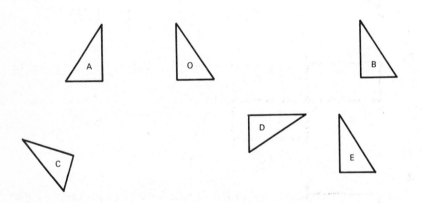

Five transformations have been carried out on triangle O. Copy these sentences. Complete each one with the word 'translation', 'reflection' or 'rotation'.

1. O maps to A by a ? .
2. O maps to B by a ? .
3. O maps to C by a ? .
4. O maps to D by a ? .
5. O maps to E by a ? .

Exercise 34

For each diagram write whether it shows a translation, a reflection or a rotation:

1.

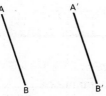

2.

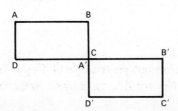

3.

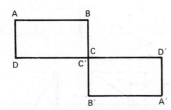

4.

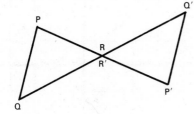

A Copy the following on to squared paper:

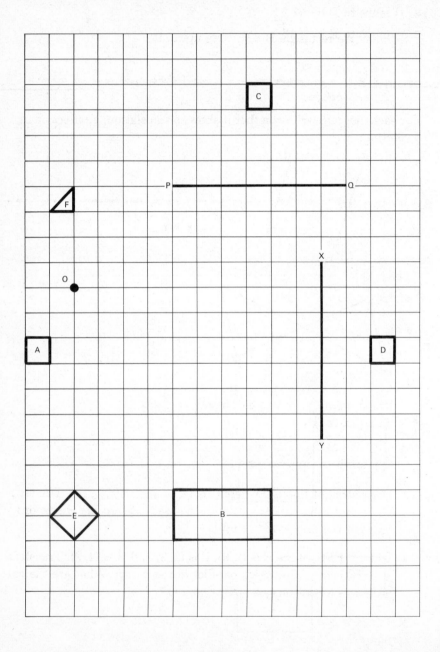

B Carry out these transformations on the shapes that you have just copied. (Note that the squares referred to in the translations are the same size as square A.)

1. Translate square A 6 squares to the right.

2. Translate rectangle B 8 squares upwards.

3. Reflect square C in mirror line PQ.

4. Reflect square D in mirror line XY.

5. Translate square E 3 squares to the right and 8 squares upwards.

6. Rotate triangle F through 90° clockwise about point O.

Exercise 36

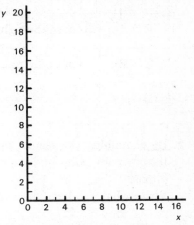

A Draw a pair of axes as shown. The x-axis should range from 0 to 16 and the y-axis from 0 to 20. Use a scale of 1 cm to 1 unit on both axes.

1. Plot the point A(3, 7). Translate it 3 cm to the right, parallel to the x-axis. Label this image point, A'. What are the co-ordinates of A'?

2. Plot point B(2, 14) then translate it 6 cm to the right, parallel to the x-axis. What are the co-ordinates of the image of B?

3. Draw straight line CD where C is (4, 8) and D is (5, 12). Translate CD 4 cm to the right, parallel to the x-axis. What are the co-ordinates of the images of C and D?

4. Draw △EFG where E is (2, 6), F is (2, 2) and G is (4, 2). Translate △EFG 5 cm to the right, parallel to the x-axis. What are the co-ordinates of the images of E, F and G?

5. Plot the point H(14, 10) then translate it to H', 2 cm to the left, parallel to the x-axis. What are the co-ordinates of H'?

6. Translate I(8, 1), 7 cm to the left to I'. What are the co-ordinates of I'?

7. Find the co-ordinates of the images of J(13, 7) and K(15, 4) if straight line JK is translated 3 cm to the left, parallel to the x-axis.

8. Plot L(12, 18), M(15, 18), N(15, 16) and P(12, 16). Draw rectangle LMNP. Translate it 8 cm to the left, parallel to the x-axis. What are the co-ordinates of the vertices of the rectangle in this new position?

B 1. Copy and complete the table for the points plotted in part A:

Point	Translation	Image
A(3, 7)	3 cm to the right	(6, 7)
B(2, 14)	6 cm to the right	(,)
C(4, 8)	4 cm to the right	(,)
D(,)		(,)

2. By examining the results in the table, work out how to find the image of any point under a given translation that is parallel to the x-axis.
Write what you have discovered.

Exercise 37

Draw another pair of axes as in Exercise 36.

1. Plot the point Q(6, 8). Translate Q 3 cm upwards, parallel to the y-axis. Label this image Q'.
What are the co-ordinates of Q'?

2. Translate R(14, 7) 6 cm downwards, parallel to the y-axis.

3. Translate the straight line ST, where S is (8, 16) and T is (12, 17), 5 cm downwards, parallel to the y-axis.

4. Plot U(2, 6), V(2, 2) and W(4, 2). Translate △UVW 10 cm upwards, parallel to the y-axis. If △U'V'W' is the image of △UVW, write the co-ordinates of U', V' and W'.

5. Plot some points and shapes of your own. Translate them upwards and downwards parallel to the y-axis. Examine the co-ordinates of the objects and their images. Write what you notice.

Exercise 38

Draw another pair of axes as in Exercise 36.

1. Translate A(2, 8) 8 cm to the right and 6 cm upwards. What are the co-ordinates of A', the image of A?

2. Point B(8, 16) is translated to B', 4 cm to the right and 5 cm downwards. What are the co-ordinates of B'?

3. C is (10, 2) and D is (14, 4). Translate straight line CD 2 cm to the left and 3 cm upwards. What are the co-ordinates of C' and D', the images of C and D?

4. Draw △EFG where E is (2, 6), F is (2, 2) and G is (4, 2). Translate △EFG to new position E'F'G' which is 3 cm to the right and 7 cm upwards.

5. Without plotting any points, find the images of H(11, 10), I(8, 8) and J(12, 8) if △HIJ is translated 6 cm to the left and 7 cm upwards. (Write the positions of the images using co-ordinates.)

Exercise 39

Draw a pair of axes as shown. The x-values should range from $^-10$ to $^+10$ and the y-values from $^-8$ to $^+8$. Use a scale of 1 cm to 1 unit on both axes.

A 1. Plot A(1, 3), B(1, 1) and C(2, 1) and join them to form a triangle. Reflect △ABC in the y-axis. Label the image A′B′C′. What are the co-ordinates of A′B′ and C′?

2. Draw a straight line from D(⁻7, 6) to E(⁻4, 5). Reflect DE in the x-axis. What are the co-ordinates of D′ and E′, the images of D and E?

3. Plot F(4, ⁻3), G(7, ⁻3), H(6, ⁻4) and I(3, ⁻4). Join them to form a parallelogram. Reflect FGHI in the x-axis. What are the co-ordinates of the images of the vertices of the parallelogram?

B 1. Plot some points and shapes of your own. Reflect them in the y-axis. Compare the co-ordinates of each object with its image. Write what you notice.

2. Plot more points and shapes of your own. Reflect them in the x-axis. Compare the co-ordinates of each object with its image. Write what you notice.

Exercise 40

A 1. Draw a pair of axes as shown. The x-values should range from ⁻4 to ⁺4 and the y-values from ⁻6 to ⁺6. Use a scale of 1 cm to 1 unit on both axes.

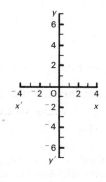

2. Plot the point A(2, 4). Rotate A through 90° anticlockwise about the origin to position A′. What are the co-ordinates of A′?

3. Draw the straight line BC where B is the point (1, 3) and C is the point (3, 1). Rotate line BC through 180° clockwise about the origin to position B′C′.
What are the co-ordinates of B′ and C′?

B 1. Draw another pair of axes as in part A.

2. Plot the points D(1, 3), E(1, 1) and F(2, 1).

3. Join D, E and F to form a triangle.

4. Rotate $\triangle$DEF through 90° clockwise about the origin to image position D'E'F'.
What are the co-ordinates of D', E' and F'?

Exercise 41

You may draw a pair of axes and plot points in this exercise if you need to do so. However, try to answer these questions without plotting points.

1. The image of the point A(1, 6) is at A'(4, 6), while B(4, 5) moves to B'(7, 5). What sort of transformation is it?

Note that we can show the transformation using mapping arrows like this:
$$A(1, 6) \rightarrow A'(4, 6)$$
$$B(4, 5) \rightarrow B'(7, 5)$$

2. Describe this transformation:
$$C(7, 1) \rightarrow (7, {}^-1)$$
$$D({}^-6, {}^-4) \rightarrow ({}^-6, 4)$$

3. Copy and complete these two tables:

(a) Translation 5 units to the right, parallel to the x-axis:

Object	Image
P = (1, 4)	P' = ([?], [?])
Q = ([?], [?])	Q' = (7, 4)
R = (0, 2)	R' = ([?], [?])

(b) Reflection in the y-axis:

Object	Image
X = ($^-$1, 1)	X' = ([?], [?])
Y = ([?], [?])	Y' = (4, $^-$2)
Z = ($^-$2, $^-$3)	Z' = ([?], [?])

4. Describe this transformation:
$$L(1, {}^-4) \rightarrow ({}^-1, 4)$$
$$M(4, {}^-4) \rightarrow ({}^-4, 4)$$
$$N(4, {}^-6) \rightarrow ({}^-4, 6)$$

5. Describe the transformation when a shape is drawn, then its image is obtained by adding 6 on to every x-co-ordinate of points on the original shape.

   e.g. $K(2, 5) \rightarrow K'(8, 5)$

6. What type of transformation changes the x-co-ordinates of points such that positive x-co-ordinates become negative and negative x-co-ordinates become positive?

Exercise 42

Name the solid obtained when the given shape is rotated through $360°$ about the given line:

1.

2.

18 Indices and Square Roots

Exercise 1 R

A Write in index form:

1. 7×7
2. $2 \times 2 \times 2 \times 2 \times 2 \times 2 \times 2$
3. $n \times n \times n \times n$
4. $x \times x \times x \times x \times x \times x \times x \times x \times x \times x$
5. $4 \times 4 \times 4 \times 4 \times 4$

6. $d \times d \times d$
7. $a \times a \times a \times a \times a \times a \times a$
8. $t \times t$
9. $10 \times 10 \times 10 \times 10 \times 10 \times 10$
10. $f \times f \times f \times f \times f$

B Find the value of:

1. 6^2
2. 11^2
3. 2^5
4. 10^4

5. 5^3
6. 8^3
7. 2^6
8. 9^3

9. 15^2
10. 2^8
11. 9^4
12. 10^7

13. 10^{10}
14. 7^4
15. 3^5
16. 6^5

C Use a calculator to find the value of:

1. 6^8
2. 9^5
3. 12^3
4. 5^7
5. 7^5

D Simplify, leaving your answers in index form:

1. $x^3 \times x^4$
2. $c^5 \times c^7$
3. $p^8 \times p^6$
4. $m^6 \times m$
5. $3^4 \times 3^5$

6. $2^7 \times 2^6$
7. $d^{13} \times d^4$
8. $7^{11} \times 7$
9. $y^3 \times y^2 \times y^4$
10. $a^5 \times a^3 \times a^4$

11. $h^4 \times h^7 \times h^2$
12. $p^3 \times p \times p^5$
13. $d \times d^7 \times p^{11}$
14. $t^4 \times t^4 \times t^4$
15. $u^3 \times u^5 \times u^7$

E Simplify, leaving your answers in index form:

1. $\dfrac{n^7}{n^2}$
2. $\dfrac{u^6}{u^4}$
3. $f^9 \div f^3$

4. $k^8 \div k$ **7.** $\dfrac{12^{11}}{12^5}$ **9.** $\dfrac{z^{16}}{z^{12}}$

5. $\dfrac{a^{10}}{a^3}$ **8.** $x^{14} \div x^4$ **10.** $\dfrac{w^{17}}{w^5}$

6. $8^6 \div 8^3$

Exercise 2   R

A Write in index form:

1. $p \times p \times p \times q \times q$
2. $c \times d \times c \times d \times c \times d$
3. $h \times e \times e \times e \times e \times h \times h$
4. $f \times f \times g \times f \times g \times g \times g \times f \times f$
5. $a \times a \times b \times c \times b \times a \times c \times c \times a$
6. $d \times e \times e \times f \times e \times d \times d \times d \times f \times d$

B Simplify, leaving your answers in index form:

1. $c^3 \times c^4 \times e^5 \times e^2$ 4. $h^4 \times h \times k^3 \times h^2 \times k^3$
2. $q^2 \times p^4 \times q^5 \times p^2$ 5. $u^3 \times v^2 \times u^2 \times w^4 \times v^3 \times u^5$
3. $s^5 \times s^2 \times t^2 \times s^7 \times t^3$ 6. $t^3 \times m \times m^5 \times t$

C 1. If $V = l^3$, find V when $l = 7$.
2. $A = 8t^2$. Find A when $t = 3$.
3. If $m = 4$, find K, where $K = 2m^2$.
4. Given that $T = 5w^4$, find T when $w = 2$.
5. If $Z = 3p^6$ find Z when $p = 10$.

Exercise 3

Simplify, leaving your answers in index form:

e.g. $3x^2 \times 3x = \underline{\underline{9x^3}}$

1. $x^2 \times x^3$ 5. $2x^2 \times 2x^2$
2. $2x \times x^2$ 6. $4x^3 \times x^2$
3. $3x \times 2x$ 7. $5x \times 3x$
4. $2x^2 \times 2x^3$ 8. $2x \times 7x$

9. $6x \times 2x^2$

10. $3x^2 \times 2x^2$

11. $3p \times 2p^5$

12. $5k^6 \times 3k^3$

13. $v^2t^3 \times t^4v^6$

14. $a^4b^4 \times a^5b^3$

15. $c^5d^3 \times cd^4$

16. $e^6n^4 \times n^6e^4$

17. $2x^2y^3 \times 3x^3y^4$

18. $4t^3u \times 2t^2u^2$

19. $5m^3n^3 \times m^4n^2$

20. $3p^2qr^3 \times 2p^2q^4$

Exercise 4

1. (a) $2 + 2 + 2 + 2 = \boxed{?}$
  (b) $4 \times 2 = \boxed{?}$
  (c) $2 \times 2 \times 2 \times 2 = \boxed{?}$
  (d) $2^4 = \boxed{?}$

2. (a) $5 + 5 + 5 = \boxed{?}$
  (b) $3 \times 5 = \boxed{?}$
  (c) $5 \times 5 \times 5 = \boxed{?}$
  (d) $5^3 = \boxed{?}$

3. Simplify:
  (a) $x + x + x + x$
  (b) $x \times x \times x \times x$

4. If $d = 3$, find the value of
  (a) $d + d + d + d + d$
  (b) $5d$
  (c) $d \times d \times d \times d \times d$
  (d) d^5

5. If $p = 7$, which is greater, p^3 or $3p$?

6. If $a = 4$, find the value of:
  (a) $2a + 2a + 2a$
  (b) $6a$
  (c) $2a \times 2a \times 2a$
  (d) $8a^3$

7. Simplify:
  (a) $3t + 2t$
  (b) $3t \times 2t$

8. If $m = 6$, find the value of:
  (a) $3m + 2m$
  (b) $5m$
  (c) $3m \times 2m$
  (d) $6m^2$

9. If $k = 5$, find the value of:
  (a) $4k + 5k$
  (b) $9k$
  (c) $4k \times 5k$
  (d) $20k^2$

10. If $n = 8$, which has the smaller value,
  (a) $3n + 4n$ or $3n \times 4n$?
  (b) $7n$ or $12n^2$?

Exercise 5

Simplify, leaving your answers in index form:

1. $x^4 \div x^2$

2. $a^7 \div a^3$

3. $\dfrac{c^6}{c^4}$

4. $\dfrac{6d^9}{2d^5}$

5. $8s^{12} \div 4s^9$

6. $\dfrac{12x^{11}}{4x^2}$

7. $18y^{15} \div 3y^{10}$

8. $\dfrac{16e^{16}}{4e^4}$

9. $\dfrac{14t^7}{2t^2}$

10. $\dfrac{100p^{13}}{5p^5}$

11. $\dfrac{d^3e^4}{d^2e^2}$

12. $\dfrac{h^7k^4}{h^4k^2}$

13. $\dfrac{8c^6f^4}{4c^2f}$

14. $\dfrac{m^5n^2}{m^2n^4}$

15. $\dfrac{12tu^5}{6t^5u}$

16. $\dfrac{24l^2m^9}{8l^3m^3}$

17. $\dfrac{9s^4n^6}{6n^3s^2}$

18. $\dfrac{12s^5t^2u^3}{18su^5}$

19. $9p^6q \div 12pq^2$

20. $\dfrac{20cf^2h^7}{15fh^3c}$

Exercise 6

A Simplify the following:

1. $x^2 \times x^2 \times x^2$

2. $m^4 \times m^4 \times m^4 \times m^4 \times m^4$

3. $k^7 \times k^7 \times k^7 \times k^7$

4. $2t^3 \times 2t^3 \times 2t^3 \times 2t^3$

5. $5y^6 \times 5y^6 \times 5y^6$

6. $3c^3 \times 3c^3$

B Simplify these:

1. $(a^2)^3$

2. $(z^4)^5$

3. $(p^6)^3$

4. $(d^2)^6$

5. $(l^3)^4$

6. $(u^4)^3$

7. $(g^8)^6$

8. $(e^7)^5$

9. $(r^4)^6$

10. $(w^7)^8$

11. $(6h^5)^2$

12. $(2b)^4$

13. $(3q^3)^3$ **16.** $(5s^4)^3$ **19.** $(9v^4)^2$

14. $(4c^4)^3$ **17.** $(7n^6)^2$ **20.** $(5y^3)^2$

15. $(2f)^6$ **18.** $(3x^2)^2$

Exercise 7

1. Fold a piece of paper in half.
(A sheet of newspaper will do.)
After one fold it is 2 sheets thick.
($2^1 = 2$)

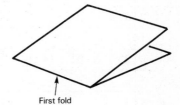

First fold

2. Fold it in half again.
After 2 folds, it is 4 sheets thick.
($2^2 = 4$)

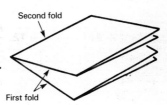

Second fold

3. Fold it in half again.
After 3 folds it is 8 (or 2^3) sheets thick.

First fold

4. How many sheets thick is it after:
(*a*) 4 folds?   (*b*) 7 folds?   (*c*) 12 folds?

5. Try to fold it in half 7 times, then tear it in half.

Exercise 8

1. Will the fifth power of every number always end in the same digit as the number itself?
For example, consider the number 3.
$3^5 = 243$, which ends in 3.
Also, $15^5 = 759\,375$. Note that both 759 375 and 15 end in 5. (It is not necessary to work out the value of a number raised to its fifth power to find the units digit. Try to find and use a quick method.)

2. Find other powers which, when numbers are raised to that power, give the same units digit as the number itself.
For example 14^7 ends in 4 so the power 7 appears to work. However 13^7 ends in 7, not 3, so the power 7 does not work.

The following table may help you to check your answers to Exercise 8. Copy and complete the table.

		1	2	3	4	5	6	7	8	9	10	11	12	13	14	15	16	17	18	etc.
												Power (or index)								
	0	0	0				0				0	0						0		
	1	1			1															
	2	2			6		4					8				8				
	3	3	9	7	1								1						9	
n	4	4																		
	5	5												5						
	6				6									6						
	7	7	9				9						1			3				
	8							2	6								6	8		
	9	9	1				1													

The main body of the table contains the last digit when n is raised to the given power.

e.g. 1 $2^4 = 16$, so the last digit, 6, is entered in the 2-row and the 4-column.

e.g. 2 $7^2 = 49$, so the last digit, 9, is entered in the 7-row and the 2-column.

1. Look carefully at the completed table and write about any patterns you notice.

2. Which rows contain the same numbers throughout?

3. (*a*) Which columns are the same as the 1-column?
   (*b*) Which columns are the same as the 2-column?
   (*c*) Which columns are the same as the 3-column?
   (*d*) Which columns are the same as the 4-column?

4. Which columns would the 25-column be like?

Exercise 10   Number Patterns

Copy and check these. For each pattern, give the next 3 steps.

1. $(1 + 2)^2$ $\qquad\qquad\quad = 1^3 + 2^3$
$\quad (1 + 2 + 3)^2 \qquad\quad = 1^3 + 2^3 + 3^3$
$\quad (1 + 2 + 3 + 4)^2 \qquad = 1^3 + 2^3 + 3^3 + 4^3$
   and so on

2. (a) $1^3 \qquad\qquad\quad = 1^2$
$\qquad 1^3 + 2^3 \qquad\quad = 3^2$
$\qquad 1^3 + 2^3 + 3^3 \qquad = 6^2$
$\qquad 1^3 + 2^3 + 3^3 + 4^3 = 10^2$
      and so on

   (b) List the first 7 triangular numbers.
        Compare the triangular numbers with the pattern above.

3. $1^2 + 2^2 = 3^2 - \mathbf{2}^2$ $\qquad$ *Note* $\quad 1 \times 2 = \mathbf{2}$
$\quad 2^2 + 3^2 = 7^2 - \mathbf{6}^2 \qquad\qquad\qquad 2 \times 3 = \mathbf{6}$
$\quad 3^2 + 4^2 = 13^2 - \mathbf{12}^2 \qquad\qquad\quad 3 \times 4 = \mathbf{12}$
$\quad 4^2 + 5^2 = 21^2 - \mathbf{20}^2 \qquad\qquad\quad 4 \times 5 = \mathbf{20}$
   and so on

4. $1^3 = 1^2$
$\quad 2^3 = (1 + 2)^2 - 1^2$
$\quad 3^3 = (1 + 2 + 3)^2 - (1 + 2)^2$
$\quad 4^3 = (1 + 2 + 3 + 4)^2 - (1 + 2 + 3)^2$
   and so on

5. $1^3 = 1^2$
$\quad 2^3 = 2(1 + 2 + 1)$
$\quad 3^3 = 3(1 + 2 + 3 + 2 + 1)$
$\quad 4^3 = 4(1 + 2 + 3 + 4 + 3 + 2 + 1)$
   and so on

Using a Calculator

Some calculators have a special key for finding powers of numbers. Check your calculator. The key probably looks like this, $\boxed{x^y}$, or this, $\boxed{y^x}$.

To find 4.6^3, key in $\boxed{4}$ $\boxed{\cdot}$ $\boxed{6}$ $\boxed{x^y}$ $\boxed{3}$ $\boxed{=}$. Note that on some calculators, a function key may need to be pressed before using $\boxed{x^y}$. If your calculator does not have a 'power' key such as $\boxed{x^y}$ you will have to use $\boxed{\times}$ as follows: $\boxed{4}$ $\boxed{\cdot}$ $\boxed{6}$ $\boxed{\times}$ $\boxed{4}$ $\boxed{\cdot}$ $\boxed{6}$ $\boxed{\times}$ $\boxed{4}$ $\boxed{\cdot}$ $\boxed{6}$ $\boxed{=}$. (You may be able to discover a faster method.)

Exercise 11

Work these out on a calculator. Give each answer correct to 4 significant figures.

1. 3^6	**4.** 2.4^4	**7.** 96.8^2	**10.** 0.48^3
2. 2^{11}	**5.** 8.3^3	**8.** 1.86^3	**11.** 0.805^4
3. 5^7	**6.** 4.1^2	**9.** 2.07^4	**12.** 0.694^3

Exercise 12

1. (a) Find what possible units digits the square numbers can have. For example, $7^2 = 49$ and the units digit is 9.
   (b) Is it possible for a square number to have a units digit of 2?

2. Consider the squares of numbers less than 10.
   (a) 1^2 has a units digit of 1.
      What other number, when squared, has a units digit of 1?
   (b) 2^2 has a units digit of 4.
      What other number, when squared, has a units digit of 4?
   (c) What number, when squared, has the same units digit as 3^2?
   (d) What number, when squared, has the same units digit as 4^2?

Exercise 13

A List the squares of all the whole numbers from 1 to 16.

B Where possible, write each of the following numbers as the sum of two squares:

1. 13	**6.** 128	**11.** 151
2. 90	**7.** 106	**12.** 269
3. 98	**8.** 160	**13.** 274
4. 97	**9.** 208	**14.** 255
5. 122	**10.** 226	**15.** 162

C Of the first 50 integers*, list those that can be written as the sum of two squares. Write down the sum that gives each of those integers.

D Write down 5 integers that can be written as a sum of two squares in more than one way. List the different sums that give each of these 5 integers. (Note that $4 + 25$ is the same as $25 + 4$. These are not two different sums.)

* See the glossary.

Exercise 14

Which of these numbers are the products of two squares, where 1 is not allowed to be one of the square numbers used? Write each product as in the example.

e.g. $144 = 4 \times 36$

1. 36	**5.** 225	**9.** 441	**13.** 676
2. 100	**6.** 375	**10.** 625	**14.** 1089
3. 16	**7.** 196	**11.** 484	**15.** 784
4. 81	**8.** 216	**12.** 392	**16.** 1225

Exercise 15

Find, without using a calculator, the value of:

A					
1.	2^2	**6.**	6^2	**11.**	9^2
2.	20^2	**7.**	60^2	**12.**	90^2
3.	200^2	**8.**	600^2	**13.**	900^2
4.	2000^2	**9.**	6000^2	**14.**	9000^2
5.	$20\,000^2$	**10.**	$60\,000^2$	**15.**	$90\,000^2$

B
1. 3000^2
2. 300^2
3. 30^2
4. 3^2
5. 0.3^2
6. 0.03^2
7. 0.003^2

8. 7000^2
9. 700^2
10. 70^2
11. 7^2
12. 0.7^2
13. 0.07^2
14. 0.007^2

15. 80^2
16. 0.8^2
17. 0.09^2
18. 0.005^2
19. 120^2
20. 0.12^2

Exercise 16

A Use a calculator to find:

1. (a) $\sqrt{4}$
   (b) $\sqrt{40}$
   (c) $\sqrt{400}$
   (d) $\sqrt{4000}$
   (e) $\sqrt{40\,000}$
   (f) $\sqrt{400\,000}$
   (g) $\sqrt{4\,000\,000}$

2. (a) $\sqrt{25}$
   (b) $\sqrt{250}$
   (c) $\sqrt{2500}$
   (d) $\sqrt{25\,000}$
   (e) $\sqrt{250\,000}$
   (f) $\sqrt{2\,500\,000}$
   (g) $\sqrt{25\,000\,000}$

3. (a) $\sqrt{6400}$
   (b) $\sqrt{640}$
   (c) $\sqrt{64}$
   (d) $\sqrt{6.4}$
   (e) $\sqrt{0.64}$
   (f) $\sqrt{0.064}$
   (g) $\sqrt{0.0064}$

B Write what you notice about the answers to the questions above.

Exercise 17

Find, *without using a calculator*, the value of:

1. $\sqrt{1600}$
2. $\sqrt{810\,000}$
3. 0.5^2
4. 0.04^2
5. 11^2
6. 1.1^2
7. 0.11^2
8. 0.011^2

9. $\sqrt{0.04}$
10. 0.08^2
11. $\sqrt{0.0025}$
12. $\sqrt{0.0009}$
13. $\sqrt{0.000\,009}$
14. 5000^2
15. 0.0005^2
16. $\sqrt{9\,000\,000}$

17. $60\,000^2$
18. $\sqrt{0.000\,064}$
19. 0.0001^2
20. 0.0007^2
21. $\sqrt{0.000\,001}$
22. $\sqrt{0.000\,000\,36}$
23. 0.25^2
24. 0.025^2

Exercise 18

Use a calculator to find (to 4 significant figures):

A **1.** 4.7^2 **4.** 1.85^2 **7.** 0.89^2 **10.** 2.34^2
    2. 5.6^2 **5.** 6.29^2 **8.** 52.3^2 **11.** 28.1^2
    3. 3.9^2 **6.** 0.63^2 **9.** 617^2 **12.** 0.906^2

B **1.** $\sqrt{47}$ **6.** $\sqrt{23.9}$ **11.** $\sqrt{0.214}$
    2. $\sqrt{12}$ **7.** $\sqrt{9.08}$ **12.** $\sqrt{0.56}$
    3. $\sqrt{5.4}$ **8.** $\sqrt{65.97}$ **13.** $\sqrt{0.172}$
    4. $\sqrt{385}$ **9.** $\sqrt{216.3}$ **14.** $\sqrt{0.075}$
    5. $\sqrt{457}$ **10.** $\sqrt{8.7}$ **15.** $\sqrt{0.083}$

Exercise 19

Find the value of:

1. $\left(\dfrac{3}{4}\right)^2$ **4.** $\left(\dfrac{6}{7}\right)^2$ **7.** $\dfrac{4^2}{8}$ **10.** $\left(\dfrac{3}{10}\right)^2$

2. $\left(\dfrac{5}{8}\right)^2$ **5.** $\left(2\dfrac{1}{2}\right)^2$ **8.** $\left(\dfrac{4}{8}\right)^2$ **11.** $\dfrac{6^2}{15^2}$

3. $\dfrac{3^2}{2^2}$ **6.** $\left(1\dfrac{3}{4}\right)^2$ **9.** $\dfrac{4}{8^2}$ **12.** $\left(6\dfrac{2}{3}\right)^2$

Exercise 20

Find the value of:

1. $\sqrt{\dfrac{4}{9}}$ **3.** $\sqrt{\dfrac{49}{100}}$ **5.** $\sqrt{\dfrac{16}{25}}$ **7.** $\sqrt{\dfrac{100}{9}}$

2. $\sqrt{\dfrac{9}{25}}$ **4.** $\sqrt{\dfrac{25}{144}}$ **6.** $\sqrt{\dfrac{81}{49}}$ **8.** $\sqrt{\dfrac{25}{4}}$

9. $\sqrt{2\frac{1}{4}}$ **12.** $\sqrt{1\frac{9}{16}}$ **15.** $\sqrt{7\frac{1}{9}}$ **18.** $\frac{2^2}{\sqrt{16}}$

10. $\sqrt{1\frac{7}{9}}$ **13.** $\sqrt{2\frac{14}{25}}$ **16.** $\frac{\sqrt{25}}{4^2}$ **19.** $(\sqrt{36})^2$

11. $\sqrt{12\frac{1}{4}}$ **14.** $\sqrt{1\frac{21}{100}}$ **17.** $\frac{\sqrt{25}}{5^2}$ **20.** $\sqrt{25^2}$

Exercise 21

Find the value of:

1. $^-3 \times {}^-3$ **5.** $(^-4)^2$ **9.** $(^-15)^2$

2. $(^-2)^2$ **6.** $^-7 \times {}^-7$ **10.** $(^-10)^2$

3. $(^-5)^2$ **7.** $(^-9)^2$ **11.** $(^-2.5)^2$

4. $(^-8)^2$ **8.** $(^-6)^2$ **12.** $(^-0.5)^2$

Exercise 22

1. Draw a pair of axes as shown. Use a scale of 1 cm to 1 unit on the x-axis and 2 cm to 5 units on the y-axis.

Let $\quad ^-7 \leqslant x \leqslant 7$

and $\quad 0 \leqslant y \leqslant 50.$

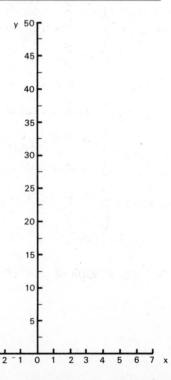

2. Copy and complete:

(a) the mapping diagram:

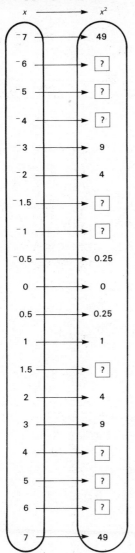

$x \longrightarrow x^2$

(b) the table:

x	$y = x^2$
$^-7$	49
$^-6$	
$^-5$	
$^-4$	
$^-3$	9
$^-2$	4
$^-1.5$	
$^-1$	
$^-0.5$	0.25
0	0
0.5	0.25
1	1
1.5	
2	4
3	9
4	
5	
6	
7	49

3. Draw a graph of $y = x^2$ using the results in your table.

Revision Exercises XIII to XVIII

Revision Exercise XIII

1. Find the value of:
- (a) $16 - {}^+7$
- (b) $8 - 11$
- (c) ${}^-4 - 6$
- (d) ${}^-6 - {}^-3$
- (e) ${}^-5 + 7$
- (f) ${}^-8 + 3$
- (g) $5 - (-4)$
- (h) $(-7) - (-2)$
- (i) $(-6) + 1$
- (j) $(-2) + 6$
- (k) $(-2) + (-6)$
- (l) $(-2) - (-6)$
- (m) ${}^-1 + 6 - 9 - 3$
- (n) $4 - 7 - 8 + 2$
- (o) ${}^-3 - 9 + 2 + 12$
- (p) ${}^-10 + 3 - 11 + 4$

2. Find the missing numbers:
- (a) $\boxed{?} - {}^+2 = {}^+6$
- (b) $4 - \boxed{?} = {}^-5$
- (c) $\boxed{?} - 7 = {}^-3$
- (d) $\boxed{?} - {}^-6 = 10$
- (e) ${}^-5 + \boxed{?} = {}^-8$
- (f) ${}^-8 - \boxed{?} = {}^-2$

3. Write in shorter form:
- (a) $3e + 5k - 2e - k$
- (b) $5x - 2z - 8x - 3z + 6x$

4. Work these out:
- (a) $8 \times {}^-3$
- (b) -6×4
- (c) ${}^-8 \times {}^-7$
- (d) $(-4) \times (-9)$
- (e) ${}^-12 \div {}^-2$
- (f) $(-7) \times (+3)$
- (g) $\dfrac{-45}{9}$
- (h) $(+32) \div (-4)$

5. Find the missing numbers:
- (a) $\boxed{?} \times {}^-4 = 28$
- (b) ${}^-3 \times \boxed{?} = {}^-27$
- (c) $48 \div \boxed{?} = {}^-4$
- (d) $\boxed{?} \div {}^-7 = {}^-7$
- (e) $9 \times \boxed{?} = {}^-63$
- (f) $\dfrac{\boxed{?}}{{}^-5} = 12$

6. If $m = {}^-6$, find the value of:
- (a) $3m$
- (b) $8 - m$
- (c) $16 - 5m$
- (d) $4 + 3m$

7. If $y = 2x + 4$, find the value of y when x equals
   (a) 6   (b) ⁻5   (c) ⁻2   (d) ⁻8

8. Which number lies exactly halfway between ⁻9 and 3?

9. Give the next three terms of the sequence:
   7, 4, 1, ⁻2, ⁻5, ⌐?⌐, ⌐?⌐, ⌐?⌐

10. Given that $V = a + 2t$, find V when $a = {}^+4$ and $t = {}^-7$.

Revision Exercise XIV

1. Copy and complete the diagram to show the relation 'is a multiple of':

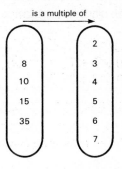

2. $X = \{28, 49, 56, 61, 74, 102, 205\}$
Draw a diagram to show the relation 'has the same remainder when divided by 5 as' from set X to X.

3. Copy and complete the mapping diagram for the mapping $x \rightarrow x - 5$:

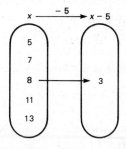

4. Show the mapping $p \rightarrow 4p + 6$ for the domain $\{1, 2, 3, 4, 5, 6\}$.

5. Use the rule 'multiply by 3 then subtract 7'. Draw a mapping diagram using the domain $\{4, 5, 6, 7, 8, 9\}$.

6. Draw a mapping diagram to show $c \rightarrow 8 - c$ using the domain $\{2, 4, 6, 8, 10, 12\}$.

7. For the mapping $t \rightarrow t + 4$:
    (*a*) What does $^-6$ map to?   (*b*) What maps to 0?

8. For the mapping $u \rightarrow 5u - 2$:
    (*a*) What does $^-4$ map to?   (*b*) What maps to 13?

Revision Exercise XV

Part One

A Draw a pair of axes as shown. (Use 2 cm to represent 1 km on both axes.)

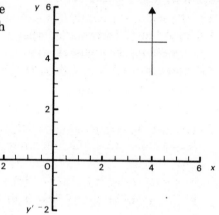

The streets of a town are given by means of pairs of co-ordinates. Each street is straight, and both end points are given. Plot the points and join them with straight lines to show a street plan of the town.

1. $(^-2, 4)$ to $(6, 4)$ **11.** $(0, \,^-2)$ to $(0, 6)$

2. $(^-4, 2)$ to $(2, 2)$ **12.** $(^-2, \,^-2)$ to $(^-2, 4)$

3. $(4, 2)$ to $(6, 2)$ **13.** $(5, 6)$ to $(5, 3.5)$

4. $(^-4, 0)$ to $(6, 0)$ **14.** $(3, 2.5)$ to $(3, 1)$

5. $(0, 1)$ to $(4, 1)$ **15.** $(^-2, 0)$ to $(5, 3.5)$

6. $(2, \,^-0.5)$ to $(1.5, \,^-0.5)$ **16.** $(^-2, 4)$ to $(^-4, 5)$

7. $(6, 4)$ to $(6, \,^-2)$ **17.** $(4, 1)$ to $(6, 0)$

8. $(4, 6)$ to $(4, \,^-2)$ **18.** $(4, \,^-1)$ to $(5, \,^-2)$

9. $(2, 4)$ to $(2, 2)$ **19.** $(1, \,^-2)$ to $(1.5, \,^-0.5)$

10. $(2, \,^-2)$ to $(2, 1)$

B Now mark on your map:

1. the bus station at $(2, 4)$
2. the railway station at $(6, {}^-1)$
3. churches at $(4, 2)$ and at $({}^-2, 4)$
4. a cinema at $(2, 3)$
5. a post office at $(0, 1)$
6. a shopping centre at $(2.5, 2)$
7. a car park at $(3.5, 3)$
8. a school at $({}^-2, 3)$
9. a swimming pool at $({}^-1, 2)$
10. a park at $(1, {}^-0.5)$
11. the police station at $(3, 0)$
12. banks at $(1, 1.5)$ and $(5, 3.5)$
13. a building society at $(4, {}^-1)$
14. hotels at $({}^-2, {}^-1)$ and $(1, 2)$
15. a restaurant at $(3, 2)$

C 1. I enter the town travelling north on the road that passes the railway station and turn first left after the railway station followed by second right. I turn right at the next junction then first left, and then I travel a further 1 km before stopping. If the scale of the map is 2 cm to 1 km, where have I stopped?

2. I then travel south, turn right at the next junction, turn second left, first right, then I turn north at the next junction. I then take the second turn right followed by the first left, and I travel north to leave the town. How far have I travelled altogether through the town?

Part Two

1. $(2, 8)$ and $({}^-6, 4)$ are opposite vertices of a square.
   Find:
   (a) the co-ordinates of the other two vertices,
   (b) the co-ordinates of the point of intersection of the diagonals.

2. $({}^-3, {}^-5)$, $({}^-2, {}^-1)$ and $(4, 1)$ are three vertices of a parallelogram when joined in the given order. Find the co-ordinates of the fourth vertex.

Part Three

1. Draw a pair of axes as shown.

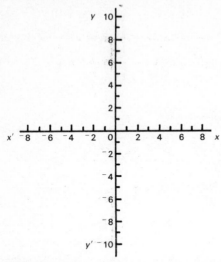

Now draw graphs of:
(*a*) $x = 6$
(*b*) $y = 5$
(*c*) $y = {}^-6$

2. What is the equation of the straight line that joins the points $(2, 7)$, $(2, 3)$, $(2, 0)$, $(2, {}^-4)$ and $(2, {}^-8)$?

3. (*a*) Draw a mapping diagram to show the relation 'is 4 less than'. (Use the same pair of axes as in question 1.)
(*b*) Draw the graph of the relation 'is 4 less than'.
(*c*) What is the equation of the graph of the relation 'is 4 less than'?
(*d*) What are the co-ordinates of the point of intersection of this graph with the line $y = 5$?

4. Using the same pair of axes as in question 1, draw graphs of:
(*a*) $y = x$
(*b*) $y = x - 5$
(*c*) $y = 2x$
(*d*) $y = 2x - 3$
Label each graph.

5. (*a*) Does the point $(2, 1)$ lie on the line $y = 4x - 7$?
(*b*) Does the point $({}^-3, 2)$ lie on the line $y = 2x + 4$?

Part Four

The table compares miles with kilometres:

km	0	8	16	24	32	40	48	56	64	72	80
miles	0	5	10	15	20	25	30	35	40	45	50

1. Draw a pair of axes as shown. Use a scale of 1 cm to 5 km on one axis and 2 cm to 5 miles on the other axis.

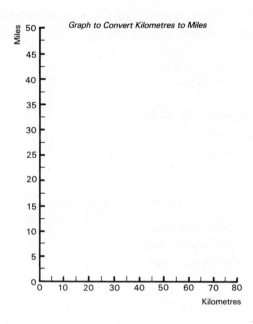

2. Plot the graph using the table above.

3. Use your graph to help you to answer these questions:
   (*a*) How many miles are there in 20 km?
   (*b*) How many kilometres are there in 37.5 miles?

Revision Exercise XVI

1. A circle has a diameter of 6.7 m. Calculate its circumference using $\pi = 3$.

2. Calculate the circumference of a circle with radius $8\frac{3}{4}$ cm. Use $\pi = 3\frac{1}{7}$.

3. Using $\pi = 3.14$, find the circumference of a circle with diameter 5.2 m.

4. The diameter of a bicycle wheel is 0.5 m. How far will the bicycle travel if the wheel makes 2000 turns? (Use $\pi = 3.14$.)

5. Calculate the length of an arc of a circle of radius 4 cm if the arc subtends an angle of 120° at the centre of the circle. (Use $\pi = 3.14$.)

6. The diameter of a tin is 72 mm. Find the length of a label that goes three-quarters of the way around the tin. (Use $\pi = 3.14$.)

Revision Exercise XVII

1. Copy the flag shown on to a piece of squared paper. Translate it 8 cm to the right. Label the image with the letter A.

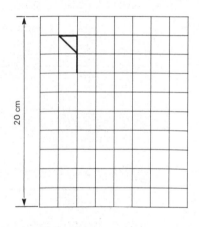

2. Now translate the first flag 4 cm to the right and 6 cm downwards. Label this image with the letter B.

3. Draw another flag and a mirror line as shown.
Now reflect the flag in the mirror line and label the image with the letter C.

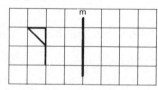

4. Copy the given shape and the mirror line. Reflect the shape in the mirror line.

5. Draw another flag on a piece of squared paper and mark a point as shown. Rotate the flag through 90° clockwise about the point.

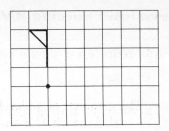

6. Trace the line PQ and the point C into your exercise book. Rotate PQ through 90° anticlockwise about point C. Label the image P′Q′. (You may use tracing paper and a set square to help you.)

7. Draw a pair of axes. The x-axis should range from ⁻8 to ⁺8 and the y-axis from ⁻10 to ⁺10. (Use 1 cm to 1 unit.) Now answer the following:

    (a) Plot the points (⁻4, 1) and (⁻4, 5). Join them using a straight line. Translate this line 5 cm to the right.

    (b) Plot the points (1, ⁻1) and (5, ⁻3). Join them with a straight line. Reflect this line in the x-axis.

    (c) Plot the points (⁻5, ⁻3) and (⁻1, ⁻5). Join them with a straight line. Rotate this line through 180° clockwise about the origin.

    (d) What sort of triangle is formed by the three images obtained from the transformations above?

8. The point (4, 5) is reflected in the x-axis. Give the co-ordinates of its image.

9. The point (⁻3, 6) is translated 8 units downwards. Give the co-ordinates of its image.

10. △ABC is transformed as follows:

$$A(6, 3) \rightarrow (1, 3)$$
$$B(2, {}^-4) \rightarrow ({}^-3, {}^-4)$$
$$C({}^-1, 6) \rightarrow ({}^-6, 6)$$

Is the transformation a translation, a reflection or a rotation?

1. Write $e \times e \times e \times e \times e \times e \times e$ in index form.

2. Find the value of: (a) 7^2 (b) 2^9

3. Simplify, leaving your answers in index form:

  (a) $c^5 \times c^3$ (d) $p \times q \times q \times p \times q$ (g) $4k \times 3k^2$

  (b) $w^7 \div w^2$ (e) $f^2 \times g^3 \times f \times g^4$ (h) $3x \times 2x$

  (c) $\dfrac{m^9}{m^6}$ (f) $a^4 \times a^2$ (i) $5d^2e \times 3d^3e^2$

4. If $A = 6l^2$, find A when $l = 5$.

5. Simplify: (a) $4y + 7y$ (b) $4y \times 7y$

6. If $h = 4$, find the value of:

  (a) $3h + 6h$ (b) $3h \times 6h$ (c) $18h^2$ (d) $9h$

7. Simplify, leaving your answers in index form:

  (a) $\dfrac{10c^5}{5c^2}$ (b) $\dfrac{18t^4u^3}{6t^2u}$ (c) $24m^7n^5 \div 4m^5n^2$

8. Simplify: (a) $(k^4)^3$ (b) $(2k^2)^3$

9. Use a calculator to find, to 4 significant figures:

  (a) 7.4^3 (b) 0.596^2 (c) 1.8^4 (d) $\sqrt{45.69}$ (e) $\sqrt{0.5904}$

10. $5\blacklozenge = 2\blacksquare07$ was written in a book. Find out whether or not the statement could be correct if the two smudged digits were properly written.
Explain your answer.

11. Find the value of:

  (a) 0.02^2 (b) $\sqrt{0.0016}$ (c) 0.07^2

12. Find the value of:

  (a) $\left(\dfrac{2}{5}\right)^2$ (b) $\left(1\dfrac{2}{3}\right)^2$ (c) $\sqrt{2\dfrac{7}{9}}$

13. Find the value of: (a) $(^-7)^2$ (b) $(-1.5)^2$

19 Basic Algebra

Formulae

Exercise 1

1. To change kilometres into miles, multiply by 5 then divide by 8. Change 72 km into miles.

2. To change miles into kilometres, multiply by 8 then divide by 5. Change 70 miles into kilometres.

3. The perimeter of a square is 4 times the length of its side. Calculate the perimeter of a square with sides of 2.9 m.

4. 1 gal is about $4\frac{1}{2}$ ℓ. To change gallons into litres, multiply by 4.5. Change 9 gal into litres.

5. To find the average speed for a journey, the distance travelled must be divided by the time taken. Find the average speed of a car that travels 320 km in 5 h.

6. The area of a kite is given as half the product of its diagonals. Calculate the area of a kite with diagonals measuring 18 cm and 8 cm.

7. (a) The perimeter of a rectangle is twice the sum of its length and breadth. Calculate the perimeter of a rectangle measuring 21 cm by 15 cm.
   (b) Test this formula for the perimeter of a rectangle: 'Double the length and double the breadth then add the two results.' Is this formula correct?

8. (a) To change pounds into kilograms, multiply by $\frac{5}{11}$. Change 88 lb into kilograms.
   (b) To change kilograms into pounds, multiply by $\frac{11}{5}$. Change 60 kg into pounds.

313

9. The current used by an electrical appliance can be found by dividing the power of the appliance (in watts) by the voltage. The current will be in ampères. Calculate the current used by:
(a) an electric kettle of 2.4 kW (2400 W) if the voltage is 240 V,
(b) a 60 W electric light bulb if the voltage is 240 V.

10. The circumference of a circle is given by the product of π and the diameter. Calculate the circumference of a circle with a diameter of 2.6 cm. Use $\pi = 3.142$.

11. To find the diameter of a circle, divide the circumference by π. Calculate the diameter of a circle with circumference 66 mm. Use $\pi = \frac{22}{7}$.

12. The volume of a cube is given as the cube of the length of an edge. Calculate the volume of a cube where each edge measures 4 cm.

Exercise 2

1. In Exercise 1, question 1, the rule for changing kilometres into miles was given as 'multiply by 5 then divide by 8'. Would the rule still work if we divided first? Try it. The new rule is 'divide by 8 then multiply by 5'.

2. Test the rule in Exercise 1, question 2, dividing before multiplying. Does the rule still work?

3. (a) Another rule for changing miles into kilometres is 'multiply by 1.6'. Test this rule. Does it work?
(b) 'To change kilometres into miles, divide by 1.6.' Test this rule. Does it work?
(c) 'To change kilometres into miles, multiply by 0.625.' Test this rule. Does it work?

Exercise 3

1. The perimeter of an equilateral triangle can be found by multiplying the length of its sides by 3. The formula can be written as $P = 3\,l$. (Remember that $3\,l$ stands for $3 \times l$.) Use this formula to find the perimeter of an equilateral triangle of side 27 cm.

2. The volume of a cuboid can be found by multiplying its length by its breadth by its height. The formula is $V = lbh$.

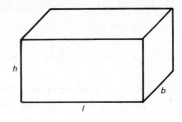

Use the formula to find the volume of a cuboid with length 8 m, breadth 6 m and height 4 m.

3. Pressure can be calculated by dividing force by area. The formula can be written as $\text{Pressure} = \dfrac{\text{force}}{\text{area}}$.

(a) Calculate the pressure if a force of 480 N (newtons) is spread over an area of 3 m².

(b) Calculate the pressure if a force of 322 N is spread over an area of 1.4 m².

4. The resistance, R (ohms), in an electric circuit can be found by dividing the voltage, V, by the current, I (ampères). The formula is $R = \dfrac{V}{I}$. Use the formula to calculate the resistance of an electric fire that works at 250 V and carries a current of 4 A.

5. The area of a triangle is given as half the product of the base and perpendicular height. The formula can be written as $A = \frac{1}{2}bh$. Calculate the area of a triangle with base 63 mm and perpendicular height 34 mm.

Exercise 4

Here are some more formulae:

1. Use $V = Ah$ to find V when $A = 9$ and $h = 4$.

2. Use $F = ma$ to find F when $m = 390$ and $a = 7$.

3. If $A = \dfrac{360}{n}$, find A when $n = 9$.

4. Use $n = \dfrac{360}{A}$ to find n when $A = 15$.

5. Use $V = \dfrac{s}{t}$ to find V when $s = 504$ and $t = 8$.

6. Use $P = mgh$ to find P when $m = 74$, $g = 10$ and $h = 9$.

7. If $V = \frac{1}{3}Ah$, find V when $A = 18$ and $h = 7$.

8. If $I = \dfrac{PRT}{100}$, find I when $P = 450$, $R = 8$ and $T = 3$.

9. Use $R = r_1 + r_2$ to find R when $r_1 = 2.8$ and $r_2 = 4.7$.

10. Use $V = IR$ to find V when $I = 7.5$ and $R = 32$.

11. If $v = u + at$, find v when $u = 8$, $a = 9$ and $t = 12$.

12. $S = (2n - 4) \times 90$. Find S when $n = 15$.

13. If $V = l^3$, find V when $l = 6$.

14. Use $V = l^2h$ to find V when $l = 5$ and $h = 14$.

15. Given that $A = \pi r^2$, find A when $\pi = 3.14$ and $r = 4$.

Exercise 5

For each of the following, write a formula using algebraic notation. Use each formula as instructed.

1. The diameter, d, of a circle, is twice its radius, r. Calculate the diameter of a circle with radius 39 mm.

2. The density, D, of a substance can be found by dividing its mass, M, by its volume, V. Find the density of wood if 1.5 m^3 has a mass of 840 kg.

3. The area of a parallelogram, A cm^2, is given as the product of its base, b cm, and its perpendicular height, h cm. Calculate the area of a parallelogram with base 6.8 cm and perpendicular height 4 cm.

4.

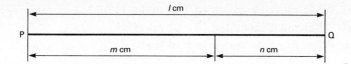

Write a formula that gives length, l, in terms of m and n. Calculate l when $m = 16$ and $n = 9$.

5. Write a formula for the perimeter, P cm, of the given isosceles triangle. Calculate its perimeter when $x = 13$ and $y = 11$.

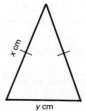

6. The volume, V mm^3, of a pyramid is given as one-third of the product of the area of its base, A mm^2 and its perpendicular height, h mm. Calculate the volume of a pyramid with a base area of 420 mm^2 and a perpendicular height of 30 mm.

7. If n articles cost l pounds each, write a formula to find the total costs, C pounds, in terms of n and l. Use the formula to find the cost of 8 articles at £13 each.

8. Write a formula to change m kg into pounds (use b). The rule is 'multiply the number of kilograms by $\frac{11}{5}$'. The formula should give b in terms of m. Use the formula to change 20 kg into pounds.

Generalised Arithmetic

Exercise 6 $\qquad$ R

1. (*a*) What number is 3 more than 5?
   (*b*) What number is 3 more than x?

2. (*a*) What is 5 less than 9?
   (*b*) What is 5 less than t?
   (*c*) What is p less than t?

3. (a) What must be added to 7 to make 11?
   (b) What must be added to c to make 11?
   (c) What must be added to c to make d?

4. What must be added to x to make y?

5. What must be added to f to make 15?

6. What must be added to 6 to make g?

7. What is u less than m?

8. What number is k more than d?

9. (a) By what must 4 be multiplied to make 20?
   (b) Write the calculation that was carried out in part (a) using the 20 and the 4. (You do not multiply!)

10. (a) By what must 3 be multiplied to make 18?
    (b) Write the calculation for part (a) using 18 and 3.

11. (a) By what must 2 be multiplied to make 14?
    (b) By what must 2 be multiplied to make f? (Write the calculation using f and 2.)
    (c) By what must e be multiplied to make f?

12. (a) By what must 14 be divided to make 2?
    (b) By what must f be divided to make 2?
    (c) By what must f be divided to make e?

13. By what must n be multiplied to make q?

14. By what must g be multiplied to make 16?

15. By what must l be divided to make r?

Exercise 7

1. (a) In a class there are 15 girls and 14 boys. How many pupils are there altogether?

   (b) In a class there are g girls and b boys. How many pupils are there altogether?

2. (a) A cyclist travelled 6 km on one day and 8 km on the following day. How far was that altogether?
   (b) A cyclist travelled x km on one day and y km on the following day. How far was that altogether?

3. (a) A girl is 14 years old now. How old will she be in 3 years' time?
   (b) A girl is y years old now. How old will she be in 3 years' time?
   (c) A girl is y years old now. How old will she be in n years' time?

4. (a) Bob will be 18 years old in 4 years' time. How old is he now?
   (b) Bob will be c years old in b years' time. How old is he now?

5. (a) There are 8 cakes in a tin. 3 were eaten. How many were left?
   (b) There are c cakes in a tin. e were eaten. How many were left?

6. What is the cost of:
   (a) 6 books at £4 each?
   (b) m books at £4 each?
   (c) m books at £x each?

7. What is the perimeter of a square with side
   (a) 7 cm?   (b) l cm?

8. (a) A car travels at 60 km/h. How far does it go in 4 h?
   (b) A car travels at v km/h. How far does it go in 4 h?

9. (a) Tammy saved £8 in 4 weeks. How much was that per week?
   (b) Peter saved £m in 4 weeks. How much was that per week?

10. Pencils cost 25 p each. How many can you buy for:
    (a) £1?   (b) £5?   (c) £x?   (d) £10y?

Exercise 8

1. There are 32 pupils in a class. If there are g girls, how many boys are there?

2. A girl is 13 years old now. How old was she y years ago?

3. A boy walks d km every day. How far does he walk in a week?

4. If a boy walks $2p$ km every day, how far does he walk in a week?

5. There were 45 l of petrol in a car's petrol tank. p l were used. How many litres were left?

6. I travel t km to work each day. b km of the journey is by bus. I walk the rest. How far do I walk?

7. I have £x. If I spend £c, how much will I have left?

8. What is the cost of 4 pencils if each pencil costs u pence?

9. What is the cost of y pencils if each pencil costs d pence?

10. What is the area of a rectangle of length x m and breadth y m?

11. A rectangle has an area of A cm²; find its breadth if its length is:
    (a) 8 cm   (b) l cm

12. How much per week is £ x per year?

Exercise 9

A 1. (a) How many millimetres are there in 6 cm?
    (b) How many millimetres are there in d cm?

2. (a) How many seconds are there in 3 min?
    (b) How many seconds are there in f min?

3. (a) How many pence are there in £1?
    (b) How many pence are there in £7?
    (c) How many pence are there in £t?

4. (a) How many metres are there in 4 km?
    (b) How many metres are there in g km?

5. (a) How many days are there in 5 weeks?
    (b) How many days are there in w weeks?

6. (a) How many months are there in 2 years?
    (b) How many months are there in y years?

B 1. (a) How many weeks are there in 21 days?
    (b) How many weeks are there in d days?

2. (a) How many hours are there in 240 min?
    (b) How many hours are there in m min?

3. (a) How many metres are there in 600 cm?
    (b) How many metres are there in l cm?

4. (*a*) How many kilograms are there in 3000 g?

(*b*) How many kilograms are there in *h* g?

5. There are 3 ft in 1 yd.

(*a*) How many yards are there in 24 ft?

(*b*) How many yards are there in *k* ft?

6. (*a*) How many days are there in 72 h?

(*b*) How many days are there in *b* h?

C How many:

1. millilitres in *t* *l*?

2. centimetres in *d* m?

3. weeks in *z* days?

4. hours in *e* days?

5. grams in *x* kg?

6. centimetres in *b* mm?

7. 20 p pieces in £ *a*?

8. £ in *f* 10 p pieces?

9. minutes in *v* s?

10. inches in *m* ft?
  (12 in = 1 ft)

11. years in *k* weeks?

12. years in *l* months?

13. minutes in *y* h?

14. 50 p pieces in £*n*?

15. feet in *u* yd?

Exercise 10

1. What is the next whole number bigger than 1?

2. *e* is even. What is the next highest even number?

3. The sum of two numbers is *t*. If one of the numbers is *u*, what is the other number?

4. What number is 6 less than *p*?

5. Write a number that is 3 times as big as *f*.

6. Write a number that is half as big as *k*.

7. Write a number that is one-quarter of *z*.

8. Which even number comes before the odd number *b*?

9. *w* is a whole number. Write the next three consecutive whole numbers that are bigger than *w*.

10. *m* is a multiple of 5. What is the next highest multiple of 5?

Sequences

Exercise 11 **R**

Copy these sequences and fill in the missing numbers:

1. 5, 8, 11, 14, $\boxed{?}$, 20, $\boxed{?}$, ...

2. 5, $\boxed{?}$, 13, 17, $\boxed{?}$, 25, 29, ...

3. 2, $\boxed{?}$, 16, $\boxed{?}$, 30, 37, ...

4. 1, 3, 6, 10, $\boxed{?}$, 21, $\boxed{?}$, 36, ...

5. 2, 5, 10, $\boxed{?}$, 26, 37, $\boxed{?}$, 65, ...

6. 1, 4, $\boxed{?}$, 16, 25, $\boxed{?}$, 49, ...

7. 2, 8, 15, $\boxed{?}$, 32, 42, $\boxed{?}$, ...

8. 85, 64, 46, $\boxed{?}$, 19, $\boxed{?}$, 4, ...

Exercise 12

Copy the following sequences, and for each question, underline the one term that is incorrect:

1. 29, 25, 21, 17, 15, 9, 5, ...

2. 1, 2, 4, 7, 11, 17, 22, 29, ...

3. 1, 2, 4, 8, 18, 32, 64, ...

4. 5, 8, 11, 14, 17, 20, 23, 27, 29, ...

5. 2, 4, 8, 16, 22, 32, 44, 58, 74, 92, ...

6. 3, 6, 11, 20, 27, 38, 51, 66, 83 ...

7. 1, 3, 6, 10, 15, 21, 27, 36, 45, ...

8. 14, 25, 36, 47, 58, 69, 70, ...

9. 6, 9, 14, 21, 30, 39, 54, 69, 86 ...

10. 6, 1, ⁻4, ⁻9, ⁻13, ⁻19, ⁻24, ⁻29, ...

Exercise 13

1. Graph the sequence 3, 6, 9, 12, 15, 18, 21, 24.

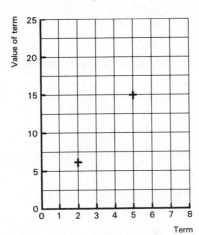

Graph of a Sequence

2. Graph the sequence 1, 2, 4, 8, 16, 32, 64, 128.

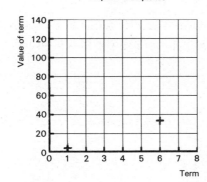

Graph of a Sequence

Exercise 14

T_n stands for nth term of a sequence.
Consider the sequence 5, 9, 13, 17, 21, 25, 29, . . .
The first term is 5 so we can write $T_1 = 5$.
The sixth term is 25 so we can write $T_6 = 25$.

Find:

1. T_2

2. the third term

3. T_5

4. T_7

5. T_8

6. Try to find a quick way of working out T_{100}

323

To find T_{100} by listing 100 terms would take some time. A formula would be useful.

Consider the formula

$$T_n = 4n + 1$$
$$T_1 = 4 \times 1 + 1 = 5$$
$$T_2 = 4 \times 2 + 1 = 9$$
$$T_3 = 4 \times 3 + 1 = 13$$
$$T_4 = 4 \times 4 + 1 = 17$$

and so on.

The formula $T_n = 4n + 1$ gives the sequence of Exercise 14. Since $T_n = 4n + 1$

$$T_{100} = 4 \times 100 + 1 = 401$$

Exercise 15

A formula is given for the nth term of each sequence. For each question, find the sequence (give the first 5 terms).

A **1.** $T_n = 2n + 3$

$T_1 = 2 + 3 = 5$

$T_2 = 4 + 3 = 7$

$T_3 = 6 + 3 = 9$

$T_4 = \boxed{?}$

$T_5 = \boxed{?}$

The sequence is

$5, 7, 9, \boxed{?}, \boxed{?}, \ldots$

2. $T_n = 4n - 3$

$T_1 = 4 - 3 = 1$

$T_2 = 8 - 3 = 5$

$T_3 = \boxed{?}$

$T_4 = \boxed{?}$

$T_5 = \boxed{?}$

The sequence is

$1, 5, \boxed{?}, \boxed{?}, \boxed{?}, \ldots$

B **1.** $T_n = 2n$

2. $T_n = 3n - 1$

3. $T_n = 3n + 5$

4. $T_n = 3n - 2$

5. $T_n = 5n - 2$

6. $T_n = 4n + 5$

7. $T_n = 4n - 1$

8. $T_n = n^2$

9. $T_n = n^2 - n$

10. $T_n = n^2 - n + 2$

11. $T_n = 2n^2 - 1$

12. $T_n = \frac{1}{2}n^2 - \frac{1}{2}n + 3$

Exercise 16

For each of these sequences, try to find a formula for its nth term:

1. 5, 7, 9, 11, 13, 15, ...
2. 7, 13, 19, 25, 31, 37, 43, 49, ...
3. 6, 10, 14, 18, 22, 26, 30, 34, ...
4. 6, 11, 16, 21, 26, 31, 36, ...
5. 3, 6, 11, 18, 27, 38, 51, ...
6. 2, 6, 12, 20, 30, 42, 56, ...

Exercise 17

1. (a) Count the number of dots on the perimeter of each square:

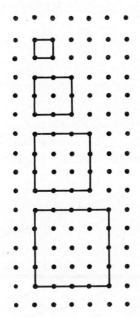

(b) Write the sequence. (Give 7 terms.) It starts:
4, 8, ? , ? , ? , ? , ? , ...

(c) Try to find a formula for the nth term of this sequence.

2. (*a*) Count the number of dots inside each square below. Start with the smallest square.

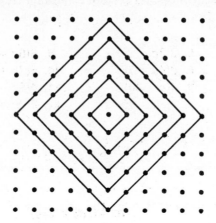

(*b*) Write the sequence. (Give 7 terms.) The sequence begins:
1, 5, 13, | ? |, | ? |, | ? |, | ? |, ...

(*c*) Is the *n*th term of this sequence given by $T_n = 2n^2 - 2n + 1$?

Brackets

The sketch shows 2 apples and 3 bananas in a box. A quick way of writing this would be $(2a + 3b)$. The *a* stands for apples, and the *b* for bananas, while the brackets stand for the box.

$2a$ means '2 apples'.

$4(2a + 3b)$ stands for 4 boxes of 2 apples and 3 bananas: a total of 8 apples and 12 bananas.

We can write: $4(2a + 3b) = 8a + 12b$

Exercise 18

In this exercise use a for apples, b for bananas and use brackets for boxes. For each question, find out how much fruit there is altogether:

A
1. $3(4a + 2b)$
2. $5(2a + 4b)$
3. $2(a + 3b)$
4. $3(2a + b)$

5. $6(3a + 2b)$
6. $2(4a + 7b)$
7. $4(a + 6b)$
8. $7(3a + 4b)$

9. $6(6a + 2b)$
10. $5(7a + 3b)$
11. $4(8a + b)$
12. $9(2a + 5b)$

B
1. $\dfrac{1}{2}(6a + 4b)$

2. $\dfrac{1}{3}(9a + 12b)$

3. $\dfrac{8a + 6b}{2}$

4. $\dfrac{2a + 10b}{2}$

5. $\dfrac{1}{2}(12a + 6b)$

6. $\dfrac{1}{4}(16a + 24b)$

7. $\dfrac{25a + 15b}{5}$

8. $\dfrac{21a + 27b}{3}$

Exercise 19

A In this exercise, each letter stands for a number and shows a length (in metres) on each rectangle.

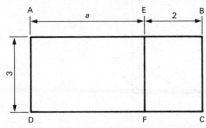

1. (a) Area of rectangle AEFD = $\boxed{?}$
   (b) Area of rectangle EBCF = $\boxed{?}$
   (c) Area of rectangle ABCD = $3(a + 2)$

   $= \boxed{?} + \boxed{?}$

2.

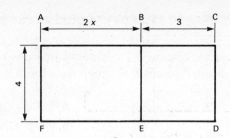

(a) Area of rectangle ABEF = ?

(b) Area of rectangle BCDE = ?

(c) Area of rectangle ACDF = $4(2x + 3)$

$$= \boxed{?} + \boxed{?}$$

B Multiply out:

1. $2(p + 4)$	**7.** $2(3c + 4)$	**13.** $6(2 + m)$
2. $3(c + 6)$	**8.** $6(2u + 3)$	**14.** $4(2 - k)$
3. $3(d - 2)$	**9.** $7(2n - 4)$	**15.** $3(5 + 2v)$
4. $5(k - 3)$	**10.** $8(3h - 5)$	**16.** $2(4 - 3t)$
5. $4(t + 4)$	**11.** $4(6l + 1)$	**17.** $3(6 - 6f)$
6. $7(m - 5)$	**12.** $3(8a - 7)$	**18.** $5(9 - 3z)$

Exercise 20

A 1.

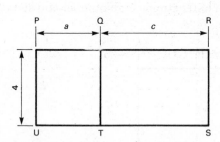

(a) Area of rectangle PQTU = ?

(b) Area of rectangle QRST = ?

(c) Area of rectangle PRSU = $4(a + c)$

$$= \boxed{?} + \boxed{?}$$

2.

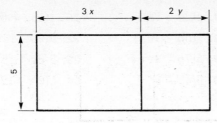

$$5(3x + 2y) = \boxed{?} + \boxed{?}$$

3.

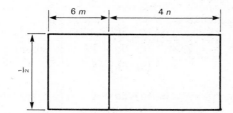

$$\tfrac{1}{2}(6m + 4n) = \boxed{?} + \boxed{?}$$

4.

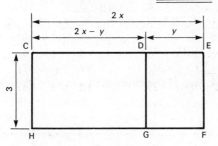

(a) Area of rectangle CEFH = $\boxed{?}$

(b) Area of rectangle DEFG = $\boxed{?}$

(c) Area of rectangle CDGH = $3(2x - y)$

$$= CEFH - DEFG$$

$$= \boxed{?} - \boxed{?}$$

B Multiply out:

1. $3(m + n)$ **5.** $6(2h - d)$ **9.** $3(4u + 2p)$

2. $4(k - l)$ **6.** $4(a + 6y)$ **10.** $5(3x + 2y)$

3. $7(g + a)$ **7.** $3(2u + e)$ **11.** $4(6b - 2c)$

4. $5(3p + q)$ **8.** $2(f - 7r)$ **12.** $\tfrac{1}{2}(4n + 6d)$

329

13. $\frac{1}{2}(8k + 2z)$ **17.** $4(2k + 7m)$ **21.** $\frac{1}{2}(10a + 6d)$

14. $6(2q - 3s)$ **18.** $\frac{1}{2}(6n - 10p)$ **22.** $2(9j - 13)$

15. $6(3s - 2q)$ **19.** $5(7b - 3u)$ **23.** $3(6e + 15)$

16. $8(1 - 3w)$ **20.** $9(4t + 1)$ **24.** $\frac{1}{3}(9k - 12c)$

Exercise 21

A Find the value of each of these expressions:

1. (a) $2x + 3$
   (b) $2(x + 3)$ when $x = 7$
   (c) $2x + 6$

4. (a) $3(2a - 3)$
   (b) $6a - 12$ when $a = 5$
   (c) $6a - 4$

2. (a) $3y + 6$
   (b) $3(y + 2)$ when $y = 4$
   (c) $3y + 2$

5. (a) $2b + 1$
   (b) $\frac{1}{2}(4b + 2)$ when $b = 6$
   (c) $2b + 2$

3. (a) $4(z - 5)$
   (b) $4z - 5$ when $z = 8$
   (c) $4z - 20$

6. (a) $12c + 2d$
   (b) $3(4c + 2d)$ when $c = 2$
   (c) $12c + 6d$ and $d = 3$

B In each question in part A, two of the three answers should be identical. Which two are they?

e.g. Question 1: $2(x + 3) = 2x + 6$, so (b) and (c) are identical.

Exercise 22

Re-write each of the following expressions without brackets:

1. $4(3c + 2)$

6. $\dfrac{(10g - 15)}{5}$

2. $5(2d + 3)$

7. $3(6 - 5p)$

3. $7(4x - 3)$

8. $2(3t + 7)$

4. $\dfrac{(6p + 4)}{2}$

9. $5(3a - 2b)$

5. $\frac{1}{2}(4m - 6)$

10. $9(2x + t)$

11. $\dfrac{(4p + 10q)}{2}$ **16.** $8(z + 2w)$

12. $\dfrac{(12r - 8s)}{4}$ **17.** $(12h + 15k) \div 3$

13. $\dfrac{18u + 12v}{6}$ **18.** $(2p - 4m) \times 7$

14. $\frac{1}{3}(6x - 9y)$ **19.** $6(\frac{1}{2}w + x)$

15. $7(3e + 5f)$ **20.** $(24q - 28r) \div 4$

Exercise 23

Re-write each of the following in its simplest form:

1. $\dfrac{(4c - 6d)}{2}$ **6.** $\dfrac{35a}{5} - 3b$

2. $\dfrac{12m}{4} + 5n$ **7.** $\dfrac{48g}{8} + \dfrac{14h}{7}$

3. $\dfrac{(15a + 25b)}{5}$ **8.** $\dfrac{8w}{2} + \dfrac{15w}{3}$

4. $7z + \dfrac{6y}{3}$ **9.** $\dfrac{24t - 18u}{6}$

5. $\dfrac{21p - 14q}{7}$ **10.** $\dfrac{36k + 6j}{12}$

Exercise 24

Re-write each of the following without brackets:

1. $^-2(3a + 4)$ **4.** $^-3(4d - 1)$
2. $^-5(2b + 3)$ **5.** $^-9(e - 6)$
3. $^-7(5c + 4)$ **6.** $^-4(2f - 3g)$

331

7. $^-6(h + 2k)$

8. $^-7(7l - 3m)$

9. $^-3(2n + m)$

10. $^-2(4p - 3q)$

11. $^-5(3r + 5s)$

12. $^-8(7t - 4u)$

13. $\dfrac{(4a + 6c)}{^-2}$

14. $\dfrac{(18d - 21e)}{^-3}$

15. $^-4(8v + 3w)$

16. $^-12(^-2x - 3y)$

17. $\dfrac{(35f - 28g)}{^-7}$

18. $\dfrac{(36h + 24k)}{^-4}$

19. $^-7(^-3j + 4h)$

20. $\dfrac{(^-42l + 54m)}{^-6}$

Exercise 25

Re-write each of the following without brackets. (The diagram illustrates question 1).

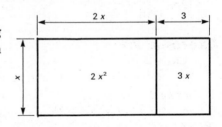

1. $x(2x + 3)$

2. $x(x + 5)$

3. $d(d - 3)$

4. $m(2 + m)$

5. $y(4 - y)$

6. $3c(c + 7)$

7. $2a(a - 4)$

8. $5p(3 - p)$

9. $4n(3n + 2)$

10. $2k(7k - 3)$

11. $7e(4 - 3e)$

12. $3x(2x^2 + 4)$

13. $4x(3x^2 - 2)$

14. $2h(6h^2 + ^{\cdot}5h)$

15. $5c^2(3c + 1)$

16. $6z^2(4 - 3z)$

17. $4g^3(g^4 + 5)$

18. $t^4(2t^2 - 7t)$

19. $3x(5x^2 - 2x + 7)$

20. $2f^2(2f^2 + f - 6)$

Once again let a stand for apples and b for bananas.

If we have a box of 5 apples and 3 bananas and a box of 2 apples and 6 bananas then altogether we have 7 apples and 9 bananas. This can be written as follows:

$$(5a + 3b) + (2a + 6b) = 5a + 3b + 2a + 6b$$
$$= \underline{\underline{7a + 9b}}$$

Note also the following example:

$$(6a + 4b) - (2a + 2b) = 6a + 4b - 2a - 2b$$
$$= \underline{\underline{4a + 2b}}$$

This next example may help with questions 24 onwards in Exercise 26:

$$(5a - 3b) - (2a - 7b)$$
$$= 5a - 3b - 2a + 7b$$
$$= 3a + 4b$$

Exercise 26

Re-write each of the following without brackets and simplify each answer:

1. $(2a + 5b) + (4a + 3b)$
2. $(6a + 3b) + (2a + 4b)$
3. $(5a + 2b) + (a + 3b)$
4. $(4t + 3u) + (5t + u)$
5. $(6k + 5) + (3k + 2)$
6. $(5l + 6) + (3l - 5)$
7. $(3b + 7e) + (b - 4e)$
8. $(5c - 2d) + (3c + 5d)$
9. $(8 + 5p) + (3 - 2p)$
10. $(7v + 3w) + (6v - 5w)$
11. $(4g - 8h) + (g + 3h)$
12. $(2x - 5y) + (4x - 6y)$
13. $(8x - 7) + (5x + 9)$
14. $(7f + h) + (2f - h)$
15. $(9q - 6r) + (3q + 6r)$

16. $(6a + 5b) - (3a + 2b)$
17. $(3n + 7m) - (n + 4m)$
18. $(9z + 4) - (4z + 3)$
19. $(7x - 3y) - (5x + 4y)$
20. $(8c - e) - (7c + e)$
21. $(3t - 5) - (3t + 5)$
22. $(6n + 8) - (4n + 8)$
23. $(5g + 7) - (4g + 6)$
24. $(3w + 3x) - (2w - 2x)$
25. $(2k - 7) - (k - 7)$
26. $(5s + 6t) - (5s - 6t)$
27. $(4t - 7u) - (4t + 7u)$
28. $(6v - 3u) - (6v - 3u)$
29. $(3w + 4x) - (5w - 2x)$
30. $(5k - 2l) - (2k - 5l)$

Factorising: Common Factors

Exercise 27

A Find the value of:

1. (a) $7 \times 6 + 7 \times 4$
(b) $7 \times (6 + 4)$

2. (a) $3 \times 9 - 3 \times 4$
(b) $3 \times (9 - 4)$

3. (a) $6 \times 4 + 3 \times 4$
(b) $4 \times (6 + 3)$

4. (a) $5 \times 8 - 6 \times 5$
(b) $5 \times (8 - 6)$

5. (a) $7 \times 42 - 5 \times 42$
(b) $(7 - 5) \times 42$
(c) $42 \times (7 - 5)$

6. (a) $3 \times 47 + 3 \times 53$
(b) $3(47 + 53)$

7. (a) $16 \times 4 + 4 \times 4$
(b) $4(16 + 4)$

8. (a) $37 \times 54 - 37 \times 44$
(b) $37(54 - 44)$

9. (a) $64 \times 29 + 36 \times 29$
(b) $29(64 + 36)$

10. (a) $87 \times 462 - 87 \times 362$
(b) $87(462 - 362)$

B **1.** 6 apples and 8 bananas are put into 2 boxes having the same number in each box.
(a) How many apples and bananas are put into each box?
(b) Copy and complete: $6a + 8b = 2(\boxed{?} + \boxed{?})$

2. Copy and complete:
(a) $12a + 9b = 3(\boxed{?} + \boxed{?})$ (e) $6a + 15b = \boxed{?}(2a + 5b)$
(b) $8a + 20b = 4(\boxed{?} + \boxed{?})$ (f) $14a + 2b = \boxed{?}(7a + b)$
(c) $10a + 6b = 2(\boxed{?} + \boxed{?})$ (g) $30a + 18b = \boxed{?}(5a + \boxed{?})$
(d) $10a + 15b = 5(\boxed{?} + \boxed{?})$ (h) $15a + 20b = \boxed{?}(\boxed{?} + 4b)$

C The rectangle shows
that $3x + 6 \equiv 3(x + 2)$
(The symbol $\equiv$ shows that the
two expressions are identical to
each other.)

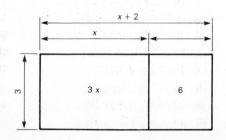

334

Draw rectangles to show that:

1. $4x + 12 \equiv 4(x + 3)$
2. $10c + 8 \equiv 2(5c + 4)$
3. $6m + 8n \equiv 2(3m + 4n)$
4. $12k + 18l \equiv 6(2k + 3l)$
5. $15g + 5h \equiv 5(3g + h)$
6. $9t + 3 \equiv 3(3t + 1)$

Exercise 28

Factorise:

e.g. $8g + 10h = 2(4g + 5h)$

1. $2a + 4b$
2. $6x + 9y$
3. $4t - 6u$
4. $9h + 12$
5. $10c - 15d$
6. $8z - 12$
7. $4p + 8$
8. $12k + 6l$
9. $4m + 2$
10. $7n + 7$

11. $6e - 18$
12. $4t + 10$
13. $5t + 10$
14. $3f - 9$
15. $12 - 8a$
16. $4b + 4d$
17. $7q - 14$
18. $9 + 18w$
19. $14m + 6l$
20. $25g - 15$

21. $12q + 8r$
22. $16v - 8w$
23. $16s - 12$
24. $16g - 8$
25. $18e + 24f$
26. $30h - 24c$
27. $26s + 39p$
28. $u^2 + 2u$
29. $m^2 - 3m$
30. $2x^2 + 3x$

Exercise 29

Find the value of the following by factorising:

1. $8 \times 64 + 8 \times 36$
2. $15 \times 37 - 15 \times 27$
3. $76 \times 29 + 24 \times 29$
4. $397 \times 6 + 6 \times 603$
5. $254 \times 23 - 154 \times 23$
6. $67 \times 58 + 58 \times 33$
7. $4 \times 17 + 4 \times 33$
8. $22 \times 36 + 22 \times 24$
9. $59 \times 32 - 32 \times 19$
10. $48 \times 74 - 34 \times 48$

11. $6 \times 4.7 + 6 \times 5.3$
12. $63.5 \times 8 + 36.5 \times 8$
13. $8.7 \times 3.5 + 1.3 \times 3.5$
14. $36.2 \times 4.7 - 26.2 \times 4.7$
15. $71.6 \times 2.8 - 2.8 \times 51.6$
16. $4.86 \times 3.2 + 5.14 \times 3.2$
17. $8.97 \times 6.24 + 8.97 \times 3.76$
18. $42.8 \times 9.8 - 9.8 \times 22.8$
19. $7.68 \times 3.54 - 7.68 \times 6.46$
20. $88.4 \times 2.107 + 11.6 \times 2.107$

20 Statistics

1. Draw a bar chart to show a newsagent's sales of six daily newspapers:

Newspaper	Sales
Gazette	48
Chronicle	20
Courier	· 37
Daily Post	24
Daily News	29
Herald	18

2. The table below shows the average monthly rainfall in Perth, Australia. Draw a jagged line graph to show the information.

Month	Jan	Feb	Mar	Apr	May	June	July	Aug	Sept	Oct	Nov	Dec
Rainfall (cm)	0.7	1	2	4.3	13	17.8	17.2	14.6	8.6	5.6	2	1.5

3. Draw a pie chart from the following information:

Attendance at School Club

Club	Attendance
computer	19
chess	16
guitar	8
wildlife	17
basketball	12

Averages (Mode, Median and Mean)

Exercise 2

Here are the shoe sizes of nine pupils:

5, 6, 4, 6, 7, 4, 8, 3, 4

1. Which size was the most common?
   (The one that occurs the most is called the *mode*.)

2. (*a*) Write the nine sizes in order of size.
   (*b*) Which is the middle size?
   (The middle size or value is called the *median*.)

3. Total the nine sizes and divide the total by the number of different sizes (by 9 in this instance).
   (This time, the average found is called the *arithmetic mean* or more usually just the *mean*.)

4. If you owned a shoe shop, which of the above three averages would be the most useful in helping you to order your shoes? Give a reason for your answer.

Exercise 3   Mode

Find the mode:

1. 7, 3, 1, 3, 4, 2, 1, 3
2. 6, 2, 2, 4, 6, 3, 6, 4
3. 5, 9, 3, 6, 3, 5, 4, 8, 6, 2, 6, 1, 3, 6
4. 4, 8, 8, 8, 3, 4, 6, 7, 1, 4, 6, 1, 7, 4, 3
5. 15, 25, 20, 25, 30, 20, 10, 10, 20, 35, 50
6. 19, 21, 14, 16, 14, 20, 17, 13, 11, 12
7. 100, 250, 125, 60, 220, 145, 220, 250, 220, 100
8. c, f, f, g, x, c, f, g, y, c, p, f, x
9. 1, 0, 4, 0, 0, 1, 3, 4, 1, 0, 4, 1, 4, 3, 1, 1, 4, 0, 4
   (Note that there could be more than one mode.)
10. 8, 6, 2, 2, 6, 4, 8, 4, 2, 6, 8, 6, 2, 4, 4, 2, 6, 8, 2, 4

Exercise 4 Median

Find the median:

1. 3, 5, 8, 3, 2, 8, 7
2. 19, 14, 13, 19, 17
3. 1, 8, 3, 3, 6, 5, 2, 9, 2, 8, 7
4. 6, 9, 3, 4, 1, 6, 5, 5, 5, 2, 1, 2, 2
5. 7, 9, 8, 1, 6, 7, 6, 8, 7, 8, 6
6. 2, 8, 11, 1, 12, 19, 3, 1, 2
7. 19, 3, 17, 12, 15, 19, 19
8. 4, 2, 1, 5, 2, 4, 7, 9, 10, 7

(Note that when there is an even number of items, the median lies half-way between the two items in the middle. In this question, the median lies half-way between the fifth and the sixth items when they are all written in order of size.)

9. 16, 3, 9, 4, 12, 2, 11, 7, 1, 8, 10, 3, 2, 14
10. 12, 2, 3, 13, 7, 9, 5, 7, 15, 1, 4, 10, 2, 7, 1, 8

Exercise 5 Mean

Calculate the mean:

1. 12, 6
2. 3, 4, 6, 7
3. 1, 8, 9
4. 2, 3, 4, 5, 6
5. 9, 8, 4
6. 7, 2, 1, 6
7. 6, 8, 10
8. 5, 6, 7
9. 1, 3, 5, 7
10. 13, 15, 17

11. 17, 25
12. 28, 40
13. 17, 5, 14
14. 72, 34
15. 10, 20, 30
16. 10, 20, 60
17. 12, 12, 15
18. 210, 248
19. 8, 25, 17, 30
20. 102, 104, 106

21. 3, 4, 5, 5, 6, 7
22. 9, 15, 21, 12, 18
23. 62, 62, 62, 62
24. 5, 12, 17, 14
25. 146, 247, 54, 12, 56
26. 108, 297, 156
27. 5, 12, 17, 14
28. 15, 22, 27, 24
29. 105, 112, 117, 114
30. 85, 92, 97, 94

Exercise 6

Find (a) the mode, (b) the median, (c) the mean of each set of data:

1. 2, 8, 9, 5, 9, 6, 10, 5, 9
2. £20, £23, £24, £23, £19, £17, £28

3. £115, £126, £161, £115, £148

4. 84, 67, 73, 69, 81, 69, 67, 75, 86, 69

5. 9 m, 7 m, 13 m, 4 m, 7 m, 4 m, 8 m, 4 m

6. 16, 43, 28, 26, 26, 35, 28, 34, 28, 41

7. 3, 4, 3, 9, 7, 6, 9, 4, 7, 3, 7, 5, 8, 2, 7

8. 14, 19, 13, 12, 13, 11, 16, 16, 13, 18, 15, 14

Exercise 7

In eight tests, each marked out of 20, Andrea scored 1, 2, 2, 15, 15, 15, 15, 15 while Kevin scored 13, 13, 13, 14, 16, 19, 20, 20.

1. Who did better?

2. (a) Find the mode of Andrea's marks.
(b) Find the mode of Kevin's marks.
(c) Whose mode was the higher?

3. (a) Find the median of Andrea's marks.
(b) Find the median of Kevin's marks.
(c) Whose median was the higher?

4. (a) Find the mean of Andrea's marks.
(b) Find the mean of Kevin's marks.
(c) Whose mean was the higher?

5. (a) Which average is the most suitable for deciding who did better in this instance?
(b) Explain your answer.

Exercise 8

1. A football team scored the following goals in 16 matches:
0, 3, 1, 1, 0, 2, 1, 2, 2, 0, 1, 4, 1, 0, 1, 2
Find the mode.

2. Two dice where thrown 20 times and their total score was noted. The totals were:
10, 7, 6, 4, 12, 7, 9, 6, 9, 7, 8, 11, 2, 7, 5, 5, 8, 6, 9, 8
Find: (a) the mode,   (b) the median.

3. The numbers of people in each car crossing a toll bridge were counted. These were the results:

3, 1, 2, 4, 2, 1, 2, 3, 2, 5, 2, 1, 1, 4, 1

Find: (*a*) the mode,   (*b*) the median.

4. The lengths of words in a paragraph of a newspaper article were noted. The results were as follows:

2, 4, 3, 5, 5, 4, 3, 4, 2, 6, 3, 3, 5, 4, 9, 2, 10, 3, 4, 3, 2 6

Find: (*a*) the mode,   (*b*) the median,   (*c*) the mean.

5. The pulse rates of several people were taken. The number of beats per minute were as follows:

74, 63, 65, 72, 73, 69, 66, 80, 72, 70, 74, 82, 64, 72, 71, 68, 75, 72, 70, 69, 73, 79

Find: (*a*) the mode,   (*b*) the median,   (*c*) the mean.

6. The numbers of ray florets (petals) were counted on several daisies. The results were:

39, 42, 41, 37, 43, 42, 39, 38, 35, 37, 42, 45, 36, 43, 42, 40, 38, 42, 38, 36

Find: (*a*) the mode,   (*b*) the median,   (*c*) the mean.

Note that if the word 'average' is used in a question and it is not clear whether the mode, median or mean is wanted, then it will probably be the mean that must be found.

Exercise 9

1. A girl spent the following sums of money each week: 94 p, 38 p, 79 p and 85 p. Calculate the average amount spent per week.

2. Calculate John's average exam mark if his marks were: maths 86%, French 65%, geography 49%, history 38%, English 57% and science 77%.

3. The temperatures at noon for one week were: 11.6 °C, 11.4 °C, 12.1 °C, 12.6 °C, 14.7 °C, 13.2 °C, 13.3 °C Calculate the average temperature.

4. My waist size was estimated to be 115 cm, 108 cm, 118 cm, 110 cm, 112 cm, 112 cm and 116 cm. Calculate the average estimate.

5. The circumference and diameter of five cylinders were measured. The results of the calculation $\dfrac{\text{circumference}}{\text{diameter}}$ were found to be 3.2, 3.1, 3.26, 3.08 and 3.06. Calculate the average result.

6. Six boys are aged 11 years 2 months, 11 years 8 months, 12 years 1 month, 11 years 0 months, 11 years 5 months and 11 years 8 months. Calculate their average age.

7. Ten estimates of an angle were: 68°, 65°, 59°, 72°, 65°, 67°, 60°, 70°, 65° and 69° Calculate the average estimate.

8. Daily barometer readings were 754 mm, 750 mm, 749 mm, 753 mm, 754 mm, 758 mm and 760 mm. Calculate the average daily reading.

9. A cricketer scored 68, 115, 32, 0, 37, 89, 108, 96 and 31.
(*a*) Calculate his average score.
(*b*) What would his average be if in one of these innings he was not out?

$$\left(\text{Note that the average score} = \frac{\text{total scored}}{\text{number of times out}}.\right)$$

10. The heights of eight pupils were 165 cm, 173 cm, 164 cm, 167 cm, 155 cm, 154 cm, 159 cm and 167 cm. Calculate the average height.

Exercise 10

1. (*a*) Find the total of the five numbers 6, 8, 3, 4 and 9.
(*b*) Calculate the mean.
(*c*) Look carefully at your answers to parts (*a*) and (*b*), then explain how to find the total of the five numbers using the mean and how many numbers there are (five in this case). (If you are unable to work out the total, then examine the total, the mean and the number of values for each question in Exercise 9. Now explain how to find the total.)

2. If the mean of five numbers is 37, what do the five numbers total?

3. The average of eight numbers is 63. Find their total.

4. The average number of children in six families is 2.5. Find the total number of children.

5. A cyclist averaged 8 miles per day for 4 days.
(a) What was the total distance travelled in the 4 days?
(b) If the cyclist travelled 23 miles during the first three days, how far did he travel on the fourth?

6. Pam's average mark in seven tests was 63%.
(a) Find her total mark.
(b) Find her chemistry mark if her other results were: English language 52%, English literature 62%, French 67%, maths 68%, physics 73% and biology 70%.

7. The average of eight numbers is 74. If seven of the numbers total 509, calculate the eighth number.

8. Seven numbers average 49. If six of the numbers average 52, find the seventh number.

9. For five successive months a man spends £32.54 on petrol. If during the sixth month he spends £29.06, find his average for the six months.

10. Calculate the average of fifteen numbers if the first four total 26, the next three total 16, the eighth and ninth total 19 and the last six total 44.

Exercise 11

In a cricket match, two bowlers, Batty and Ball have identical bowling averages after the first innings. Both took 2 wickets for 12 runs, an average of 6 runs per wicket (the lower the average the better the bowler). In the second innings, Batty took 1 wicket for 15 runs (an average of 15 runs per wicket), while Ball took 4 wickets for 48 runs (an average of only 12 runs per wicket).

Who had the better bowling averages for the whole match?

Exercise 12

1. Write six numbers that have a mode of 8.

2. Write six numbers that have a median of 8.

3. Write six numbers that have a mean of 8.

4. Find three numbers where the mode = 6 and the mean = 7.

5. Four numbers have a mean of 5. If the mode and median both equal 6, find the other two numbers.

Exercise 13

1. Consider the numbers 3, 6, 2, 2, 8, 5, 2.
   (a) What is the mode?
   (b) Add 10 to each number.
   (c) What is the mode of the new set of numbers?

2. Repeat question 1 for the median.

3. Repeat question 1 for the mean.

4. Investigate adding any number to a given set of numbers. Find out what happens to the mode, median and mean. Write what happens.

Histograms

Exercise 14

The *histogram** given below shows the marks out of 10 obtained by some pupils in a test:

1. How many pupils took the test?

2. Which mark was the mode?

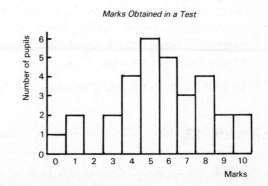

Marks Obtained in a Test

* See the glossary.

Here are some more test marks. This time, the marks are out of 100.

12	28	47	39	72	61	54	19	51	40
53	60	49	57	32	84	65	55	50	39
25	58	52	48	62	93	51	42	46	73
37	67	70	21	8	17	65	59	69	37
31	46	82	56	66	42	57	31	76	42

1. What is the *range* of the marks? (The range is the difference between the largest and smallest marks.)

2. Copy and complete the following tally chart (or *frequency table*). Write the marks in groups 0–9, 10–19, 20–29, and so on. (Each group is called a *class interval*.)

Marks	Tally	Frequency
0– 9		
10–19		3
20–29		
30–39		
40–49		9
50–59		
60–69		
70–79		
80–89		
90–99		

3. Draw a histogram using your frequency table.

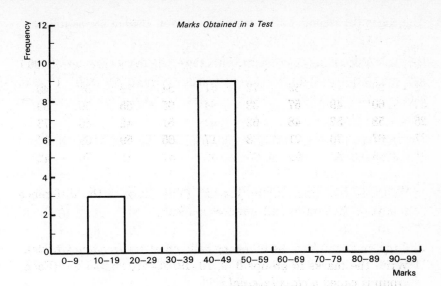

Marks Obtained in a Test

4. Which is the modal class? (The *modal class* is the class interval where the greatest frequency of marks occurs. It is the class where the highest bar is on the graph.)

Exercise 16

For each of the surveys below:

1. Find the range.

2. Make a frequency table using the given class intervals.

3. Draw a histogram.

4. Give the modal class.

A The masses (in kilograms) of 60 pupils are as follows:

42	50	43	36	31	38	44	56	45	49
63	56	33	43	43	50	37	46	54	33
38	42	35	41	48	39	51	47	44	42
37	45	40	42	52	59	62	34	39	44
49	53	57	36	49	46	42	45	50	46
52	43	37	55	36	52	36	57	32	39

Use the class intervals 30–34, 35–39, 40–44, 45–49, 50–54, 55–59, 60–64.

345

B The times (in seconds) of 34 runners who ran 1500 m are as follows:

485,	372,	324,	379,	425,	448,	399,	418
331,	438,	524,	461,	442,	400,	453,	365
327,	361,	445,	525,	533,	444,	500,	503
396,	354,	366,	411,	484,	434,	317,	389
388,	446						

Use the class intervals 300–329, 330–359, 360–389, 390–419, 420–449, 450–479, 480–509, 510–539.

C Here are the heights of some trees (measured in metres):

7	3	8	2	5	7	13	4	10	8	16	8
7	10	4	7	6	17	2	16	19	6	7	12
6	11	8	9	4	14	16	5	7	3	3	8
11	4	9	12	2	8	10	16	10	12	15	6
4	3	7	10	10	16	11	12	4	6	5	12

Use the class intervals 0–2, 3–5, 6–8, 9–11, 12–14, 15–17, 18–20.

D Here are the ages of the residents in a village, given in years:

24	27	2	49	25	36	35	13	10	72	64	69
51	49	83	78	29	32	2	4	7	36	36	14
11	9	57	56	52	49	60	62	73	47	48	22
20	19	54	50	43	40	17	13	11	32	28	1
4	34	33	7	4	26	25	48	45	17	15	49
52	58	51	73	41	65	63	59	57	32	31	9
7	4	28	25	27	25	26	24	2	27	28	5
3	27	4	32	60	45	43	19	18	26	34	64
66	44	68	54	50	48	51	54	57	55		

Use the class intervals 0–9, 10–19, 20–29, 30–39, 40–49, 50–59, 60–69, 70–79, 80–89.

Note In drawing a histogram, we should try to have between 6 and 15 classes.

Exercise 17

Carry out at least one of the surveys below. For each survey carried out:

1. Find the range.
2. Make a frequency table (decide on the class interval).

3. Draw a histogram.

4. Give the modal class.

A Find the heights of the pupils in your class. (Work to the nearest centimetre.)

B Find the times taken for pupils in your class to come to school. (Work to the nearest minute.)

C For each pupil in your class (or year group), find the total time spent per week watching television. (Work to the nearest hour.)

Scattergrams

Exercise 18

The graph shown is called a *scattergram* or *scatter diagram* (because the points are scattered).

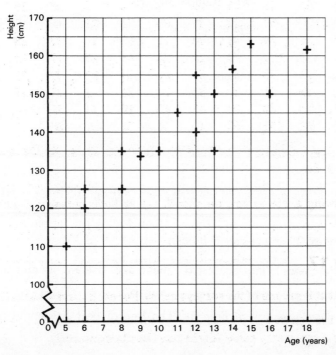

Heights and Ages of some Girls

Such a graph shows two independent *variables* at the same time. Height and age are both variables because they vary from person to person.

1. How many girls are shown on the graph?

2. How tall is the tallest girl?

3. What is the age of the youngest girl?

4. What is the difference in height between the 12-year old girls?

From the graph, it can be seen that some younger girls are taller than some older girls. However, it is still clear from the graph that older girls tend to be taller than younger girls.

The total height of the girls is $(110 + 120 + 125 + 125 + 135 + 133 + 135 + 145 + 140 + 155 + 136 + 150 + 157 + 163 + 150 + 161)$ cm, which is 2240 cm.

$$\text{Their mean height} = \frac{\text{total height}}{\text{total number of girls}}$$

$$= \frac{2240}{16} \text{ cm}$$

$$= 140 \text{ cm}$$

Exercise 19

1. Calculate the mean age of the girls given in the graph in Exercise 18.

2. Copy the scattergram in Exercise 18, including the jagged lines on both axes. They are called *broken scales**.

3. Plot the mean height against the mean age. Use a cross and circle it.

4. Now draw the *line of best fit*. The line of best fit should pass

* See the glossary.

through the point that was plotted from the two means. It should also have about the same number of points on each side.

Heights and Ages of some Girls

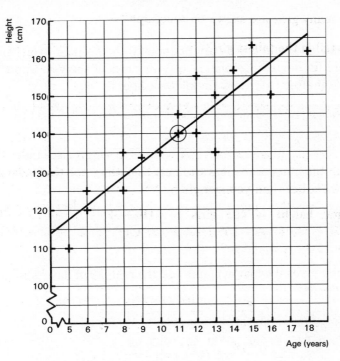
Age (years)

5. Use your graph to find the height of a girl aged 7 years.

Exercise 20

For each survey:
(a) draw a scattergram,
(b) calculate and plot the mean for both variables,
(c) draw the line of best fit (if there is one; sometimes there is no line of best fit!),
(d) answer the questions using your graph.

1. Here are the maths and science exam results for ten pupils:

Maths marks	50	40	70	60	24	66	80	20	34	56
Science marks	70	50	86	79	40	70	88	26	34	57

(a) From your graph, find the maths mark of someone who got 80 marks in science.

(b) Someone got 30 marks in maths. Find that person's science mark.

2. The table gives, for the Smith household, the average room temperature (in degrees Celsius) at certain times of the year and the amount of electricity used (in kilowatt-hours):

Temperature (°C)	10	15	6	20	9	16	4	10	3	6	19	14
Electricity used (kW h)	24	18	35	14	28	24	35	31	38	31	20	26

(a) Find the number of kilowatt hours used when the temperature was 13 °C.

(b) What was the temperature when 34 kW h of electricity were used?

3. This table gives the maths marks and the number of days' absence of ten pupils:

Maths marks	80	30	52	68	34	48	52	20	10	66
Days absent	10	30	10	8	20	22	18	30	37	15

(a) From your graph, find the possible number of days' absence for someone who got 72 marks.

(b) Someone was absent for 24 days. What mark does your graph suggest that person got?

4. The maths marks and the house numbers of fifteen pupils are given in this table:

Maths marks	30	20	50	26	84	70	52	13	66	56	38	40	10	66	84
House number	60	80	120	42	76	116	42	132	28	84	96	142	28	154	148

Write what you notice about your graph.

5. Twelve golfers played two rounds of golf in a competition. Here are their scores:

Player number	1	2	3	4	5	6	7	8	9	10	11	12
Round 1	73	71	69	72	73	69	70	74	71	71	75	76
Round 2	74	68	69	73	70	68	70	73	69	72	72	74

DO NOT DRAW A SCATTERGRAM UNTIL YOU READ THESE NOTES:

The scores in round 1 range from 69 to 76 (a very narrow range). Similarly, round 2 has a narrow range: from 68 to 74.

If you used a full scale from 0 to 76 then the graph would be drawn on a small part of the page and would be too small to use (see fig. 1).

Fig. 1

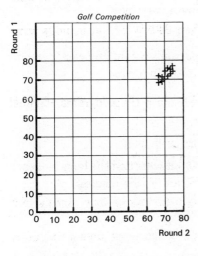

Fig. 2

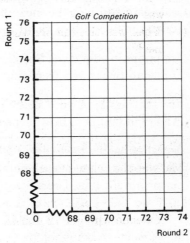

Since the axes ought to be labelled from zero, a *broken scale** is used on both axes (see fig. 2).

Now draw your scattergram setting the work out using a broken scale as in fig. 2.

Answer these:

(a) Which golfer won the competition? (The winner is the person with the smallest total score.)

(b) A golfer scored 70 in round 1. What did that golfer score in round 2? (Use your graph.)

* See the glossary.

6. Here are the masses (in kilograms) and the heights (in centimetres) of 12 boys:

Height (cm)	144	158	172	160	164	148	180	172	148	156	150	168
Mass (kg)	34	60	50	55	40	30	63	55	42	41	48	58

(*a*) Find the height of someone with a mass of 36 kg.

(*b*) A boy is 164 cm tall. Find his mass.

Exercise 21

For each survey:

(*a*) draw a scattergram,

(*b*) calculate and plot the mean for both variables,

(*c*) draw the line of best fit (if there is one).

1. For pupils in your class, find each person's height and each person's arm span (measured from fingertip to fingertip).

2. For the pupils in your class, graph mass (in kilograms) against height (in cm). Are heavier people taller?

3. Do taller people have bigger feet?
Measure the height of each pupil in your class and the length of each person's right foot. Draw a scattergram of the results.

4. If your class has sat a maths and a science exam then draw a scattergram of the results.

5. Draw a scattergram to show a maths mark and the size of each pupil's head (measure the distance around) for pupils in your class.

Probability

Exercise 22

Here are some words that we probably use when we decide whether or not something is likely to happen (we are, in fact, describing probabilities):

impossible, highly unlikely, fifty-fifty chance, most probable, certain

For each of the following sentences, select from the five choices above, the word (or words) that best describes what is likely to happen:

1. The next vehicle you see travelling along the road will be a bus.

2. The next person you will see in the street will be over 10 ft tall.

3. You will watch TV tonight.

4. It will snow on 8 July.

5. The next person you will see in the street will be taller than you.

6. The next person you will see in the street will be male.

7. When you throw a die the number you get will be bigger than 2.

8. You will eat something today.

9. When you toss a coin it will be a head.

10. You will get full marks in your next maths test.

Exercise 23

1. Try this game.
   Three people should play. Two coins are needed.
   Before you start to play the game, decide who you think will win.
   (a) Copy this table first:

Name	Outcome	Tally	Frequency
	two heads		
	one head and one tail		
	two tails		

   (b) The two coins should be tossed together. Record the result.
   The first person gets a point if two heads are shown.
   The second person gets a point for a head and a tail.
   The third person gets a point for two tails.

(c) Repeat this. Toss the two coins about forty times altogether. The winner is the person who gets the most points.

(d) Show your results on a bar chart.

(e) Write a sentence about your bar chart.

(f) Which *outcome** is most likely to win, two heads, a head and a tail or two tails?

2. If you tossed two coins eighty times, how many times would you expect to get two heads?

* See the glossary.

Let us look at the game in question 1 where two coins were tossed.

The possible outcomes are:

First coin	Second coin
heads	heads
heads	tails
tails	heads
tails	tails

4 possible outcomes

Using H for heads and T for tails,
the first person wins if the outcome is HH
the second person wins if the outcome is HT or TH
the third person wins if the outcome is TT.

Since the second person can win with two outcomes while the others can win with only one outcome, the second person has the best *chance* of winning.

Since the second person can win with 2 out of 4 outcomes
the probability that the second person wins is $\frac{1}{2}$ (2 out of 4 $= \frac{2}{4} = \frac{1}{2}$)
the probability that the first person wins is $\frac{1}{4}$ and
the probability that the third person wins is $\frac{1}{4}$.

Since one of them must win and since $\frac{1}{2} + \frac{1}{4} + \frac{1}{4} = 1$, it can be seen that a probability of 1 means that the *event** is certain to happen.
Also, a probability of 0 means the event will definitely not happen.

* See the glossary.

Exercise 24

1. Make out a table to show the possible outcomes when three coins are tossed. The table has been started for you.

Tossing Three Coins

First coin	Second coin	Third coin
H	H	H
H	H	T
H	T	H

2. How many different outcomes are there?

3. How many of these outcomes show:
   (*a*) 3 heads? (*c*) 1 head?
   (*b*) 2 heads? (*d*) 0 heads?

4. Make out a tally chart and carry out an experiment with three coins. Toss the coins 120 times.

Number of heads	Tally	Frequency
3		
2		
1		
0		

5. Draw a bar chart to show your results.

6. Write what you notice. Compare the theoretical results with the experimental results.

Here is a *tree diagram*. It shows the outcome from tossing two coins.

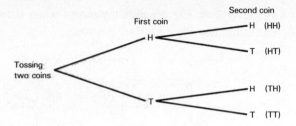

Exercise 25

1. Copy and complete this tree diagram for tossing three coins:

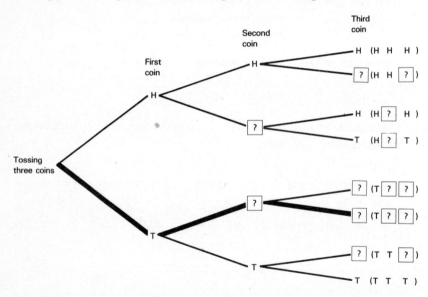

The route marked with a heavy line shows the outcome tail, head, tail.

2. Draw a tree diagram for tossing four coins.

3. List the outcomes as follows:

H H H H
H H H T
H H T H

and so on.

4. Copy this table. Write the results of questions 2 and 3 in your table.

Tossing Four Coins

Outcome	Number of ways
4 heads	1
3 heads	
2 heads	6
1 head	
0 heads	

5. There are 6 different ways of getting 2 heads out of a total of 16 different outcomes.

We say that the *probability** of 2 heads is $\frac{3}{8}$ (since $\frac{6}{16} = \frac{3}{8}$).

(*a*) What is the probability of 3 heads?
(*b*) What is the probability of 3 tails?

* See the glossary.

Exercise 26

In throwing a die, there are 6 possible outcomes (1, 2, 3, 4, 5 or 6).

e.g. The probability of getting a 2 or a 5 is $\frac{1}{3}$
(since these are 2 events out of 6 outcomes and 2 out of $6 = \frac{2}{6} = \frac{1}{3}$).

Find the probability from throwing a die of getting:

1. a 3 or a 4
2. an odd number
3. a prime number
4. 5 or more

5. 3 or less
6. less than 2
7. 6 or less
8. a factor of 77 that is greater than 1

357

Exercise 27

A Find the probability of:

1. Choosing a spade from a pack of 52 cards.

2. Choosing an ace from a pack of 52 cards.

3. Choosing a picture card from a pack of 52 cards.

4. Choosing a black jelly baby from a packet containing 6 black and 9 red jelly babies.

5. Choosing a vowel in a game of Scrabble® if there are 4 vowels and 10 consonants.

6. Choosing a piece of walnut fudge from a bag containing 5 pieces of walnut fudge and 10 pieces of plain fudge.

7. Choosing a blue bead from a bag containing 14 red beads and 6 blue beads.

8. Choosing a 10 p coin from a purse containing £1.75 in 5 p and 10 p coins where 25 p-worth of the coins were 5 p coins.

9. Choosing a £5 note from a wallet containing £100 in £5 and £10 notes if exactly half the money in the wallet is in £10 notes.

10. Choosing a black marble from a bag containing 6 red, 3 green and 15 black marbles.

11. Choosing a blue pen refill from a box containing 15 red, 5 black and 28 blue.

12. One of your 5 raffle tickets winning if 240 tickets were sold.

B What is the probability of:

1. Getting a double 6 when two dice are thrown?

2. Getting two draws out of two games of football if each result (win, draw or loss) is equally likely?

21 Simple Equations

Solve these equations (use any method):

1. $x + 4 = 9$
2. $t + 5 = 14$
3. $p - 7 = 4$
4. $19 - a = 13$

5. $6n = 24$

6. $3k = 27$
7. $f \div 3 = 6$
8. $6m = 54$
9. $c \times 4 = 20$

10. $\dfrac{d}{3} = 5$

11. $6t = 72$
12. $5b = 45$
13. $9e = 63$
14. $3x = 12$

15. $3x + 2 = 14$

Exercise 2

A Find the value of:

1. $7 - 7$
2. $11 - 11$
3. $36 - 36$
4. $97 - 97$

5. $8 + 7 - 7$
6. $12 + 4 - 4$
7. $43 + 18 - 18$
8. $67 + 34 - 34$

9. $10 - 7 + 7$
10. $22 - 6 + 6$
11. $31 - 31 + 13$
12. $58 - 39 + 39$

B Simplify:

1. $x + 7 - 7$
2. $p + 9 - 9$
3. $2y + 5 - 5$
4. $3k + 12 - 12$
5. $8 + t - 8$

6. $11 + 4c - 11$
7. $d - 7 + 7$
8. $f - 14 + 14$
9. $2v - 15 + 15$
10. $5g - 10 + 10$

C Copy and complete:

1. $n + 7 - \boxed{?} = n$
2. $u + 8 - \boxed{?} = u$

3. $h + 11 - \boxed{?} = h$
4. $2e + 6 - \boxed{?} = 2e$

5. $4m + 13 - \boxed{?} = 4m$ **9.** $q - 17 + \boxed{?} = q$

6. $4 + k - \boxed{?} = k$ **10.** $z - 30 + \boxed{?} = z$

7. $16 + a - \boxed{?} = a$ **11.** $3w - 1 + \boxed{?} = 3w$

8. $l - 2 + \boxed{?} = l$ **12.** $5x - 20 + \boxed{?} = 5x$

Exercise 3

You have probably been able to find the answers to the equations given so far without using any particular method. For some equations you need to be better organised.

Here is a balance. A packet of jelly babies and 3 jelly babies on one pan are balanced by 7 jelly babies on the other pan we can write this as a simple equation:

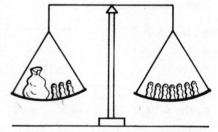

$$n + 3 = 7$$

where n stands for the number of jelly babies in the bag.

1. If we take 3 jelly babies off the left-hand pan, the balance tips as shown. What should we do to balance the scales again? (Do not put the 3 jelly babies back on the pan!)

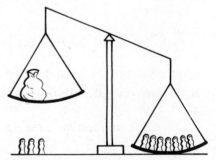

2. How many jelly babies are left on the right-hand pan?

3. How many jelly babies are in the packet?

Exercise 4

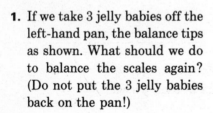

e.g. 1 $x + 5 \quad\quad = 8$

         $x + 5 - 5 = 8 - 5$

         $\therefore \quad x = 3$

e.g. 2 $p - 3 \quad\quad = 7$

         $p - 3 + 3 = 7 + 3$

         $p = 10$

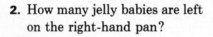

Solve these equations: *Odd numbers*

1. $a + 2 = 7$
2. $d + 5 = 9$
3. $c + 4 = 11$
4. $y + 7 = 13$
5. $m + 9 = 16$
6. $k + 8 = 23$
7. $h + 6 = 17$
8. $f + 12 = 21$
9. $n + 20 = 43$
10. $g + 19 = 56$

11. $e - 3 = 5$
12. $b - 6 = 9$
13. $q - 4 = 5$
14. $u - 8 = 10$
15. $l - 6 = 4$
16. $t - 2 = 8$
17. $z - 9 = 4$
18. $v - 4 = 10$
19. $a - 10 = 25$
20. $w - 14 = 33$

21. $t + 4 = 14$
22. $k - 7 = 8$
23. $m - 8 = 6$
24. $w + 6 = 14$
25. $h - 20 = 12$
26. $l - 11 = 5$
27. $u + 9 = 23$
28. $x - 18 = 34$
29. $c - 12 = 49$
30. $e + 15 = 37$

Exercise 5

This balance shows the equation $2x = 8$ (where there are x jelly babies in each packet).

1. If you halve the number of packets on the left-hand pan, what must you do to the jelly babies on the right-hand pan?

2. How many jelly babies are there in each packet?

The answer to question 2 can be worked out like this:

$$2x = 8$$
$$\therefore \quad x = 4$$

So there are 4 jelly babies in each packet.

Exercise 6

e.g. 1 $5x = 30$ e.g. 2 $\dfrac{x}{2} = 5$

$\therefore \quad x = 6$ $\therefore \quad x = 10$

A Solve these equations: ~~odd nos.~~

1. $2x = 14$ **11.** $\dfrac{c}{2} = 7$ **16.** $8e = 120$

2. $3m = 15$

3. $5a = 40$ **12.** $\dfrac{z}{5} = 3$ **17.** $\dfrac{n}{8} = 7$

4. $4t = 24$

5. $6u = 18$ **13.** $\dfrac{h}{4} = 7$ **18.** $\dfrac{l}{9} = 12$

6. $6k = 30$

7. $9p = 36$ **14.** $\dfrac{b}{7} = 7$ **19.** $6f = 36$

8. $10g = 40$

9. $7w = 49$ **15.** $\dfrac{s}{6} = 12$ **20.** $\dfrac{v}{6} = 14$

10. $3d = 36$

B Solve these equations:

1. $2c = 5$ **11.** $6l = 3$ **21.** $\dfrac{z}{2} = 3\frac{1}{2}$

2. $5n = 17$ **12.** $4t = 6$

3. $3p = 5$ **13.** $10g = 15$ **22.** $\dfrac{w}{3} = 1\frac{2}{3}$

4. $4a = 11$ **14.** $4u = 30$

5. $7d = 16$ **15.** $8h = 20$ **23.** $\dfrac{d}{4} = 2\frac{1}{2}$

6. $9k = 23$ **16.** $8r = 26$

7. $6e = 25$ **17.** $12y = 21$ **24.** $\dfrac{s}{2} = 1\frac{1}{6}$

8. $2q = 11$ **18.** $9m = 21$

9. $3f = 13$ **19.** $14v = 21$ **25.** $\dfrac{a}{5} = 3\frac{7}{10}$

10. $4b = 3$ **20.** $15x = 40$

Exercise 7

Solve these equations:

1. $10 = x + 6$ **6.** $18 = 2k$ **11.** $9 = 2n$

2. $14 = 8 + t$ **7.** $18 = y + 8$ **12.** $6 = 9p$

3. $8 = u - 6$ **8.** $9 = g - 11$ **13.** $9 = 6f$

4. $15 = 5m$ **9.** $30 = 21 + h$ **14.** $22 = 6d$

5. $9 = \dfrac{w}{2}$ **10.** $24 = 8e$ **15.** $5 = v + 1\frac{1}{2}$

Exercise 8

For each problem, form an equation.

Solve each equation.

1. When 6 is added to a number, x, we get 15. Find the number, x.

2. When 9 is added to a number, the answer is 15. Find the number.

3. I think of a number then add 3. If the answer is 12, what is the number?

4. I think of a number then subtract 8. If the answer is 9, what is the number?

5. I think of a number and multiply it by 4. The answer is 32. Find the number.

6. I think of a number and divide it by 4. If the answer is 8, find the number.

7. John has p felt-tipped pens and Jim has 6. If they have 13 pens altogether, how many has John?

8. Jane is 15 years old and Joan is x years old. If their ages total 26 years, how old is Joan?

9. My house number and my friend's house number total 53. If I live at number 29, at what number does my friend live?

10. Richard has x sweets. If 8 times that number is 56, find the value of x.

11. Samantha is one-third the age of her dad who is d years old. If Samantha is 14 years old, how old is her dad?

12. The sum of p and q is 60. If $q = 39$, find p.

Exercise 9

Copy and complete:

e.g. 1 $\quad u + 7 \xrightarrow{\;-7\;} u$

e.g. 2 $\quad 5k \xrightarrow{\;\div 5\;} k$

1. $x + 5 \xrightarrow{\boxed{?}} x$

9. $z - 12 \xrightarrow{\boxed{?}} z$

2. $m - 4 \xrightarrow{\boxed{?}} m$

10. $\quad 7h \xrightarrow{\boxed{?}} h$

3. $p + 8 \xrightarrow{\boxed{?}} p$

11. $\quad \dfrac{w}{7} \xrightarrow{\boxed{?}} w$

4. $\quad 3d \xrightarrow{\boxed{?}} d$

12. $a + 19 \xrightarrow{\boxed{?}} a$

5. $\quad \dfrac{e}{6} \xrightarrow{\boxed{?}} e$

13. $y \div 13 \xrightarrow{\boxed{?}} y$

6. $f \div 9 \xrightarrow{\boxed{?}} f$

14. $\quad 9t \xrightarrow{\boxed{?}} t$

7. $7 + q \xrightarrow{\boxed{?}} q$

15. $19 + g \xrightarrow{\boxed{?}} g$

8. $c \times 2 \xrightarrow{\boxed{?}} c$

Exercise 10

Copy and complete:

1. $2m + 5 \xrightarrow{\boxed{?}} 2m \xrightarrow{\boxed{?}} m$

2. $3b - 7 \xrightarrow{\boxed{?}} 3b \xrightarrow{\boxed{?}} b$

3. $4k + 9 \xrightarrow{\boxed{?}} 4k \xrightarrow{\boxed{?}} k$

4. $\dfrac{s}{2} + 3 \xrightarrow{\boxed{?}} \dfrac{s}{2} \xrightarrow{\boxed{?}} s$

5. $\dfrac{v}{5} - 6 \xrightarrow{\boxed{?}} \dfrac{v}{5} \xrightarrow{\boxed{?}} v$

6. $6y + 2 \xrightarrow{\boxed{?}} 6y \xrightarrow{\boxed{?}} y$

7. $\dfrac{l}{4} + 6 \xrightarrow{\boxed{?}} \dfrac{l}{4} \xrightarrow{\boxed{?}} l$

8. $9 + 4u \xrightarrow{\boxed{?}} 4u \xrightarrow{\boxed{?}} u$

9. $7 + \dfrac{x}{3} \xrightarrow{\boxed{?}} \dfrac{x}{3} \xrightarrow{\boxed{?}} x$

10. $5n - 9 \xrightarrow{\boxed{?}} 5n \xrightarrow{\boxed{?}} n$

Exercise 11

Solve these equations:

1. (a) $2x = 12$
  (b) $2x + 3 = 15$

2. (a) $2x = 16$
  (b) $2x + 6 = 22$

3. (a) $5c = 25$
  (b) $5c + 8 = 33$

4. (a) $7t = 28$
  (b) $7t - 3 = 25$

5. (a) $8f = 48$
  (b) $8f - 10 = 38$

6. (a) $3y = 30$
  (b) $3y - 7 = 23$

7. (a) $2m = 9$
  (b) $2m + 8 = 17$

8. (a) $3v = 8$
  (b) $3v - 2 = 6$

9. $2d - 5 = 15$

10. $5c + 6 = 41$

11. $4f - 7 = 29$

12. $10u + 8 = 68$

13. $19 = 2x + 9$

14. $6p + 7 = 19$

15. $16 = 3a + 7$

16. $9z - 11 = 34$

17. $10e - 8 = 22$ **21.** $4b - 1 = 13$
18. $4h + 9 = 9$ **22.** $3w + 4 = 15$
19. $12 = 7k - 9$ **23.** $5g + 3 = 16$
20. $2l + 6 = 9$ **24.** $7n - 11 = 13$

Exercise 12   R

Simplify:

1. $4x - 2 + x + 3$ **6.** $4a - 3 - 3a + 3$
2. $3p - p + 4 - 7$ **7.** $8g + 7 - 5 - 6g$
3. $6m - 3 + 2m - 4$ **8.** $9 - 3d - 6 + 8d$
4. $7t + 2 - 3t - 9$ **9.** $9l + 7 + 3l + 5 - l$
5. $5k + 6 + 8 - 4k$ **10.** $14 - 2y - 3y - 9 + 6y$

Exercise 13   R

odds

Solve these equations. Exercise 12 may help.

1. $4x - 2 + x + 3 = 16$ **6.** $4a - 3 - 3a + 3 = 12$
2. $3p - p + 4 - 7 = 9$ **7.** $8g + 7 - 5 - 6g = 8$
3. $6m - 3 + 2m - 4 = 9$ **8.** $9 - 3d - 6 + 8d = 23$
4. $7t + 2 - 3t - 9 = 13$ **9.** $9l + 7 + 3l + 5 - l = 34$
5. $5k + 6 + 8 - 4k = 15$ **10.** $14 - 2y - 3y - 9 + 6y = 14$

Exercise 14

Solve these equations:

1. $2y - 3 + y - 7 = 11$ **11.** $5k + 2 + 4k + 13 = 69$
2. $5a + 2 - 3a - 7 = 19$ **12.** $3t + 18 + 3t + 10 = 40$
3. $h - 7 + 3h + 7 = 32$ **13.** $l + 21 - 9 + 3l = 20$
4. $4u - 1 + 3u + 9 = 71$ **14.** $9v - 4 - 2v - 10 = 0$
5. $e + 8 + 10 + 4e = 63$ **15.** $8s + 5 + s = 14$
6. $8m - 7 - 2m - 4 = 31$ **16.** $3c - 11 - c - 17 = 18$
7. $3f + 6 - f - 3 = 31$ **17.** $4q - 8 - 1 = 6$
8. $6w - 5 - 8 + 2w = 19$ **18.** $2n - 1 + n - 9 = 0$
9. $4x + 6 - x - 15 = 15$ **19.** $5z + 2 - 3z - 2 = 17$
10. $p + 12 + 4p - 13 = 49$ **20.** $3d - 4 + 2d - 8 = 11$

Exercise 15 ✓

Solve these equations:

1. $4g + 2 = 3g + 8$
2. $5b - 2 = 3b + 4$
3. $4w - 15 = w + 18$
4. $3a - 12 = 16 + a$
5. $7z + 8 = 56 + 3z$
6. $12k + 30 = 2k + 100$
7. $8c - 25 = 3c + 40$
8. $9f - 14 = 4f + 56$

9. $6d - 34 = 18 + 2d$
10. $8n + 6 = 6n + 60$
11. $2h + 19 = 5h - 5$
12. $80 + 4v = 9v - 20$
13. $m + 40 = 8m + 5$
14. $3x - 50 = x - 4$
15. $7t - 65 = 4t - 23$
16. $11p + 18 = 7p + 82$

Exercise 16   R

Work these out:

1. $7 - 9$
2. $^-4 + 6$
3. $^-8 + 3$
4. $^-6 + {}^-2$
5. $^-4 - 7$
6. $9 - {}^-4$
7. $2 - {}^-6$
8. $^-3 - {}^-8$

9. $^-10 - {}^-4$
10. $5 - {}^-12$
11. $4 \times {}^-3$
12. $^-8 \times {}^-2$
13. $^-9 \times {}^-6$
14. $^-3 \times {}^+7$
15. $^-8 \div 2$
16. $15 \div {}^-3$

17. $\dfrac{^-12}{4}$
18. $\dfrac{^-18}{^-6}$
19. $\dfrac{^-20}{2}$
20. $\dfrac{^-18}{3}$

Exercise 17

A Solve these equations:

1. $x - 3 = {}^-2$
2. $a - 5 = {}^-8$
3. $p + 4 = 2$
4. $d + 9 = 5$
5. $y - 8 = {}^-3$
6. $k + 7 = {}^-3$
7. $s - 10 = {}^-12$
8. $n + 12 = 8$

9. $3h = {}^-9$
10. $2m = {}^-12$
11. $5x = {}^-20$
12. $4q = {}^-28$
13. $\dfrac{b}{4} = {}^-6$
14. $\dfrac{z}{^-3} = {}^-5$

15. $t + 6 = 0$
16. $6u = 0$
17. $^-2c = 8$
18. $^-7l = {}^-42$
19. $\dfrac{e}{6} = {}^-3$
20. $\dfrac{v}{^-5} = {}^-8$

367

B Solve these equations:

1. $2x + 9 = 5$
2. $2n - 3 = {}^-13$
3. $3h - 7 = {}^-4$
4. $4d + 11 = 3$
5. $3k + 2 = {}^-13$

6. $5v + 6 = {}^-9$
7. $4e + 4 = 0$
8. $3a - 2 = {}^-23$
9. $4f + 12 = {}^-20$
10. $2y - 15 = {}^-5$

11. $6z + 50 = 8$
12. $8t + 12 = {}^-12$
13. $5m - 9 = {}^-9$
14. $2u - 2 = {}^-20$
15. $7p + 15 = 1$

Exercise 18

For each problem, form an equation.
Solve each equation.

1. 30 pupils are in a class. $2x$ are present and 4 are absent. Find x.

2. When 5 is added to 4 times a number the result is 21. Find the number.

3. Two boys share 29 marbles. If Stephen gets $3m$ marbles and Valji 11 marbles:
   (a) find the value of m,
   (b) how many marbles does Stephen get?

4. Angela is $5d$ years old and Gina is 14 years old. Their ages total 34 years.
   (a) Find d.   (b) Find Angela's age.

5. Two classes share 63 books. The first class gets $2g$ books while the second class gets 29.
   (a) Find g.   (b) How many books does the first class get?

6. $6x + y = 50$. If $y = 8$, find x.

7. $7m + n = 70$. If $n = 14$, find m.

8. $8g + 4h = 100$. If $h = 7$, find g.

9. Helen has $3s$ sweets and Brian has 12. If they have 45 sweets altogether, find:
   (a) the value of s,   (b) the number of sweets Helen has.

10. There are 352 pages in a book. I have read $8p$ of them. I still have 216 pages to read.
   (a) Find p.   (b) How many pages have I read?

22 Length, Volume, Capacity and Mass

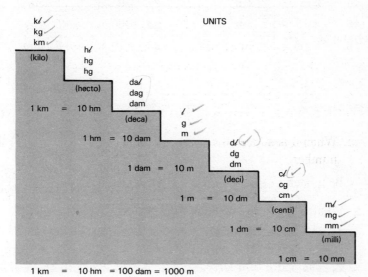

UNITS

kℓ
kg
km
(kilo)

hℓ
hg
hg
(hecto)

daℓ
dag
dam
(deca)

ℓ
g
m

dℓ
dg
dm
(deci)

cℓ
cg
cm
(centi)

mℓ
mg
mm
(milli)

1 km = 10 hm

1 hm = 10 dam

1 dam = 10 m

1 m = 10 dm

1 dm = 10 cm

1 cm = 10 mm

1 km = 10 hm = 100 dam = 1000 m

1 m = 10 dm = 100 cm = 1000 mm

Length

$$10 \text{ mm} = 1 \text{ cm}$$
$$1000 \text{ mm} = 1 \text{ m}$$
$$100 \text{ cm} = 1 \text{ m}$$
$$1000 \text{ m} = 1 \text{ km}$$

Exercise 1   R

Copy and complete:

1. 6 cm = ? mm

2. 4 cm = ? mm

3. 70 mm = ? cm

4. 50 mm = ? cm

5. 2.4 cm = ? mm

6. 5.7 cm = ? mm

7. 36 mm = ? cm

8. 92 mm = ? cm

9.	2 m = [?] mm		**17.**	3.7 km = [?] m	
10.	3 m = [?] cm		**18.**	5000 mm = [?] m	
11.	8 m = [?] mm		**19.**	400 cm = [?] m	
12.	7.4 m = [?] mm		**20.**	2000 m = [?] km	
13.	1.68 m = [?] mm		**21.**	4.62 km = [?] m	
14.	9 m = [?] cm		**22.**	2.05 m = [?] cm	
15.	4.3 m = [?] cm		**23.**	8160 m = [?] km	
16.	6 km = [?] m		**24.**	0.19 m = [?] mm	

Exercise 2

1. What is most likely to be 20 mm thick?
  A. a coin   C. a brick
  B. a book   D. a pencil

2. What is likely to be about 10 m?
  A. The height of a tree.
  B. The length of a cricket bat.
  C. The width of a lorry.
  D. The diameter of a tennis ball.

3. The height of a chair seat is about:
  A. 1 m   B. 100 mm   C. 5 cm   D. 500 mm

4. The length of a 53-seater coach is about:
  A. 12 m   B. 18 m   C. 24 m   D. 30 m

5. The height of a small tin is about:
  A. 6 mm   B. 60 mm   C. 600 mm   D. 6 m

6. The diameter of a jam jar is about:
  A. 70 mm   B. 120 mm   C. 200 mm   D. 240 mm

7. The height of a house is about:
  A. 21 m   B. 15 m   C. 11 m   D. 7 m

8. The height of a table is about:
  A. 75 mm   B. 750 mm   C. 1.5 m   D. 20 cm

9. The length of a brick is about:

   A. 20 mm   B. 30 mm   C. 200 mm   D. 300 mm

10. The width of a car is about:

    A. 1.6 m   B. 2.8 m   C. 3.5 m   D. 4 m

Exercise 3

For each question, write L if AB is longer than CD, S if AB is shorter than CD and E if AB and CD are of equal length. DO NOT measure.

1.

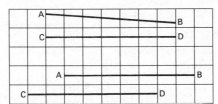

2.

3.

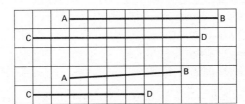

4.

Exercise 4

1. Draw a straight line AB, 82 mm long. Mark a point C on the line such that AC = 56 mm. How long is BC?

2. Draw a straight line PQ, 67 mm in length. Using a pair of compasses, bisect PQ. Draw the perpendicular bisector. Label it XY where X lies on PQ and where XY = 38 mm. How long is PY?

3. Draw a straight line XY, 67 mm long. Mark a point L on XY where XL = 25 mm. Draw a line LM such that ∠MLY = 40° and where LM = 54 mm. How long is MY?

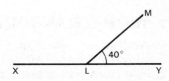

371

4. Draw a straight line QR, 75 mm long. Mark a point S on the line where QS = 52 mm. Draw a straight line TU at any angle to intersect QR at S. TS = 40 mm and TU = 65 mm. Measure QT.

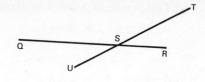

5. Construct △ABC where AB = 70 mm, BC = 88 mm and ∠ABC = 34°. Construct a straight line AX, parallel to CB such that AX = 51 mm. (Use a set square and ruler.) How long is BX?

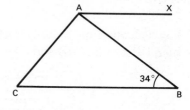

6. Where possible, construct isosceles triangles with the following lengths of sides:
 (*a*) 6 cm, 6 cm, 3 cm
 (*b*) 3 cm, 3 cm, 6 cm
 (*c*) 50 mm, 50 mm, 35 mm
 (*d*) 35 mm, 35 mm, 50 mm

The measurements made so far in this chapter have been in the *metric system*. The units used are called *metric units*. Before metrication (the change to the metric system) most measurements in Britain were in *imperial units*.

Using imperial units of length:

$$12 \text{ in} = 1 \text{ ft}$$
$$3 \text{ ft} = 1 \text{ yd}$$
$$1760 \text{ yd} = 1 \text{ mile}$$

Inches are marked along the edge of this page.

Exercise 5

1. How many inches are there in 5 ft?
2. How many inches are there in 1 yd?
3. How many feet are there in 7 yd?

4. Change 9 yd to feet.
5. Change 4 ft to inches.
6. Change 3 yd to inches.
7. Change 8 yd to inches.
8. How many feet are there in 22 yd?
9. How many feet are there in 220 yd?
10. How many feet are there in 1 mile?

Exercise 6

Measure the lengths of six items (such as a pencil or a pen) using imperial units. If you do not have a suitable ruler or tape measure, use the inches marked along the edge of p. 372.

Exercise 7

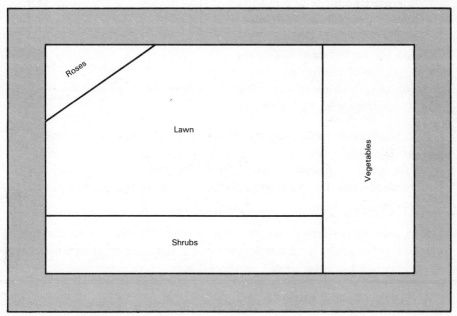

Scale: 1 cm to 2 m

The drawing above is a plan of a garden. A path surrounds the garden. By careful measuring, find:

1. the perimeter of the vegetable plot,

2. the perimeter of the outer edge of the path,

3. the perimeter of the inner edge of the path,

4. the perimeter of the lawn,

5. the length of the edge of the lawn that is next to the roses,

6. the difference between the length and the breadth of the shrubbery,

7. the length of string needed to stretch across a diagonal of the vegetable plot.

Exercise 8

1. The sketch shows a picture which has been framed. If the picture framing is 18 mm wide and if the picture itself measures 475 mm by 350 mm, find:

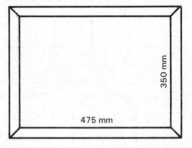

  (a) the perimeter of the inside edge of the frame,
  (b) the perimeter of the outside edge of the frame.

2. A rectangular room measures 18 ft by 12 ft. What is the perimeter of the room?
If a carpet is placed in the room so that there is a border of uncovered floor 1 ft wide around it, calculate the perimeter of the carpet.

3. A rectangular room measures 8 m by 5 m. Another room is 1 m shorter in length than this first room, but it has the same perimeter. Calculate the breadth of this second room.

4. A strip of paper measures 200 cm by 3 cm.

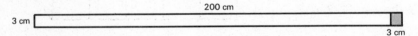

  (a) What is the perimeter of the strip of paper?
  (b) A 3 cm square piece of paper is cut off the end of this 200 cm strip. What is the perimeter of this 3 cm square?

374

(c) What is the perimeter of the strip of paper that is left after the 3 cm square has been cut off?

(d) What is the perimeter of the strip of paper that is left after five 3 cm squares have been cut off the original strip?

Volume of a Cuboid

Exercise 9

Copy and complete the sentences:

1.

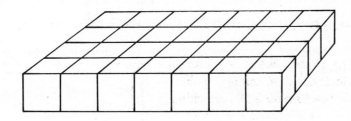

(a) There are ? small cubes in the diagram above.

(b) If there were 2 layers there would be ? small cubes.

(c) If there were 5 layers there would be ? small cubes.

(d) If each small cube has a volume of 1 cm³, the volume of the cuboid in the diagram above is ? cm³.

2. (a) There are ? small cubes in each layer of the cuboid.

(b) There are ? layers.

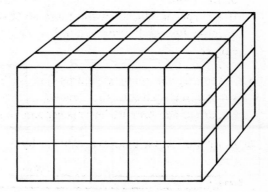

(c) There are ? small cubes in the cuboid.

(d) If each small cube has a volume of 1 cm³, the volume of the cuboid is ? cm³.

Exercise 10

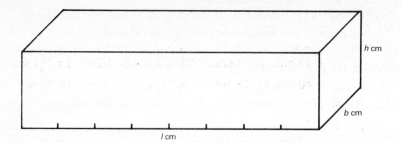

If a cuboid was l cm long, b cm wide and h cm high, then:

1. The number of 1 cm cubes in the length = $\boxed{?}$.

2. The number of 1 cm cubes in the bottom layer of the cuboid = $l \times \boxed{?}$.

3. The total number of 1 cm cubes = $l \times \boxed{?} \times \boxed{?}$.

4. The volume of the cuboid, $V = l \times \boxed{?} \times \boxed{?}$.

Exercise 11

Calculate the volume of the cuboid given in each question. (Use m³, cm³ or mm³ depending on the units given in the question.)

1.

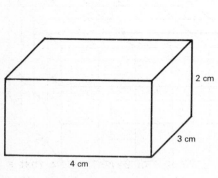

2.

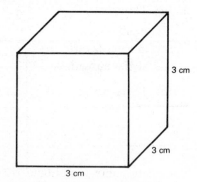

3. 4 cm by 4 cm by 2 cm
4. 4 cm by 3 cm by 3 cm
5. 5 cm by 3 cm by 2 cm
6. 6 cm by 2 cm by 3 cm

7. 8 m by 3 m by 2 m
8. 7 m by 3 m by 2 m
9. 9 m by 2 m by 2 m
10. 10 m by 4 m by 1 m

11. 7 m by 6 m by 5 m	18. 13 cm by 8 cm by 6 cm
12. 5 m by 5 m by 5 m	19. 1.6 m by 1.5 m by 2 m
13. 9 cm by 1 cm by 3 cm	20. 8.7 m by 6 m by 2.5 m
14. 8 cm by 7 cm by 5 cm	21. 7.4 m by 4.6 m by 3 m
15. 9 m by 4 m by 7 m	22. 4.2 cm by 3.1 cm by 1.8 cm
16. 30 mm by 20 mm by 10 mm	23. 6 cm by 5 cm by $2\frac{1}{2}$ cm
17. 45 mm by 40 mm by 15 mm	24. 8 m by $3\frac{1}{2}$ m by $1\frac{1}{2}$ m

Exercise 12

1.

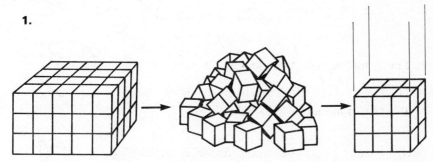

The cubes in the cuboid above have been re-arranged to form a new cuboid having six cubes as a base. How many cubes high is the new cuboid?

2. A cuboid measuring 6 cm by 4 cm by 3 cm is re-arranged to form a new cuboid of length 4 cm and width 2 cm. What is the height of the new cuboid?

Exercise 13

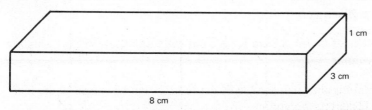

1 cm

3 cm

8 cm

The sketch shows a cuboid with a volume of 24 cm³. (Note that a cuboid with length 3 cm, width 1 cm and height 8 cm is the same as that in the sketch but in a different position.)

Sketch five more cuboids (all different) each having a volume of 24 cm³.

The internal measurements of the given box are: 5 cm long, 3 cm wide and 2 cm high.

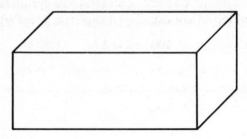

1. How many 1 cm cubes would fit inside the box?

2. How many $\frac{1}{2}$ cm cubes would fit inside the box?

Exercise 15

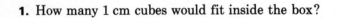

1. Find the volume of:
   (*a*) a 2 cm cube
   (*b*) a 3 cm cube
   (*c*) a 6 cm cube
   (*d*) a 10 cm cube
   (*e*) a 15 cm cube
   (*f*) a 20 cm cube

2. A block of metal is 8 cm long, 5 cm wide and 2 cm thick. Calculate its volume.

3. A 'rectangular' fish tank is 60 cm long, 30 cm wide and 40 cm high.
   (*a*) Calculate its volume.
   (*b*) If it is only three-quarters full of water, find the number of cubic centimetres of water in the tank.

4. A kitchen measures 10 ft by 9 ft by 8 ft. Calculate the number of cubic feet of air in the room.

Capacity

The *capacity* of a container is the amount of liquid it will hold.

Small amounts of liquid are usually measured in millilitres (mℓ) while large amounts of liquid are usually measured in litres (ℓ).

$$1000 \text{ m}\ell = 1 \ell$$

In the imperial system, gallons (gal) are used for large amounts of liquid and pints (pt) for small amounts:

$$8 \text{ pt} = 1 \text{ gal}$$

Exercise 16

A Change to millilitres:

1. 2 ℓ	**7.** 18 ℓ	**13.** 64 ℓ	**19.** 2.73 ℓ
2. 4 ℓ	**8.** 20 ℓ	**14.** 125 ℓ	**20.** 0.9 ℓ
3. 7 ℓ	**9.** 25 ℓ	**15.** 100 ℓ	**21.** 0.5 ℓ
4. 9 ℓ	**10.** 42 ℓ	**16.** 5.8 ℓ	**22.** 0.46 ℓ
5. 11 ℓ	**11.** 76 ℓ	**17.** 8.6 ℓ	**23.** 0.802 ℓ
6. 15 ℓ	**12.** 99 ℓ	**18.** 12.4 ℓ	**24.** 15.09 ℓ

B Change to litres:

1. 3000 mℓ	**9.** 52 000 mℓ	**17.** 4305 mℓ
2. 5000 mℓ	**10.** 70 000 mℓ	**18.** 5102 mℓ
3. 6000 mℓ	**11.** 118 000 mℓ	**19.** 508 mℓ
4. 8000 mℓ	**12.** 200 000 mℓ	**20.** 760 mℓ
5. 10 000 mℓ	**13.** 4700 mℓ	**21.** 800 mℓ
6. 12 000 mℓ	**14.** 7200 mℓ	**22.** 400 mℓ
7. 21 000 mℓ	**15.** 1460 mℓ	**23.** 100 mℓ
8. 14 000 mℓ	**16.** 2810 mℓ	**24.** 58 mℓ

C Change to pints:

1. 2 gal	**4.** 9 gal	**7.** 17 gal	**10.** 30 gal
2. 4 gal	**5.** 12 gal	**8.** 21 gal	**11.** 42 gal
3. 7 gal	**6.** 15 gal	**9.** 25 gal	**12.** 50 gal

D Change to gallons:

1. 24 pt **4.** 64 pt **7.** 104 pt **10.** 216 pt
2. 40 pt **5.** 80 pt **8.** 128 pt **11.** 280 pt
3. 48 pt **6.** 88 pt **9.** 160 pt **12.** 320 pt

Exercise 17

Choose the answer that is correct or almost correct:

1. A milk bottle holds:
   A. 4 l B. 20 l C. 600 ml D. 20 ml

2. A teaspoonful of medicine is:
   A. 5 ml B. 20 ml C. 100 ml D. 1 l

3. A bucket holds:
   A. 1000 ml B. 9 l C. 24 l D. 600 ml

4. A kettle holds:
   A. 1.7 l B. 3 l C. 6.6 l D. 4000 ml

5. A cup holds:
   A. 200 ml B. 50 ml C. 400 ml D. 100 ml

6. A bath holds:
   A. 85 l B. 12 l C. 250 l D. 110 l

7. A public swimming pool holds:
   A. 250 l B. 2500 l C. 25 000 l D. 250 000 l

8. A can of lemonade is:
   A. 75 ml B. 330 ml C. 675 ml D. 3.75 l

9. A car's petrol tank holds:
   A. 60 l B. 15 l C. 5 l D. 10 000 ml

10. A wash-basin holds:
   A. 950 ml B. 3 l C. 8 l D. 20 l

Exercise 18

Choose the answer that is correct or almost correct:

1. A kettle holds:
   A. 1 gal   B. 3 pt   C. 1 pt   D. $\frac{1}{2}$ pt

2. A tall, thin glass holds:
   A. 1 gal   B. 3 pt   C. 1 pt   D. $\frac{1}{2}$ pt

3. A bath holds:
   A. 100 pt   B. 15 gal   C. 35 gal   D. 55 gal

4. A watering can holds:
   A. 2 pt   B. 5 pt   C. 2 gal   D. 5 gal

5. A milkpan holds:
   A. 8 pt   B. 4 pt   C. 2 pt   D. $\frac{1}{2}$ pt

Exercise 19

Copy this list of containers. Write them one under the other. Alongside each container, write how many millilitres or litres it holds.

bucket, watering can, kettle, saucepan, tea-pot, lemonade bottle, milk bottle, medicine bottle, shampoo bottle, glass tumbler, mug, cup, wineglass, wash-basin, washing-up bowl, perfume bottle, nail polish bottle, teaspoon, tablespoon, wine bottle, can of drink

Exercise 20

1. I have four 500 ml cartons of milk. How many litres is that?

2. A tall glass holds 320 ml.
   (a) How many glasses can be filled from 1 l of milk?
   (b) How many millilitres would be left?

3. A mug holds 250 ml.
   (a) How many millilitres will two mugs hold?
   (b) How many mugs can be filled from 1 l of water?
   (c) How many litres will ten mugs hold?

4. A tea-pot holds 1 *l* and a cup holds 200 m*l*.
   (*a*) How many cups can be filled from one tea-pot?
   (*b*) I need to pour tea for eight people using 200 m*l* cups. How many
       pots of tea must I make?

5. A wine-glass holds 150 m*l*. How many glasses can be filled from
   (*a*) a 1 *l* bottle of wine?
   (*b*) a 70 c*l* (700 m*l*) bottle of wine?
   (*c*) two 700 m*l* bottles of wine?
   (*d*) 2 *l* of wine?

6. Chris must take two 5 m*l* spoonfuls of medicine four times a day.
   Each bottle holds 100 m*l*. How many days will two bottles last?

7. A kettle holds 1.5 *l*, a tea-pot 1 *l*, a tall glass 300 m*l*, a mug 250 m*l*,
   a cup 200 m*l* and a wine-glass 150 m*l*. Make a list showing how many
   of each can be filled from 3 *l*. The list has been started for you. Copy
   and complete it.

            2   kettles
            3   tea-pots

Mass

WEIGHING IN ANCIENT EGYPT ABOUT 2000 B.C.

The main metric unit of *mass** (often wrongly called weight) is the *kilogram* (kg). Other units of mass are the gram (g), milligram (mg) and metric tonne (t).

$$1\,t\ =\ 1000\ kg$$
$$1\,kg\ =\ 1000\ g$$
$$1\,g\ =\ 1000\ mg$$

Note that 1 ℓ of water has a volume of 1000 cm³ and has a mass of about 1 kg.

* See the glossary.

Exercise 21

Copy these sentences but replace the boxes with t, kg, g or mg to make each sentence correct:

1. A jar of jam has a mass of 454 ⬚ .

2. A teabag has a mass of 3 ⬚ .

3. A packet of flour has a mass of 1.5 ⬚ .

4. A drawing pin has a mass of 0.5 ⬚ .

5. A loaf of bread has a mass of 800 ⬚ .

6. A car has a mass of 1 ⬚ .

7. A lorry has a mass of 10 ⬚ .

8. A bar of chocolate has a mass of 100 ⬚ .

Exercise 22

A Collect about ten different objects. Find the mass of each one.
List the objects. Alongside each one, write its mass.

B Find the mass of about twenty common objects such as a jar of jam, a tin of fruit, a packet of tea, a suitcase, a bag of potatoes, and so on. The mass of a jar of jam is usually printed on the label. (This does not normally include the mass of the jar. You can weigh it if you wish to include the mass of the jar.)

Exercise 23

A Change to grams:

1. 4 kg	**6.** 24 kg	**11.** 4.5 kg	**16.** 5.62 kg
2. 7 kg	**7.** 50 kg	**12.** 7.2 kg	**17.** 0.04 kg
3. 2 kg	**8.** 1 kg	**13.** 2.8 kg	**18.** 0.007 kg
4. 12 kg	**9.** 0.5 kg	**14.** 6.3 kg	**19.** 12.5 kg
5. 16 kg	**10.** 1.5 kg	**15.** 1.47 kg	**20.** 0.625 kg

B Change to kilograms:

1. 5000 g	**6.** 45 000 g	**11.** 6940 g	**16.** 3164 g
2. 8000 g	**7.** 3500 g	**12.** 6000 g	**17.** 2008 g
3. 9000 g	**8.** 7800 g	**13.** 900 g	**18.** 409 g
4. 13 000 g	**9.** 1700 g	**14.** 40 g	**19.** 273 g
5. 21 000 g	**10.** 700 g	**15.** 2985 g	**20.** 84 g

Exercise 24

Copy and complete:

1. 6 kg = ? g
2. 9 kg = ? g
3. 3000 g = ? kg
4. 7000 g = ? kg
5. 2500 g = ? kg
6. 3500 g = ? kg
7. 4700 g = ? kg
8. 9200 g = ? kg
9. 8.6 kg = ? g
10. 2.4 kg = ? g
11. 9.1 kg = ? g
12. 500 g = ? kg
13. 5000 mg = ? g
14. 8000 mg = ? g
15. 7 g = ? mg

16. 4 g = ? mg
17. 2000 kg = ? t
18. 9000 kg = ? t
19. 3 t = ? kg
20. 7 t = ? kg
21. 1500 mg = ? g
22. 2.6 g = ? mg
23. 8.2 t = ? kg
24. 4900 kg = ? t
25. 7.5 kg = ? g
26. 0.2 kg = ? g
27. 0.25 kg = ? g
28. 0.613 kg = ? g
29. 600 g = ? kg
30. 290 g = ? kg

31. $9134 \text{ g} = \boxed{?} \text{ kg}$ **36.** $8.47 \text{ g} = \boxed{?} \text{ mg}$

32. $9134 \text{ mg} = \boxed{?} \text{ g}$ **37.** $0.16 \text{ g} = \boxed{?} \text{ mg}$

33. $9134 \text{ kg} = \boxed{?} \text{ t}$ **38.** $0.9 \text{ t} = \boxed{?} \text{ kg}$

34. $8.47 \text{ t} = \boxed{?} \text{ kg}$ **39.** $42 \text{ kg} = \boxed{?} \text{ t}$

35. $8.47 \text{ kg} = \boxed{?} \text{ g}$ **40.** $0.025 \text{ g} = \boxed{?} \text{ mg}$

Exercise 25

Choose the best answer:

1. An apple has a mass of about
   A. 130 mg   B. 130 g   C. 500 mg   D. 500 g

2. A marble has a mass of about
   A. 75 mg   B. 200 mg   C. 850 mg   D. 6 g

3. A woman has a mass of about
   A. 25 kg   B. 150 kg   C. 55 kg   D. 940 g

4. A textbook has a mass of about
   A. 540 mg   B. 5.4 g   C. 54 g   D. 540 g

5. A 10 p piece has a mass of about
   A. 113 mg   B. 113 g   C. 1.13 g   D. 11.3 g

6. A new-born baby has a mass of about
   A. 1 kg   B. 3 kg   C. 9 kg   D. 15 kg

7. A 53-seater coach has a mass of about
   A. 7 t   B. 4 t   C. 1 t   D. 870 kg

8. A television set has a mass of about
   A. 25 kg   B. 75 kg   C. 100 kg   D. 140 kg

9. An iron has a mass of about
   A. 1.5 kg   B. 8 kg   C. 280 g   D. 890 mg

10. A cricket ball has a mass of about
   A. 80 g   B. 420 g   C. 160 g   D. 420 mg

The main units of mass in the imperial system are ounces (oz), pounds (lb), stones (st), hundredweights (cwt) and tons.

$$16 \text{ oz} = 1 \text{ lb}$$
$$14 \text{ lb} = 1 \text{ st}$$
$$112 \text{ lb} = 1 \text{ cwt}$$
$$20 \text{ cwt} = 1 \text{ ton}$$

Exercise 26

1. How many pounds are there in 1 ton?

2. How many stones are there in 1 cwt?

3. How many ounces are there in:
   (*a*) 2 lb?   (*b*) 5 lb?   (*c*) $\frac{1}{2}$ lb?   (*d*) $\frac{1}{4}$ lb?

4. How many pounds are there in:
   (*a*) 2 st?   (*b*) 8 st?   (*c*) 12 st?   (*d*) 20 st?

5. How many hundredweights are there in:
   (*a*) 3 tons?   (*b*) 7 tons?   (*c*) 10 tons?   (*d*) 14 tons?

6. Change 6 st 9 lb to pounds.

Exercise 27

If 1 kg = 2.2 lb:

1. Change 10 kg to pounds
2. Change 5 kg to pounds
3. Change 44 lb to kilograms
4. Change 33 lb to kilograms
5. Change 22 kg to pounds

Exercise 28

1. A golf ball has a mass of 50 g. Find the total mass of 6 golf balls.

2. A packet of sweets has a mass of 125 g.
   (*a*) Find the total mass of 3 packets.
   (*b*) How many packets have a total mass of 1 kg?

3. A jar of coffee has a mass of 670 g including the jar. The label states that the coffee has a mass of 200 g.
   (a) What is the mass of the jar?
   (b) Find the mass, in kilograms, of 4 jars of coffee.

4. A textbook has a mass of 650 g. If you carry 30 of the textbooks, what mass, in kilograms, are you carrying?

5. Find the total mass, in kilograms, of a box of 100 bars of soap if each bar of soap has a mass of 142 g and if the box has a mass of 380 g.

6. Which is heavier and by how many grams, £1's worth of 5 p pieces or 34 p worth of 2 p pieces, if a 5 p piece has a mass of 5.6552 g and a 2 p piece has a mass of 7.128 g?

Miscellaneous Units of Measure

Exercise 29

Copy these, but replace each box with $<$, $>$ or $=$ to make each statement correct:

1. kilometre $\boxed{?}$ mile   4. tonne $\boxed{?}$ ton
2. metre $\boxed{?}$ yard   5. kilogram $\boxed{?}$ pound
3. litre $\boxed{?}$ pint   6. gram $\boxed{?}$ ounce

Exercise 30

1. Which is heavier, 10 kg or 100 000 g?

2. Which is longer, 200 m or 2000 cm?

3. A metal carpet bar is 1 m long. What length is wasted if it is used for a doorway that is 842 mm wide?

4. If Andrew drinks 500 mℓ of milk each day, how many litres would he have drunk during the month of June?

387

5. A kettle holds 1.7 l of water. If it is filled three times, how many litres is that?

6. I need to draw a line 140 mm long. After drawing 6 cm of the line, how many millimetres are left?

7. If £10's worth of 50 p pieces have a total mass of 265 g, find the mass of one 50 p piece.

8. A water container holds 5 l of water.
 (a) How many 300 ml bottles can be filled from this?
 (b) How many mililitres would be left over?

9. A cyclist has completed 7 laps of a cycle track. If each lap is 750 m, how many more metres must he cycle to have cycled exactly 8 km?

10. If I fill six 250 ml glasses, three 300 ml glasses and eight 200 ml glasses with lemonade, how many litres of lemonade do I use?

11. Several people received equal shares of 10.5 l of orange juice. They each received 300 ml. How many people shared the orange juice?

12. A lift will carry a total mass of up to 1 t. Find the maximum number of people each weighing 75 kg that the lift will carry at the same time.

13. A piece of wood is 2 m long. Six equal lengths are cut off leaving 80 mm waste. How long are the lengths that have been cut off?

14. A box holds 40 identical containers full of talcum powder, the total mass being 7 kg. If the box itself has a mass of 600 g and if each container holds 100 mg of talcum powder, calculate the mass of one container.

15. 1 cm^3 of brass has a mass of 8.4 g (we say that its *density* is 8.4 g per cubic centimetre). Calculate the mass of a brass article having a volume of 12 cm^3.

16. How many 250 cm^3 mugs can be filled from 8 l of water?

Exercise 31

e.g. 480 pages of a certain type of paper make a pile 50 mm thick.
 (*a*) Find the thickness of 36 sheets.
 (*b*) How many pages have a total thickness of 45 mm?

Look carefully at this method:

Number of pages	Thickness	Notes
480	50 mm	
240	25 mm	240 is half of 480
48	5 mm	48 is $\frac{1}{10}$ of 480
24	2.5 mm	24 is $\frac{1}{2}$ of 48
12	1.25 mm	12 is $\frac{1}{2}$ of 24
36	3.75 mm	36 = 24 + 12

(*a*) 36 sheets are 3.75 mm thick.

(*b*) 50 mm − 5 mm = 45 mm
 $\therefore$ 480 pages − 48 pages = 432 pages

hence, 432 pages have a total thickness of 45 mm.

1. Copy the table above then add further rows to help you to answer these questions:
 (*a*) Find the thickness of 30 sheets.
 (*b*) Find the thickness of 18 sheets.
 (*c*) Find the thickness of 126 sheets.
 (*d*) How many sheets have a total thickness of 15 mm?
 (*e*) How many sheets have a total thickness of 22.5 mm?

2. 360 kg of a certain type of seed cost £ 100. Make a table as before then use it to help you to answer these questions.
 (*a*) Find the cost of 4.5 kg of seed.
 (*b*) What is the cost of 13.5 kg?
 (*c*) How much does 31.5 kg cost?
 (*d*) How many kilograms can you buy for £1?
 (*e*) How many kilograms can you buy for £30.25?

Container ships, lorries and railway flat cars carry three basic sizes of containers. All three are 8 ft wide and 8 ft 6 in ($8\frac{1}{2}$ ft) high. The three lengths are 40 ft, 30 ft and 20 ft.
Using 1 ft = 0.3048 m:

1. (a) Change the width of 8 ft to metres.
   (b) Change the height of 8 ft 6 in to metres.

2. Change the three different lengths of containers to metres.

Lorries and railway flat cars can carry containers up to a total length of 60 ft (a 40 ft and a 20 ft, two 30 ft, and so on).

3. Change 60 ft to metres.

Some trailers are 2.5 m wide.

4. Calculate the amount of space in millimetres left on each side of a trailer when the 8 ft wide container is placed centrally on the trailer.

5. Calculate in cubic feet the volumes of all three sizes of container.

6. Calculate in cubic metres the volumes of all three sizes of container.

A 6-wheeled tractor unit (lorry without a trailer) has a mass of 7.6 t.
A 4-wheeled tractor unit has a mass of 6.72 t.
A 30 ft trailer has a mass of 4.08 t and an empty 30 ft container has a mass of 3.48 t.
A 6-wheeled tractor unit can pull a maximum of 38 t including its own mass while a 4-wheeled tractor unit can pull a maximum of 32.5 t.

7. Find the largest mass of goods that can be carried in a 30 ft container pulled by:
   (a) a 6-wheeled tractor unit,
   (b) a 4-wheeled tractor unit.

Containers can be stacked five high. The bottom container can stand a maximum load of 80 t.

8. If all containers have the same mass, find the maximum mass of each.

9. If the bottom container has a mass of 16 t, the second 17.9 t, the third 15.6 t and the fourth 25.3 t, calculate the mass of the top container if the bottom container supports its maximum load.

A container ship of about 35 000 t can carry up to 800 of the largest containers.

10. If the average mass of these containers is 21.4 t, calculate the load carried by the ship.

11. If the maximum mass of a container is 26.32 t, calculate the maximum load carried by the ship.

A small coaster carries sixty 40 ft containers each of mass 28.7 t, fifty 30 ft containers each having a mass of 24.6 t and twenty 20 ft containers each with a mass of 18 t.

12. Calculate the load carried by the ship.

Miscellaneous Information

The heaviest recorded man in Great Britain was William Campbell who was born in Glasgow in 1856 and died in 1878. He was 191 cm (6 ft 3 in) tall and had a mass of 340 kg (53 st 8 lb). His waist measured 216 cm (85 in) and his chest 244 cm (96 in). His coffin had a total mass of 680 kg (107 st 2 lb).

The largest blue whale ever recorded was 33.58 m long. Another blue whale of length 29.48 m was believed to have a total mass of 177 t (174 tons). A 27.6 m blue whale taken by the Slava whaling fleet in the Antarctic on 17 March 1947 had a tongue that weighed 4.29 t (4.22 tons).

The longest animal ever recorded is the ribbon worm. In 1864, one measuring more than 54 m (180 ft) was washed ashore at St Andrews, Fifeshire, Scotland.

The main span of the Humber Estuary Bridge measures 1410 m (4626 ft).

In Austria, the Arlberg road tunnel is 14 km (8.7 miles) long.

23 Conversion Graphs and Tables

8 km is about the same distance as 5 miles.
We can write 8 km ≈ 5 miles.

The relationship between kilometres and miles can be shown on a graph:

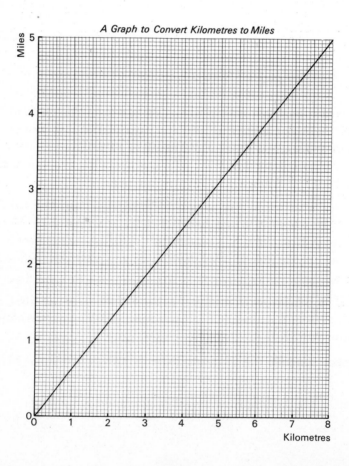

A Graph to Convert Kilometres to Miles

Exercise 1

1. Copy the graph opposite. (Do not forget the title.)
   Use a scale of 2 cm to 1 km on the horizontal axis and 4 cm to 1 mile on the vertical axis.

2. From your graph, change:
   (a) 4 km into miles
   (b) 1 mile into kilometres
   (c) 2 miles into kilometres
   (d) 3 miles into kilometres
   (e) 4 miles into kilometres
   (f) 2 km into miles
   (g) 6 km into miles

Exercise 2

A Draw a graph to convert miles to kilometres. This time draw the graph so that any number of miles up to 100 miles can be converted to kilometres.
Use a scale of 1 cm to 5 miles and 1 cm to 10 km.

Use 5 miles = 8 km and 100 miles = 160 km.
Use your graph to convert to kilometres:

(a) 50 miles
(b) 60 miles
(c) 40 miles
(d) 25 miles
(e) 85 miles
(f) $52\frac{1}{2}$ miles

Now use your graph to convert to miles:

(g) 120 km
(h) 48 km
(i) 112 km
(j) 72 km
(k) 128 km
(l) 28 km

B Draw a graph to convert kilograms to pounds.

Use a scale of 1 cm to 5 kg and 1 cm to 10 lb.

Use 5 kg = 11 lb and 80 kg = 176 lb.

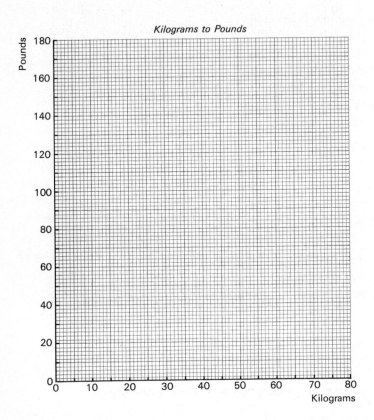

Now use your graph to help you with these questions:

1. Change to pounds:

(a) 20 kg	(c) 40 kg	(e) 35 kg	(g) 25 kg
(b) 60 kg	(d) 75 kg	(f) 55 kg	(h) 62 kg

2. Change to kilograms:

(a) 110 lb	(c) 22 lb	(e) 99 lb	(g) 33 lb
(b) 66 lb	(d) 154 lb	(f) 143 lb	(h) 50 lb

394

c Draw a conversion graph to change litres to gallons.

Use a scale of 1 cm to 5 ℓ and 4 cm to 5 gal.
Use 91 ℓ = 20 gal.

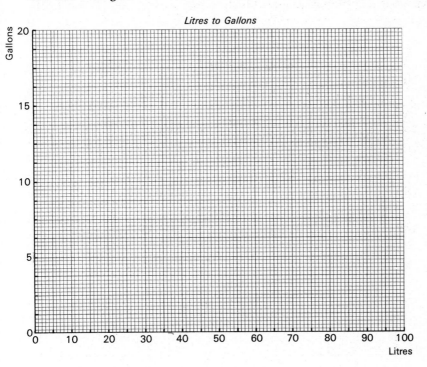

Litres to Gallons

Now use your graph to help you with these questions:

1. Change to gallons:

(a) 50 ℓ (e) 41 ℓ
(b) 75 ℓ (f) 34 ℓ
(c) 25 ℓ (g) 57 ℓ
(d) 66 ℓ

2. Change to litres:

(a) 2 gal   (e) 13 gal
(b) 18 gal   (f) 8 gal
(c) 7 gal   (g) 3.5 gal
(d) 10 gal

395

D Draw a graph to change French francs to £.

Use a scale of 1 cm to 5 francs and 2 cm to £1.
Use £8 = 92 francs.

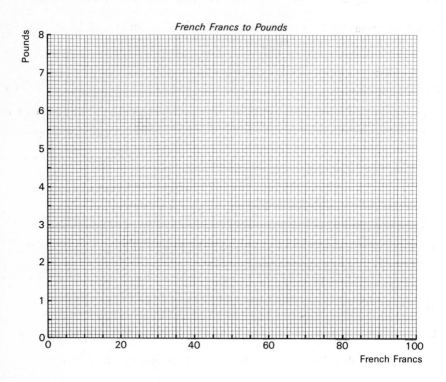

Now use your graph to help with these:

1. Change to francs:

(a) £2

(b) £6

(c) £7

(d) 50 p

(e) £4.80

(f) £3.40

(g) £5.50

2. Change to £:

(a) 46 francs

(b) 20 francs

(c) 72 francs

(d) 10 francs

(e) 60 francs

(f) 85 francs

(g) 31 francs

Conversion Tables

A table can be used to convert from one unit to another. Four different conversion tables are given on p. 399. Look at the first table of length. Look carefully at the row of figures having an **8** in the centre column.

The row gives	cm	cm or in	in
	20.32	**8**	3.15

This row shows that 8 cm = 3.15 in.
It also shows that 8 in = 20.32 cm.

(Note that the values are more accurate in the tables than on the graphs you have drawn.)

Exercise 3

Use the tables on p. 399 to change:

A centimetres to inches:

1. 6 cm   **2.** 9 cm   **3.** 20 cm   **4.** 40 cm   **5.** 50 cm

B inches to centimetres:

1. 5 in   **2.** 7 in   **3.** 30 in   **4.** 40 in   **5.** 50 in

C kilometres to miles:

1. 2 km   **2.** 5 km   **3.** 8 km   **4.** 30 km   **5.** 50 km

D miles to kilometres:

1. 3 miles   **2.** 6 miles   **3.** 10 miles   **4.** 20 miles   **5.** 50 miles

E pounds to kilograms:

1. 4 lb   **2.** 7 lb   **3.** 9 lb   **4.** 30 lb   **5.** 50 lb

F kilograms to pounds:

1. 1 kg   **2.** 3 kg   **3.** 6 kg   **4.** 20 kg   **5.** 50 kg

G litres to gallons:

1. 1 ℓ **2.** 3 ℓ **3.** 6 ℓ **4.** 20 ℓ **5.** 50 ℓ

H gallons to litres:

1. 3 gal   **2.** 6 gal   **3.** 10 gal   **4.** 30 gal   **5.** 50 gal

Exercise 4

Some values are not in the conversion tables.

e.g. Convert 46 km into miles.

From the table, 40 km = 24.85 miles

and   6 km = 3.73 miles

so   46 km = 28.58 miles

Use the given tables to convert:

1. 25 kg to pounds
2. 36 in to centimetres
3. 48 km to miles
4. 13 ℓ to gallons
5. 27 miles to kilometres
6. 80 lb to kilograms
7. 60 cm to inches
8. 11 gal to litres

9. 15 kg to pounds
10. 15 lb to kilograms
11. 24 gal to litres
12. 57 ℓ to gallons
13. 69 km to miles
14. 85 miles to kilometres
15. 93 cm to inches
16. 52 in to centimetres

Conversion Tables

Length			Mass		
centimetres	cm or in	inches	kilograms	kg or lb	pounds
2.54	1	0.39	0.45	1	2.20
5.08	2	0.79	0.91	2	4.41
7.62	3	1.18	1.36	3	6.61
10.16	4	1.58	1.81	4	8.82
12.70	5	1.97	2.27	5	11.02
15.24	6	2.36	2.72	6	13.23
17.78	7	2.76	3.18	7	15.43
20.32	8	3.15	3.63	8	17.64
22.86	9	3.54	4.08	9	19.84
25.40	10	3.94	4.54	10	22.05
50.80	20	7.87	9.07	20	44.09
76.20	30	11.81	13.61	30	66.14
101.60	40	15.75	18.14	40	88.18
127.00	50	19.69	22.68	50	110.2

Length			Capacity		
kilometres	km or miles	miles	litres	ℓ or gal	gallons
1.61	1	0.62	4.55	1	0.22
3.22	2	1.24	9.09	2	0.44
4.83	3	1.86	13.64	3	0.66
6.44	4	2.49	18.18	4	0.88
8.05	5	3.11	22.73	5	1.10
9.66	6	3.73	27.28	6	1.32
11.27	7	4.35	31.82	7	1.54
12.87	8	4.97	36.37	8	1.76
14.48	9	5.59	40.91	9	1.98
16.09	10	6.21	45.46	10	2.20
32.19	20	12.43	90.92	20	4.40
48.28	30	18.64	136.4	30	6.60
64.37	40	24.85	181.8	40	8.80
80.47	50	31.07	227.3	50	11.00

24 Vectors

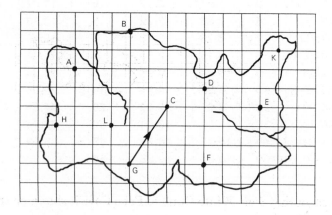

Look at the map above.

A journey from G to C can be written $\overrightarrow{GC} = \begin{pmatrix} 2 \\ 3 \end{pmatrix}$.

C to K can be written $\overrightarrow{CK} = \begin{pmatrix} 6 \\ 3 \end{pmatrix}$ and

A to B can be written $\overrightarrow{AB} = \begin{pmatrix} 3 \\ 2 \end{pmatrix}$.

The journey from C to B is $\overrightarrow{CB} = \begin{pmatrix} -2 \\ 4 \end{pmatrix}$.

Other journeys are $\overrightarrow{DE} = \begin{pmatrix} 3 \\ -1 \end{pmatrix}$, $\overrightarrow{DC} = \begin{pmatrix} -2 \\ -1 \end{pmatrix}$ and $\overrightarrow{DF} = \begin{pmatrix} 0 \\ -4 \end{pmatrix}$.

Write these journeys in the same way:

1. H to A
2. C to D
3. E to K
4. A to L
5. G to H

6. B to C
7. D to B
8. E to D
9. G to L
10. A to H

11. D to G
12. C to E
13. E to C
14. B to G
15. F to D

Exercise 2 M

Copy this map on to 1 cm squared paper:

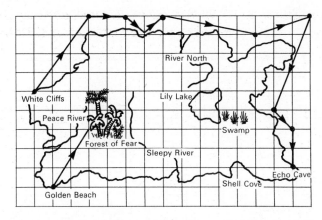

1. A sea journey from White Cliffs to Echo Cave is shown on the map above. The journey can be written as

$$\binom{3}{4}, \binom{2}{0}, \binom{1}{-1}, \quad \binom{1}{?}, \binom{?}{?},$$

$$\binom{?}{1}, \binom{?}{?}, \binom{?}{?}, \binom{?}{?}$$

Copy and complete the journey.

2. Here is a route to some treasure:

$$\binom{2}{3}, \binom{1}{4}, \binom{2}{-1}, \binom{3}{0}, \binom{-2}{-1}, \binom{4}{1}, \binom{1}{-3},$$

$$\binom{1}{-2}, \binom{-3}{2}, \binom{0}{-1}, \binom{-3}{1}$$

On your copy of the map, start at Golden Beach and mark the route to the treasure. (The first stage of the journey, $\binom{2}{3}$, has already been given.)

In this chapter we have been using *displacement vectors*.

To describe a straight journey we need to know the distance travelled (the *magnitude* of the journey), and its *direction*.

A *vector* is defined as having both *magnitude* and *direction*.

Exercise 3 M

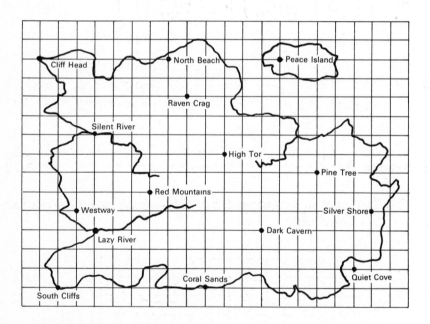

A In each question the vectors describe a journey from the given place to another place on the map above. Find the place at the end of each journey.

1. $\binom{2}{4}, \binom{3}{1}, \binom{1}{-2}, \binom{3}{-4}, \binom{5}{0}, \binom{1}{2}$

from Lazy River.

2. $\begin{pmatrix} 1 \\ 6 \end{pmatrix}, \begin{pmatrix} 4 \\ 1 \end{pmatrix}, \begin{pmatrix} -2 \\ 2 \end{pmatrix}, \begin{pmatrix} -3 \\ -1 \end{pmatrix}, \begin{pmatrix} -4 \\ 0 \end{pmatrix}, \begin{pmatrix} 2 \\ 4 \end{pmatrix}$

from Coral Sands.

3. $\begin{pmatrix} 3 \\ -2 \end{pmatrix}, \begin{pmatrix} 0 \\ -1 \end{pmatrix}, \begin{pmatrix} 3 \\ 1 \end{pmatrix}, \begin{pmatrix} 5 \\ -2 \end{pmatrix}, \begin{pmatrix} -1 \\ -6 \end{pmatrix}, \begin{pmatrix} 2 \\ 1 \end{pmatrix}$

from Cliff Head.

4. $\begin{pmatrix} 2 \\ -5 \end{pmatrix}, \begin{pmatrix} -1 \\ -3 \end{pmatrix}, \begin{pmatrix} -3 \\ 0 \end{pmatrix}, \begin{pmatrix} 1 \\ 1 \end{pmatrix}, \begin{pmatrix} -5 \\ 2 \end{pmatrix}, \begin{pmatrix} 1 \\ 3 \end{pmatrix}$

from Peace Island.

5. $\begin{pmatrix} 0 \\ 4 \end{pmatrix}, \begin{pmatrix} -3 \\ 2 \end{pmatrix}, \begin{pmatrix} 1 \\ -4 \end{pmatrix}, \begin{pmatrix} -6 \\ 0 \end{pmatrix}, \begin{pmatrix} -2 \\ 3 \end{pmatrix}, \begin{pmatrix} -2 \\ -3 \end{pmatrix}, \begin{pmatrix} -3 \\ 1 \end{pmatrix}$

from Quiet Cove.

B Now draw your own map. Mark about fifteen places on it. Name a starting point. Give a route using vectors. Ask someone to find where your route leads.

Exercise 4 ══════════════════════════════ M

Copy this map on to squared paper. You may use larger squares and obtain a larger map.

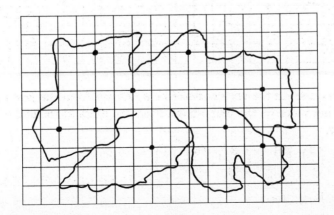

The ten points marked on the map are the starting points of ten different journeys.

Question 1 gives the vector $\overrightarrow{AA'} = \begin{pmatrix} 5 \\ 2 \end{pmatrix}$. Label one of the ten points on your map as A, then find, mark and label the end point A′. Note that you must carefully select the point A so that if AA′ is drawn with a straight line segment, the line segment does not cross a river and the point A′ does not land in the sea. Use the same rule for all ten journeys. Try not to get wet!

1. $\overrightarrow{AA'} = \begin{pmatrix} 5 \\ 2 \end{pmatrix}$ **5.** $\overrightarrow{EE'} = \begin{pmatrix} 0 \\ 4 \end{pmatrix}$ **9.** $\overrightarrow{II'} = \begin{pmatrix} -3 \\ 0 \end{pmatrix}$

2. $\overrightarrow{BB'} = \begin{pmatrix} 1 \\ 4 \end{pmatrix}$ **6.** $\overrightarrow{FF'} = \begin{pmatrix} 2 \\ -3 \end{pmatrix}$ **10.** $\overrightarrow{KK'} = \begin{pmatrix} -4 \\ 1 \end{pmatrix}$

3. $\overrightarrow{CC'} = \begin{pmatrix} 3 \\ -2 \end{pmatrix}$ **7.** $\overrightarrow{GG'} = \begin{pmatrix} -2 \\ 2 \end{pmatrix}$

4. $\overrightarrow{DD'} = \begin{pmatrix} -3 \\ 1 \end{pmatrix}$ **8.** $\overrightarrow{HH'} = \begin{pmatrix} -2 \\ -3 \end{pmatrix}$

Exercise 5

In the diagram, *all* the arrows show the vector $\begin{pmatrix} 3 \\ 2 \end{pmatrix}$

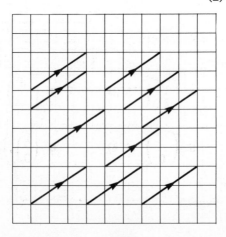

On squared paper, draw three arrows to show each of these vectors:

1. $\begin{pmatrix} 4 \\ 2 \end{pmatrix}$ **5.** $\begin{pmatrix} 3 \\ -2 \end{pmatrix}$ **9.** $\begin{pmatrix} -4 \\ 1 \end{pmatrix}$ **13.** $\begin{pmatrix} 4 \\ -3 \end{pmatrix}$ **17.** $\begin{pmatrix} 3 \\ 0 \end{pmatrix}$

2. $\begin{pmatrix} 3 \\ 1 \end{pmatrix}$ **6.** $\begin{pmatrix} 2 \\ -3 \end{pmatrix}$ **10.** $\begin{pmatrix} -4 \\ -1 \end{pmatrix}$ **14.** $\begin{pmatrix} -4 \\ 3 \end{pmatrix}$ **18.** $\begin{pmatrix} -4 \\ 0 \end{pmatrix}$

3. $\begin{pmatrix} 1 \\ 3 \end{pmatrix}$ **7.** $\begin{pmatrix} -2 \\ 5 \end{pmatrix}$ **11.** $\begin{pmatrix} -2 \\ -3 \end{pmatrix}$ **15.** $\begin{pmatrix} 4 \\ 3 \end{pmatrix}$ **19.** $\begin{pmatrix} 0 \\ -4 \end{pmatrix}$

4. $\begin{pmatrix} 2 \\ -1 \end{pmatrix}$ **8.** $\begin{pmatrix} -3 \\ 3 \end{pmatrix}$ **12.** $\begin{pmatrix} -1 \\ -1 \end{pmatrix}$ **16.** $\begin{pmatrix} -4 \\ -3 \end{pmatrix}$ **20.** $\begin{pmatrix} 0 \\ -2 \end{pmatrix}$

Exercise 6

In each question, a vector and the co-ordinates of its starting point have been given.

Find the co-ordinates of its end point.

e.g. $\begin{pmatrix} 5 \\ 3 \end{pmatrix}$, (2, 3)

     End point is <u>(7, 6)</u>

Try to answer these without plotting the points.

1. $\begin{pmatrix} 2 \\ 3 \end{pmatrix}$, (3, 1)   **4.** $\begin{pmatrix} -3 \\ -2 \end{pmatrix}$, (5, 2)   **7.** $\begin{pmatrix} 3 \\ -4 \end{pmatrix}$, (1, 4)

2. $\begin{pmatrix} 4 \\ 1 \end{pmatrix}$, (2, 4)   **5.** $\begin{pmatrix} -1 \\ 0 \end{pmatrix}$, (4, 4)   **8.** $\begin{pmatrix} 1 \\ 0 \end{pmatrix}$, (2, 1)

3. $\begin{pmatrix} -2 \\ 4 \end{pmatrix}$, (4, 6)   **6.** $\begin{pmatrix} 5 \\ -1 \end{pmatrix}$, (0, 3)   **9.** $\begin{pmatrix} 4 \\ -2 \end{pmatrix}$, (⁻2, 1)

10. $\begin{pmatrix} -5 \\ 1 \end{pmatrix}$, $(3, \, ^-4)$ **13.** $\begin{pmatrix} 2 \\ -4 \end{pmatrix}$, $(^-3, 0)$ **16.** $\begin{pmatrix} -2 \\ -7 \end{pmatrix}$, $(0, 0)$

11. $\begin{pmatrix} 0 \\ 1 \end{pmatrix}$, $(0, \, ^-1)$ **14.** $\begin{pmatrix} 1 \\ -1 \end{pmatrix}$, $(^-2, 2)$ **17.** $\begin{pmatrix} -6 \\ -4 \end{pmatrix}$, $(3, \, ^-4)$

12. $\begin{pmatrix} -2 \\ -3 \end{pmatrix}$, $(5, 1)$ **15.** $\begin{pmatrix} 0 \\ -4 \end{pmatrix}$, $(^-4, 3)$ **18.** $\begin{pmatrix} -6 \\ 4 \end{pmatrix}$, $(3, \, ^-4)$

Exercise 7

Given a vector and its end point, find the co-ordinates of its starting point:

1. $\begin{pmatrix} 3 \\ 4 \end{pmatrix}$, $(5, 5)$ **5.** $\begin{pmatrix} -1 \\ 4 \end{pmatrix}$, $(1, 4)$ **9.** $\begin{pmatrix} -3 \\ -1 \end{pmatrix}$, $(^-4, \, ^-1)$

2. $\begin{pmatrix} 1 \\ 3 \end{pmatrix}$, $(4, 7)$ **6.** $\begin{pmatrix} -3 \\ -2 \end{pmatrix}$, $(^-3, 2)$ **10.** $\begin{pmatrix} 0 \\ -2 \end{pmatrix}$, $(^-1, \, ^-3)$

3. $\begin{pmatrix} 2 \\ 5 \end{pmatrix}$, $(3, 5)$ **7.** $\begin{pmatrix} -4 \\ -2 \end{pmatrix}$, $(^-3, 1)$ **11.** $\begin{pmatrix} 5 \\ -6 \end{pmatrix}$, $(^-1, \, ^-1)$

4. $\begin{pmatrix} 1 \\ -2 \end{pmatrix}$, $(3, 2)$ **8.** $\begin{pmatrix} -5 \\ 3 \end{pmatrix}$, $(^-1, \, ^-1)$ **12.** $\begin{pmatrix} -4 \\ -3 \end{pmatrix}$, $(^-7, \, ^-4)$

Exercise 8

Given the starting point and the end point of a displacement vector, find the vector:

Start	End		Start	End
1. $(2, 1)$	$(5, 7)$		**6.** $(0, 0)$	$(3, 6)$
2. $(3, 0)$	$(7, 2)$		**7.** $(0, 0)$	$(^-2, 1)$
3. $(1, 3)$	$(4, 0)$		**8.** $(0, 0)$	$(^-5, \, ^-3)$
4. $(^-2, 4)$	$(0, \, ^-3)$		**9.** $(4, \, ^-1)$	$(^-2, \, ^-2)$
5. $(4, \, ^-2)$	$(1, \, ^-1)$		**10.** $(^-5, \, ^-1)$	$(^-3, \, ^-4)$

Translations can be described using vectors. In Exercise 3, question 1, on p. 257, an L-shape was translated 4 cm to the right and 3 cm upwards (as in the diagram).

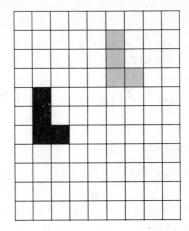

The vector $\begin{pmatrix} 4 \\ 3 \end{pmatrix}$ describes the translation.

Exercise 9

In the diagram, A has been translated to A′. The pair of co-ordinates for the object A is (3, 2) while the image A′ is (6, 7).

The vector for this translation is $\begin{pmatrix} 3 \\ 5 \end{pmatrix}$.

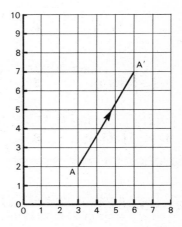

A Given a translation vector and a point, find the image of that point under the given translation:

1. $\begin{pmatrix} 5 \\ 1 \end{pmatrix}$, (2, 3)

3. $\begin{pmatrix} 1 \\ 2 \end{pmatrix}$, (⁻3, 0)

5. $\begin{pmatrix} -2 \\ -5 \end{pmatrix}$, (2, 1)

2. $\begin{pmatrix} 3 \\ 6 \end{pmatrix}$, (5, ⁻2)

4. $\begin{pmatrix} -3 \\ 4 \end{pmatrix}$, (1, ⁻6)

6. $\begin{pmatrix} 3 \\ -6 \end{pmatrix}$, (⁻2, ⁻7)

B 1. On to what point would the translation vector $\begin{pmatrix} 4 \\ -3 \end{pmatrix}$ map the point:

(a) $(1, 0)$?   (b) $(^-2, 1)$?   (c) $(^-5, 5)$?   (d) $(^-4, 3)$?

2. (a) $\begin{pmatrix} 1 \\ -2 \end{pmatrix}$ maps $(3, 4) \rightarrow (\boxed{?} , \boxed{?})$

(b) $\begin{pmatrix} -3 \\ -4 \end{pmatrix}$ maps $(3, 3) \rightarrow (\boxed{?} , \boxed{?})$

Exercise 10

1. What translation vector would map:
    (a) $(2, 6)$ on to $(3, 9)$?   (d) $(^-3, 4)$ on to $(^-1, 2)$?
    (b) $(1, 5)$ on to $(4, 3)$?   (e) $(^-5, 0)$ on to $(0, 5)$?
    (c) $(^-1, 2)$ on to $(^-4, 0)$?   (f) $(4, \ ^-7)$ on to $(0, 0)$?

2. (a) $\begin{pmatrix} 4 \\ 3 \end{pmatrix}$ maps $(\boxed{?} , \boxed{?}) \rightarrow (^-1, 5)$

(b) $\begin{pmatrix} 2 \\ -5 \end{pmatrix}$ maps $(\boxed{?} , \boxed{?}) \rightarrow (0, 0)$

(c) $\begin{pmatrix} -3 \\ 6 \end{pmatrix}$ maps $(1, \boxed{?}) \rightarrow (\boxed{?} , 2)$

(d) $\begin{pmatrix} -1 \\ -5 \end{pmatrix}$ maps $(\boxed{?} , 2) \rightarrow (1, \boxed{?})$

Exercise 11

1. Draw a pair of axes as shown. Use a scale of 1 cm to 1 unit on both axes.

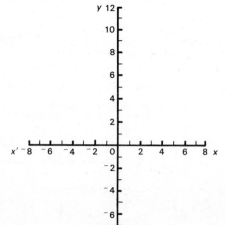

2. (a) Plot the points A$(1, 1)$, B$(1, 3)$ and C$(2, 1)$ and join them to form $\triangle$ABC.

408

(b) Translate $\triangle ABC$ to the image position A'B'C' using the vector

$$\begin{pmatrix} 4 \\ 2 \end{pmatrix}.$$

3. (a) Draw rectangle PQRS where P, Q, R and S are the points $(^-2, \ ^-4)$, $(4, \ ^-4)$, $(4, \ ^-7)$, $(^-2, \ ^-7)$ respectively.

(b) Translate the rectangle to its image position P'Q'R'S' using the

vector $\begin{pmatrix} ^-5 \\ 6 \end{pmatrix}.$

4. (a) Draw $\triangle LMN$ where $L = (^-6, 7)$, $M = (^-3, 11)$ and $N = (0, 8)$.

(b) Translate $\triangle LMN$ to position L'M'N' using the vector $\begin{pmatrix} 6 \\ 0 \end{pmatrix}.$

Exercise 12

1. Draw a pair of axes as in Exercise 9, on p. 407.

2. Plot the points A(1, 3), B(1, 1) and C(2, 1) and join them to give triangle ABC.

3. Translate $\triangle ABC$ to position A'B'C' using the vector $\begin{pmatrix} 2 \\ 1 \end{pmatrix}.$

4. Translate $\triangle A'B'C'$ to position A"B"C" using the vector $\begin{pmatrix} 1 \\ 4 \end{pmatrix}.$

5. Which vector would have translated $\triangle ABC$ directly to image position A"B"C"?

6. Find a rule connecting the vectors in questions 3, 4 and 5.

7. Test the rule using your own shapes and your own vectors.

Exercise 13

1. Draw a pair of axes. The x-values should range from $^-6$ to $^+10$ and the y-values from $^-6$ to $^+14$. (Use a scale of 1 cm to 1 unit.)

2. Use the vector $\begin{pmatrix} 2 \\ 4 \end{pmatrix}$ to map A → A′ where A is the point (2, 3). What are the co-ordinates of A′?

3. Use the vector $\begin{pmatrix} 4 \\ 1 \end{pmatrix}$ to map A′ → A″. What are the co-ordinates of A″?

4. Which vector maps A to A″?

5. Try to find a rule connecting the vectors in questions 2, 3 and 4.

6. Test the rule using your own choice of points and vectors.

Exercise 14

A

e.g. 1 $\begin{pmatrix} 3 \\ 5 \end{pmatrix} + \begin{pmatrix} 3 \\ 2 \end{pmatrix} = \begin{pmatrix} 6 \\ 7 \end{pmatrix}$ *e.g. 2* $\begin{pmatrix} 2 \\ -4 \end{pmatrix} + \begin{pmatrix} -3 \\ -1 \end{pmatrix} = \begin{pmatrix} -1 \\ -5 \end{pmatrix}$

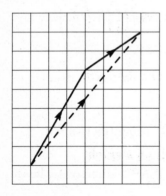 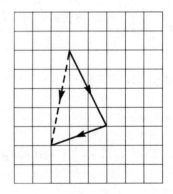

Add these vectors and show your results on a graph:

1. $\begin{pmatrix} 4 \\ 3 \end{pmatrix} + \begin{pmatrix} 2 \\ 5 \end{pmatrix}$ **3.** $\begin{pmatrix} 3 \\ 1 \end{pmatrix} + \begin{pmatrix} 2 \\ 6 \end{pmatrix}$ **5.** $\begin{pmatrix} 1 \\ 0 \end{pmatrix} + \begin{pmatrix} 3 \\ 6 \end{pmatrix}$

2. $\begin{pmatrix} 2 \\ 5 \end{pmatrix} + \begin{pmatrix} 6 \\ 1 \end{pmatrix}$ **4.** $\begin{pmatrix} 7 \\ 2 \end{pmatrix} + \begin{pmatrix} 2 \\ 5 \end{pmatrix}$ **6.** $\begin{pmatrix} 3 \\ 6 \end{pmatrix} + \begin{pmatrix} 1 \\ -2 \end{pmatrix}$

7. $\begin{pmatrix} 7 \\ -5 \end{pmatrix} + \begin{pmatrix} 2 \\ 3 \end{pmatrix}$ 　　**9.** $\begin{pmatrix} -3 \\ -2 \end{pmatrix} + \begin{pmatrix} 4 \\ -2 \end{pmatrix}$ 　　**11.** $\begin{pmatrix} -5 \\ -4 \end{pmatrix} + \begin{pmatrix} -4 \\ -5 \end{pmatrix}$

8. $\begin{pmatrix} -7 \\ -5 \end{pmatrix} + \begin{pmatrix} -2 \\ 3 \end{pmatrix}$ 　　**10.** $\begin{pmatrix} 2 \\ -3 \end{pmatrix} + \begin{pmatrix} -5 \\ -2 \end{pmatrix}$ 　　**12.** $\begin{pmatrix} 3 \\ 5 \end{pmatrix} + \begin{pmatrix} -8 \\ -2 \end{pmatrix}$

B Add these vectors:

1. $\begin{pmatrix} 7 \\ 2 \end{pmatrix} + \begin{pmatrix} 3 \\ 4 \end{pmatrix}$ 　　**6.** $\begin{pmatrix} 4 \\ 8 \end{pmatrix} + \begin{pmatrix} 2 \\ -5 \end{pmatrix}$ 　　**11.** $\begin{pmatrix} -7 \\ -3 \end{pmatrix} + \begin{pmatrix} -7 \\ -3 \end{pmatrix}$

2. $\begin{pmatrix} 1 \\ 6 \end{pmatrix} + \begin{pmatrix} 4 \\ 2 \end{pmatrix}$ 　　**7.** $\begin{pmatrix} 2 \\ -3 \end{pmatrix} + \begin{pmatrix} -1 \\ 4 \end{pmatrix}$ 　　**12.** $\begin{pmatrix} 4 \\ -6 \end{pmatrix} + \begin{pmatrix} 4 \\ -6 \end{pmatrix}$

3. $\begin{pmatrix} 3 \\ 8 \end{pmatrix} + \begin{pmatrix} 8 \\ 3 \end{pmatrix}$ 　　**8.** $\begin{pmatrix} 5 \\ -4 \end{pmatrix} + \begin{pmatrix} -1 \\ 2 \end{pmatrix}$ 　　**13.** $\begin{pmatrix} 9 \\ -4 \end{pmatrix} + \begin{pmatrix} -4 \\ 9 \end{pmatrix}$

4. $\begin{pmatrix} 9 \\ 0 \end{pmatrix} + \begin{pmatrix} 0 \\ 4 \end{pmatrix}$ 　　**9.** $\begin{pmatrix} -6 \\ 1 \end{pmatrix} + \begin{pmatrix} 6 \\ -1 \end{pmatrix}$ 　　**14.** $\begin{pmatrix} 5 \\ -3 \end{pmatrix} + \begin{pmatrix} 2 \\ 1 \end{pmatrix}$

5. $\begin{pmatrix} 7 \\ 9 \end{pmatrix} + \begin{pmatrix} 0 \\ 0 \end{pmatrix}$ 　　**10.** $\begin{pmatrix} 7 \\ 8 \end{pmatrix} + \begin{pmatrix} 7 \\ 8 \end{pmatrix}$ 　　**15.** $\begin{pmatrix} 2 \\ 1 \end{pmatrix} + \begin{pmatrix} 5 \\ -3 \end{pmatrix}$

Exercise 15

Answer these:

1. (a) Find $\begin{pmatrix} 6 \\ 4 \end{pmatrix} + \begin{pmatrix} 2 \\ 5 \end{pmatrix}$ and show the result on a graph.

(b) Find $\begin{pmatrix} 2 \\ 5 \end{pmatrix} + \begin{pmatrix} 6 \\ 4 \end{pmatrix}$ and show the result on a graph.

(c) Does $\begin{pmatrix} 6 \\ 4 \end{pmatrix} + \begin{pmatrix} 2 \\ 5 \end{pmatrix} = \begin{pmatrix} 2 \\ 5 \end{pmatrix} + \begin{pmatrix} 6 \\ 4 \end{pmatrix}$?

2. (a) Does $\begin{pmatrix} 5 \\ -6 \end{pmatrix} + \begin{pmatrix} 3 \\ 2 \end{pmatrix} = \begin{pmatrix} 3 \\ 2 \end{pmatrix} + \begin{pmatrix} 5 \\ -6 \end{pmatrix}$?

(b) Show your results on a graph.

3. (a) Find $\begin{pmatrix} 8 \\ -5 \end{pmatrix} + \begin{pmatrix} -3 \\ 4 \end{pmatrix}$

    (b) Find $\begin{pmatrix} -3 \\ 4 \end{pmatrix} + \begin{pmatrix} 8 \\ -5 \end{pmatrix}$

    (c) Does $\begin{pmatrix} 8 \\ -5 \end{pmatrix} + \begin{pmatrix} -3 \\ 4 \end{pmatrix} = \begin{pmatrix} -3 \\ 4 \end{pmatrix} + \begin{pmatrix} 8 \\ -5 \end{pmatrix}$?

4. Copy and complete: $\begin{pmatrix} 7 \\ -9 \end{pmatrix} + \begin{pmatrix} -2 \\ -1 \end{pmatrix} = \begin{pmatrix} -2 \\ -1 \end{pmatrix} + \begin{pmatrix} \boxed{?} \\ \boxed{?} \end{pmatrix}$

5. Copy and complete: $\begin{pmatrix} 12 \\ 2 \end{pmatrix} + \begin{pmatrix} -5 \\ -2 \end{pmatrix} = \begin{pmatrix} -5 \\ \boxed{?} \end{pmatrix} + \begin{pmatrix} \boxed{?} \\ 2 \end{pmatrix}$

Exercise 16

Copy and complete:

1. $\begin{pmatrix} 3 \\ 7 \end{pmatrix} + \begin{pmatrix} \boxed{?} \\ 2 \end{pmatrix} = \begin{pmatrix} 7 \\ \boxed{?} \end{pmatrix}$
      8. $\begin{pmatrix} \boxed{?} \\ \boxed{?} \end{pmatrix} + \begin{pmatrix} -3 \\ -1 \end{pmatrix} = \begin{pmatrix} 2 \\ 6 \end{pmatrix}$

2. $\begin{pmatrix} 4 \\ \boxed{?} \end{pmatrix} + \begin{pmatrix} \boxed{?} \\ 3 \end{pmatrix} = \begin{pmatrix} 9 \\ 4 \end{pmatrix}$
      9. $\begin{pmatrix} -6 \\ \boxed{?} \end{pmatrix} + \begin{pmatrix} \boxed{?} \\ -7 \end{pmatrix} = \begin{pmatrix} 2 \\ -3 \end{pmatrix}$

3. $\begin{pmatrix} 3 \\ 8 \end{pmatrix} + \begin{pmatrix} 5 \\ \boxed{?} \end{pmatrix} = \begin{pmatrix} \boxed{?} \\ 10 \end{pmatrix}$
      10. $\begin{pmatrix} 3 \\ 10 \end{pmatrix} + \begin{pmatrix} \boxed{?} \\ \boxed{?} \end{pmatrix} = \begin{pmatrix} -6 \\ 6 \end{pmatrix}$

4. $\begin{pmatrix} \boxed{?} \\ 7 \end{pmatrix} + \begin{pmatrix} 6 \\ \boxed{?} \end{pmatrix} = \begin{pmatrix} 11 \\ 12 \end{pmatrix}$
      11. $\begin{pmatrix} 8 \\ 2 \end{pmatrix} + \begin{pmatrix} \boxed{?} \\ \boxed{?} \end{pmatrix} = \begin{pmatrix} 0 \\ 0 \end{pmatrix}$

5. $\begin{pmatrix} -5 \\ 4 \end{pmatrix} + \begin{pmatrix} 2 \\ \boxed{?} \end{pmatrix} = \begin{pmatrix} \boxed{?} \\ 8 \end{pmatrix}$
      12. $\begin{pmatrix} 7 \\ -9 \end{pmatrix} + \begin{pmatrix} \boxed{?} \\ \boxed{?} \end{pmatrix} = \begin{pmatrix} 0 \\ 0 \end{pmatrix}$

6. $\begin{pmatrix} -6 \\ -2 \end{pmatrix} + \begin{pmatrix} 9 \\ \boxed{?} \end{pmatrix} = \begin{pmatrix} \boxed{?} \\ 5 \end{pmatrix}$
      13. $\begin{pmatrix} -5 \\ -2 \end{pmatrix} + \begin{pmatrix} \boxed{?} \\ \boxed{?} \end{pmatrix} = \begin{pmatrix} 0 \\ 0 \end{pmatrix}$

7. $\begin{pmatrix} \boxed{?} \\ -1 \end{pmatrix} + \begin{pmatrix} 8 \\ \boxed{?} \end{pmatrix} = \begin{pmatrix} 5 \\ 4 \end{pmatrix}$
      14. $\begin{pmatrix} \boxed{?} \\ \boxed{?} \end{pmatrix} + \begin{pmatrix} -10 \\ 8 \end{pmatrix} = \begin{pmatrix} 0 \\ 0 \end{pmatrix}$

15. $\begin{pmatrix} 9 \\ -9 \end{pmatrix} + \begin{pmatrix} -9 \\ 9 \end{pmatrix} = \begin{pmatrix} \boxed{?} \\ \boxed{?} \end{pmatrix}$ **18.** $\begin{pmatrix} -6 \\ \boxed{?} \end{pmatrix} + \begin{pmatrix} \boxed{?} \\ -6 \end{pmatrix} = \begin{pmatrix} 3 \\ 3 \end{pmatrix}$

16. $\begin{pmatrix} 5 \\ -8 \end{pmatrix} + \begin{pmatrix} \boxed{?} \\ \boxed{?} \end{pmatrix} = \begin{pmatrix} 0 \\ -4 \end{pmatrix}$ **19.** $\begin{pmatrix} -6 \\ \boxed{?} \end{pmatrix} + \begin{pmatrix} \boxed{?} \\ -6 \end{pmatrix} = \begin{pmatrix} -3 \\ -3 \end{pmatrix}$

17. $\begin{pmatrix} 1 \\ 0 \end{pmatrix} + \begin{pmatrix} \boxed{?} \\ \boxed{?} \end{pmatrix} = \begin{pmatrix} 0 \\ 1 \end{pmatrix}$ **20.** $\begin{pmatrix} -7 \\ 10 \end{pmatrix} + \begin{pmatrix} \boxed{?} \\ -9 \end{pmatrix} = \begin{pmatrix} -10 \\ \boxed{?} \end{pmatrix}$

Exercise 17

1.

	Mon	Tues	Wed	Thurs	Fri	Sat	Sun
Jogging	1	0	$\frac{1}{2}$	$1\frac{1}{2}$	2	2	1
Cycling	2	3	3	1	0	3	5

The table above shows the number of hours per day that someone spends jogging and cycling.

The information can be written as vectors. If the vector $\begin{pmatrix} 1 \\ 5 \end{pmatrix}$ stands for Sunday,

(a) Which day does $\begin{pmatrix} 2 \\ 0 \end{pmatrix}$ stand for?

(b) Why does $\begin{pmatrix} 3 \\ \frac{1}{2} \end{pmatrix}$ not stand for Wednesday?

(c) Which vector does stand for Wednesday?

The total times spent jogging and cycling on Monday and Tuesday can be worked out as follows:

$$\begin{pmatrix} 1 \\ 2 \end{pmatrix} + \begin{pmatrix} 0 \\ 3 \end{pmatrix} = \begin{pmatrix} 1 \\ 5 \end{pmatrix}$$

Which shows that 1 h was spent jogging and 5 h were spent cycling.

(d) By adding vectors, show the total times spent jogging and cycling on Saturday and Sunday.

(e) Using vectors, find the total times spent jogging and cycling on Wednesday and Thursday.

(f) Using vectors, find the total times spent jogging and cycling for the full week.

2. The table shows the number of packets of tea, jars of coffee, packets of sugar, cartons of eggs and loaves of bread used during three months.

	June	July	Aug
Tea	4	2	4
Coffee	1	2	2
Sugar	3	2	3
Eggs	4	7	3
Bread	9	11	7

The vector $\begin{pmatrix} 2 \\ 2 \\ 2 \\ 7 \\ 11 \end{pmatrix}$ shows July's groceries.

(a) Write the vector for August.

(b) By adding vectors, find the totals used for the months of July and August together.

(c) Using vectors, find the totals for the three months.

(d) Why is it important to keep the order the same in all the vectors to be added?

3. The vectors given show the number of hours spent on housework each week for four successive weeks. The vectors are given in the order of the weeks.

$$\begin{pmatrix} 1 \\ \frac{1}{2} \\ \frac{1}{2} \\ 10 \\ 6 \\ 1\frac{1}{2} \end{pmatrix}, \begin{pmatrix} \frac{1}{2} \\ 1 \\ 1 \\ 14 \\ 7 \\ 2 \end{pmatrix}, \begin{pmatrix} 2 \\ 1 \\ \frac{1}{2} \\ 12 \\ 6 \\ 2 \end{pmatrix}, \begin{pmatrix} 1\frac{1}{2} \\ 1 \\ 1 \\ 13 \\ 7 \\ 1\frac{1}{2} \end{pmatrix}$$

(a) One of the values (components*) in each vector is for ironing. Why is it not possible to say how many hours' ironing were carried out in the third week?

* See the glossary.

If each vector shows window cleaning, hoovering, dusting, cooking, washing-up and ironing in that order, then:

(b) add vectors to find the totals for the third and fourth weeks,

(c) add vectors to find the totals for all four weeks,

(d) make a table from the given information.

Exercise 18

1. A bus is 12 m long. The distance between two bus stops is 600 m. The bus starts with the driver opposite the first bus stop then stops again when the driver is opposite the second bus stop. How far has:

   (a) the driver travelled?

   (b) a passenger on the back seat travelled?

   (c) a passenger sitting 4.5 m from the front of the bus travelled?

2. A train travels a certain journey. Who travels further, a person in the first carriage or somone in the last carriage?

3. (a) A ship sails from R to S, the vector for the journey being $\begin{pmatrix} 3 \\ -4 \end{pmatrix}$.

   It then sails for T in the direction given by the vector $\begin{pmatrix} -5 \\ -1 \end{pmatrix}$.

   What vector gives the journey back to R from T?

   (b) Answer part (a) again but this time use the vectors $\begin{pmatrix} 8 \\ 4 \end{pmatrix}$ and $\begin{pmatrix} 2 \\ -7 \end{pmatrix}$ for the journeys from R to S and from S to T respectively.

Revision Exercises XIX to XXIV

Revision Exercise XIX

Part One

1. The volume of a cylinder can be found by multiplying the area of its base by its perpendicular height. Calculate the volume of a cylinder with base area 28 cm^2 and perpendicular height 12 cm.

2. The total surface area of a cube can be found by multiplying the square of the length of an edge by 6. The formula can be written as $A = 6l^2$. Use the formula to find the total surface area of a cube where the length of each edge is 7 cm.

3. The power of a machine (measured in watts) can be found by dividing the work done (in joules) by the time taken (in seconds). Find a formula giving the power P, in terms of W (work done) and t (time). Use the formula to find the power of a crane that does 4800 joules of work in 8 s in lifting a load.

4. (a) What number is d less than 12?
   (b) What number is d less than f?

5. What is the cost of g pounds of apples at m p per pound?

6. James walked s km in 7 days. How many kilometres did he walk each day if he walked the same distance each day?

7. What angle, when added to $p°$, will make a right-angle?

8. How many pence are there in £a?

9. c is an odd number. What is the next highest odd number?

10. What number is 4 more than n?

Part Two

1. Copy this sequence and fill in the missing numbers:

5, 8, 12, 17, 23, $\boxed{?}$, 38, $\boxed{?}$, ...

2. Copy this sequence and underline the term that is incorrect:

3, 6, 12, 21, 33, 48, 64, 87, ...

3. The nth term of a sequence is given by $T_n = 3n + 4$. Find the first 5 terms of the sequence.

4. $T_n = n^2 + 3$ gives the nth term of a sequence. Find the first 5 terms.

Part Three

Re-write without brackets:

1. (a) $6(2v + 7)$
(b) $\frac{1}{2}(4m + 12)$
(c) $4(3t - 6u)$

(d) $(4p + 3) \times 3$

(e) $\dfrac{(25 - 15h)}{5}$

2. (a) $^-3(2c + 5)$
(b) $^-4(5a - 7b)$
(c) $^-2(6d + 1)$

(d) $\dfrac{(12m + 3n)}{^-3}$

(e) $\dfrac{(6u - 14)}{^-2}$

3. (a) $x(3x + 7)$
(b) $2k(3k - 2)$
(c) $6z(3z - 3)$

(d) $3v^2(2v + 1)$
(e) $5l^2(l^2 - 2l + 3)$

4. (a) $(4a + 5b) + (2a + b)$
(b) $(6m - 3n) + (2m + 7n)$
(c) $(3j - 6k) + (j + 2k)$

(d) $(7h + 9i) - (3h + 4i)$
(e) $(6x - 3y) - (4x - 5y)$

Part Four

A Factorise:

1. $8v + 12$
2. $9y - 15$

3. $5k + 20$
4. $18n + 6$

5. $24 - 12g$
6. $10 + 4z$

7. $2d - 14f$ **9.** $32h + 24w$ **11.** $r^2 + 4r$

8. $6p - 12n$ **10.** $8 - 24u$ **12.** $4x^2 - 6x$

B By factorising, find the value of each of the following:

1. $9 \times 18 + 9 \times 2$

2. $13 \times 71 + 13 \times 29$

3. $46 \times 24 - 36 \times 24$

4. $49 \times 63 + 51 \times 63$

5. $7 \times 329 - 7 \times 229$

6. $14 \times 3.7 + 14 \times 6.3$

7. $9 \times 65.2 + 9 \times 34.8$

8. $7 \times 38.7 - 7 \times 28.7$

9. $4.8 \times 3.8 + 4.8 \times 6.2$

10. $9.7 \times 12.4 + 7.6 \times 9.7$

Revision Exercise XX

Part One

1. For the lengths 5 cm, 8 cm, 7 cm, 6 cm, 2 cm, 9 cm, 8 cm, 3 cm, 6 cm, 8 cm and 4 cm, find:
  (*a*) the mode,
  (*b*) the median,
  (*c*) the mean.

2. The mean of 6 numbers is 14. Find the total.

3. The mean age of 5 pupils is 13 years. If a 14 year old leaves the group and a 19 year old joins it, calculate the new mean age.

4. Write five numbers that have a mode of 9.

5. Write seven numbers that have a median of 6.

6. Write three numbers where the mode is 5 and the mean is 6.

Part Two

These are the heights of sixty pupils measured to the nearest centimetre:

149 136 138 161 150 167 132 139 167 174 152 153 144 155 154
143 168 141 160 143 146 132 158 168 135 150 142 171 137 159
136 148 172 169 144 138 146 145 148 161 170 164 136 154 152
148 167 139 134 156 164 132 150 163 143 155 167 153 147 154

1. Make out a tally chart then draw a histogram. Use the class intervals 130–134, 135–139, 140–144, 145–149, 150–154, 155–159, 160–164, 165–169, 170–174.

2. What is the range of the heights?

3. Which is the modal class?

Part Three

In an ice-skating competition there were twelve competitors. Two judges' marks were compared.
The marks awarded were as follows:

Competitor	1	2	3	4	5	6	7	8	9	10	11	12
Judge A	5.6	5.6	5.7	5.9	5.5	5.5	5.4	5.9	6	5.8	5.7	5.8
Judge B	5.4	5.5	5.5	5.6	5.3	5.5	5.3	5.8	5.9	5.8	5.7	5.9

1. Draw a scattergram.

2. Calculate the mean number of marks awarded by each judge and plot them.

3. Draw the line of best fit.

4. If judge B awarded a mark of 5.7, use the graph to find the mark awarded by judge A.

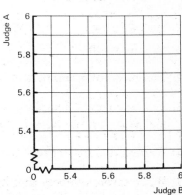

Ice-skating Competition

Part Four

1. (*a*) List the eight different outcomes from tossing three coins. HTH is one of the outcomes (the first coin shows a head, the second a tail and the third a head).
   (*b*) What is the probability of exactly one head when three coins are tossed?

2. What is the probability of getting an even number when a fair die is thrown?

3. Find the probability of choosing a king or a queen from an ordinary pack of 52 playing cards.

419

4. Find the probability of choosing a white marble from a bag containing 5 black and 4 white marbles.

5. A bag contains 6 black and 4 white marbles. What is the probability of choosing a white marble?

6. There are 6 similar keys on a key ring. Two of the keys will open my front door. What is the probability that I will choose a key that will open the front door?

7. (*a*) Write two events which have a probability of 1 of occurring.
(*b*) Write two events that have a probability of 0 of occurring.

Revision Exercise XXI

A Solve these equations:

1. $k + 7 = 11$

2. $y - 6 = 15$

3. $t - 9 = 20$

4. $m + 8 = 20$

5. $5z = 50$

6. $\dfrac{n}{4} = 6$

7. $9f = 27$

8. $\dfrac{c}{7} = 8$

9. $\dfrac{h}{2} = 17$

10. $d - 8 = 14$

11. $17 = a + 3$

12. $64 = 8x$

B Solve these equations:

1. $2e = 7$

2. $3b = 14$

3. $5w = 21$

4. $10p = 25$

5. $6l = 15$

6. $4m = 18$

7. $\dfrac{t}{2} = 4\frac{1}{2}$

8. $\dfrac{s}{6} = 1\frac{1}{3}$

C Solve the problems by using simple equations:

1. When 7 is added to a number, n, the answer is 16. Find the number.

2. There are 24 people on a bus. x get off and 11 remain. How many got off the bus?

D Solve these equations:

1. $3x - 6 = 15$

2. $4g + 5 = 33$

3. $5k - 4 = 1$

4. $2t + 11 = 35$

5. $5n + 2 - 2n - 6 = 23$

6. $7a - 9 - 11 - a = 4$

7. $5f + 2 = 4f + 11$

8. $9p - 15 = 3p + 33$

E Solve these equations:

1. $c - 6 = {}^-2$ 5. $3z = {}^-18$ 8. $3l - 6 = {}^-12$

2. $x + 8 = 5$ 6. $4u + 12 = 0$ 9. $2u + 7 = 1$

3. $m + 5 = {}^-5$

4. $6d = {}^-30$ 7. $\dfrac{b}{2} = {}^-9$ 10. $\dfrac{e}{{}^-6} = {}^-7$

Revision Exercise XXII

1. Copy and complete:

(a) 9 cm   = ? mm   (k) 5.97 km   = ? m

(b) 20 mm   = ? cm   (l) 6020 m   = ? km

(c) 7.3 cm   = ? mm   (m) 7.5 l = ? ml

(d) 59 mm   = ? cm   (n) 2480 ml = ? l

(e) 4.6 m   = ? mm   (o) 4.7 kg   = ? g

(f) 0.21 m   = ? mm   (p) 3270 g   = ? kg

(g) 5200 mm = ? m   (q) 2660 mg   = ? g

(h) 2980 mm = ? m   (r) 0.53 g   = ? mg

(i) 8.4 m   = ? cm   (s) 1.6 t   = ? kg

(j) 490 cm   = ? m   (t) 6920 kg   = ? t

2. (a) The length of a car is about

     A. 2.4 m   B. 4.3 m   C. 180 cm   D. 920 mm

(b) A mug holds about

     A. 250 ml B. 150 l C. 1.5 l D. 9.5 ml

(c) A packet of tea has a mass of about

     A. 125 mg   B. 825 mg   C. 125 g   D. 785 g

3. (a) Which is the most water, 4000 ml or 40 l?

   (b) Which is the longer, 7000 mm or 0.7 m?

   (c) Write 3.5 km in metres.

   (d) Forty people each have a glass of fruit juice. Each glass holds 150 ml. How many litres of fruit juice are used?

   (e) Denise ran 3.7 km. How many more metres should she run to cover a total distance of 4 km?

   (f) How many 150 g packets of sweets can be made up out of 4.5 kg of sweets?

4. (*a*) Calculate the volume of a 4 cm cube.

(*b*) Calculate the volume of the cuboid given in the diagram.

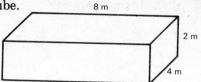

(*c*) Calculate the volume of a cuboid measuring 7 cm by 4 cm by 3 cm.

(*d*) Calculate the volume of a cuboid measuring 2.4 m by 2 m by 1.5 m.

Revision Exercise XXIII

A Draw a graph to convert litres to pints.

Use a scale of 2 cm to 5 litres and 1 cm to 5 pints. Use 44 *l* = 77 pt.

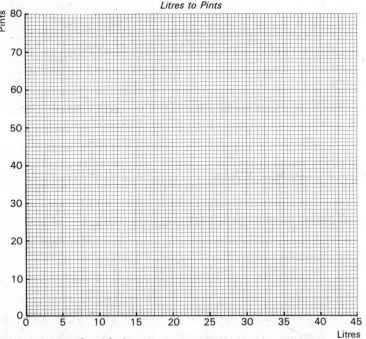

Now use your graph to help you to answer these questions:

1. Change to pints:

(*a*) 20 *l*   (*c*) 8 *l*   (*e*) 42 *l*   (*g*) 26 *l*

(*b*) 24 *l*   (*d*) 34 *l*   (*f*) 18 *l*

2. Change to litres:
- (a) 70 pt
- (c) 7 pt
- (e) 49 pt
- (g) 28 pt
- (b) 56 pt
- (d) 21 pt
- (f) 63 pt

B Use the conversion table given to change:

1. °C to °F:
- (a) 100 °C
- (e) 20 °C
- (b) 0 °C
- (f) 50 °C
- (c) 40 °C
- (f) 150 °C
- (d) 80 °C

2. °F to °C:
- (a) 50 °F
- (e) 10 °F
- (b) 0 °F
- (e) 100 °F
- (c) 60 °F
- (g) 200 °F
- (d) 30 °F

Temperature

°Celsius	°C or °F	°Fahrenheit
⁻23	⁻10	14
⁻18	0	32
⁻12	10	50
⁻7	20	68
⁻1	30	86
4	40	104
10	50	122
16	60	140
21	70	158
27	80	176
32	90	194
38	100	212
66	150	302
93	200	392

Revision Exercise XXIV

1. Write the vectors shown by the arrows in the form $\begin{pmatrix} x \\ y \end{pmatrix}$:

(a)

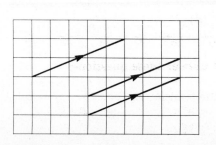

(b)

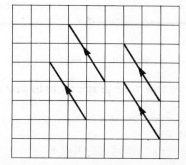

(c)

(d)

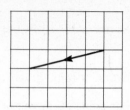

2. On squared paper draw arrows to show these vectors (one arrow for each vector is acceptable):

    (a) $\begin{pmatrix} 3 \\ 5 \end{pmatrix}$ (b) $\begin{pmatrix} ^-1 \\ 4 \end{pmatrix}$ (c) $\begin{pmatrix} 2 \\ ^-6 \end{pmatrix}$ (d) $\begin{pmatrix} ^-5 \\ ^-3 \end{pmatrix}$ (e) $\begin{pmatrix} 0 \\ 4 \end{pmatrix}$

3. Given a vector and the co-ordinates of its starting point, find the co-ordinates of its end point:

    (a) $\begin{pmatrix} 4 \\ 2 \end{pmatrix}$, (1, 5)   (d) $\begin{pmatrix} 3 \\ ^-2 \end{pmatrix}$, (6, 2)   (g) $\begin{pmatrix} 5 \\ 3 \end{pmatrix}$, ($^-2$, $^-6$)

    (b) $\begin{pmatrix} ^-3 \\ 5 \end{pmatrix}$, (6, 2)   (e) $\begin{pmatrix} ^-1 \\ ^-4 \end{pmatrix}$, (5, 2)   (h) $\begin{pmatrix} ^-2 \\ 6 \end{pmatrix}$, (4, $^-4$)

    (c) $\begin{pmatrix} 1 \\ ^-1 \end{pmatrix}$, (0, 4)   (f) $\begin{pmatrix} 2 \\ 3 \end{pmatrix}$, ($^-3$, 4)   (i) $\begin{pmatrix} ^-2 \\ 4 \end{pmatrix}$, (2, $^-4$)

4. Given a vector and its end point, find the co-ordinates of its starting point:

    (a) $\begin{pmatrix} 2 \\ 6 \end{pmatrix}$, (3, 9)   (c) $\begin{pmatrix} ^-1 \\ ^-3 \end{pmatrix}$, (3, $^-2$)   (e) $\begin{pmatrix} 6 \\ ^-2 \end{pmatrix}$, ($^-1$, $^-4$)

    (b) $\begin{pmatrix} 1 \\ 0 \end{pmatrix}$, ($^-1$, $^-2$)   (d) $\begin{pmatrix} ^-3 \\ 5 \end{pmatrix}$, ($^-5$, 1)   (f) $\begin{pmatrix} ^-4 \\ ^-4 \end{pmatrix}$, (2, $^-2$)

5. Given the starting point and end point of a displacement vector, find the vector:

	(a)	(b)	(c)	(d)
Start	(4, 3)	(1, 6)	(4, 2)	($^-1$, $^-6$)
End	(7, 5)	(4, 4)	(1, $^-3$)	($^-4$, $^-2$)

6. (a) On to what point would the translation vector $\begin{pmatrix} ^-2 \\ 1 \end{pmatrix}$ map the point (3, $^-1$)?

(b) $\begin{pmatrix} 4 \\ -5 \end{pmatrix}$ maps $(2, 3) \to (\boxed{?} , \boxed{?})$

(c) Find the image of the point $(4, \,^-2)$ under the translation vector $\begin{pmatrix} -3 \\ -3 \end{pmatrix}$.

(d) What translation vector would map $(\,^-2, 4)$ on to $(5, \,^-3)$?

(e) $\begin{pmatrix} -2 \\ -1 \end{pmatrix}$ maps $(\boxed{?} , \boxed{?}) \to (4, \,^-2)$

(f) $\begin{pmatrix} 3 \\ 2 \end{pmatrix}$ maps $(\,^-1, \boxed{?}) \to (\boxed{?} , \,^-1)$

7. (a) Do $\begin{pmatrix} 4 \\ 2 \end{pmatrix}$ and $\begin{pmatrix} 2 \\ 4 \end{pmatrix}$ give the same change of position?

(b) Do $\begin{pmatrix} 4 \\ -2 \end{pmatrix}$ and $\begin{pmatrix} -4 \\ 2 \end{pmatrix}$ give the same change of position?

(c) Do $\begin{pmatrix} 4 \\ 2 \end{pmatrix}$ and $\begin{pmatrix} 2 \\ 4 \end{pmatrix}$ translate points through the same distance?

8. Draw a pair of axes. The x-values should range from $^-6$ to $^+10$ and the y-values from $^-6$ to $^+12$. (Use a scale of 1 cm to 1 unit.) Plot the points $A(\,^-1, 1), B(5, \,^-2), C(\,^-1, \,^-5), D(\,^-4, \,^-2)$ and join them to give a kite.

Translate ABCD to position $A'B'C'D'$ using the vector $\begin{pmatrix} 3 \\ 9 \end{pmatrix}$.

9. Add the vectors and show the results on squared paper:

(a) $\begin{pmatrix} 3 \\ 5 \end{pmatrix} + \begin{pmatrix} 4 \\ 1 \end{pmatrix}$ (b) $\begin{pmatrix} -2 \\ 6 \end{pmatrix} + \begin{pmatrix} -3 \\ -1 \end{pmatrix}$ (c) $\begin{pmatrix} -5 \\ -9 \end{pmatrix} + \begin{pmatrix} 7 \\ 2 \end{pmatrix}$

10. Copy and complete:

(a) $\begin{pmatrix} 5 \\ 6 \end{pmatrix} + \begin{pmatrix} \boxed{?} \\ 3 \end{pmatrix} = \begin{pmatrix} 9 \\ \boxed{?} \end{pmatrix}$ (c) $\begin{pmatrix} -4 \\ \boxed{?} \end{pmatrix} + \begin{pmatrix} \boxed{?} \\ -7 \end{pmatrix} = \begin{pmatrix} 0 \\ 0 \end{pmatrix}$

(b) $\begin{pmatrix} -9 \\ -2 \end{pmatrix} + \begin{pmatrix} \boxed{?} \\ \boxed{?} \end{pmatrix} = \begin{pmatrix} -6 \\ 1 \end{pmatrix}$ (d) $\begin{pmatrix} -9 \\ 8 \end{pmatrix} + \begin{pmatrix} \boxed{?} \\ \boxed{?} \end{pmatrix} = \begin{pmatrix} 0 \\ 0 \end{pmatrix}$

11. The table shows the number of hours spent sleeping, eating, working and on leisure during three days.

	Fri	Sat	Sun
Sleeping	8	6	7
Eating	2	4	3
Working	8	4	0
Leisure	6	10	14

(a) Give Saturday's activities as a vector.

(b) Which day does the vector $\begin{pmatrix} 8 \\ 2 \\ 8 \\ 6 \end{pmatrix}$ show?

(c) By adding vectors, find the totals for Saturday and Sunday.

(d) Use vectors to find the totals over the three days.

Appendix

A B C D E F G H I J
K L M N O P Q R S
T U V W X Y Z

Glossary

broken scale   (pp. 348, 351)

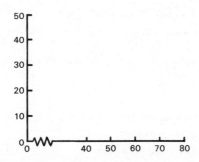

The diagram shows a broken scale used on the 'horizontal' axis. It is used when the full range of values will not fit on an axis.

In the example, 0 to 80 is shown on the horizontal axis. Since 0 to 80 will not fit completely, unless a small scale is used, and since only the range of values from 40 to 80 is needed, the scale is broken, as shown, between 0 and 40. A larger scale can then be used.

component of a vector   (p. 414)

Each value in a vector is called a component. In the example, 3 is the first component and 4 the second component.

$$\begin{pmatrix} 3 \\ 4 \end{pmatrix}$$

domain (p. 222)

A domain is the first set in a mapping. The arrows used in a mapping diagram point from the domain.
(The second set is called the *co-domain*.)

event (p. 354)

An event is the occurrence of a set of outcomes. In a statistical experiment, the probability of an event is the probability of *a* set of outcomes happening.

histogram (p. 343)

A histogram looks like a bar chart. But in a *bar chart* the *length* of each block shows the frequency, while in a *histogram* the frequency is shown by the *area* of each block.
When each block or bar has the same width, a histogram is the same as a bar chart. The difference will be more clearly shown in book 3G.

integer (p. 299)

An integer is a member of the set $\{ \dots, {}^-3, {}^-2, {}^-1, 0, 1, 2, 3, \dots \}$.
1, 2, 3, ... are called positive integers
and ${}^-1, {}^-2, {}^-3, \dots$ are negative integers.

mapping (p. 221)

A mapping is a relation in which *every* member of the first set is linked by some rule to one or more members of the second set. On p. 219, Exercise 1, question 4 does not show a mapping since the number 1 in the first set is not used.
In Exercise 2, on p. 220, questions 3, 4, 5 and 6 are not mappings.
Note Some texts define a mapping differently. Such texts would probably define a mapping and a function as being the same. All texts probably agree on the definition of a function. A function will be defined in book 3G.

mass (p. 383)

Mass is the amount of matter in a body. It is often confused with weight, which is a force. For example, on the Earth, the weight of a body is the force with which it is attracted towards the centre of the Earth (the force of gravity). On the Moon, the force of gravity is less than on Earth, so the weight of a body is less on the Moon than on Earth.
However, the mass of the body remains the same.

natural number (p. 2)

The set of natural numbers = $\{1, 2, 3, 4, \ldots\}$
They are the counting numbers.

outcome (p. 354)

In a statistical experiment, an outcome is a happening. For example, in tossing a coin, the outcome could be a head or it could be a tail.

p.a. (p. 187)

p.a. means per annum (that is, 'per year' or 'each year').

probability (p. 357)

Probability is a measure of how likely an event is.
If all outcomes are equally likely we can write:

$$\text{the probability of an event} = \frac{\text{the number of ways the event can happen}}{\text{the total number of possible outcomes}}$$

For example, in taking a card from a pack of cards there are 52 possible outcomes (there are 52 cards). Each outcome is equally likely. (Each card has the same chance of being selected.) Since there are 4 kings in the pack there are 4 ways a king can be selected.

$$\text{The probability of a king} = \frac{4}{52} = \frac{1}{13}.$$

The values used in measuring probability vary between 0 and 1. A probability of 0 means that it is impossible for the event to happen, whereas if the probability of an event is 1, that event is certain to happen.

real numbers (p. 230)

A real number is a number that can be written as a decimal. 5, 2.8, $^-3$, $2\frac{1}{2}$ and $\sqrt{2}$ are all real numbers.

subtended (p. 250)

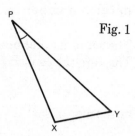

Fig. 1

to be opposite to.

In fig. 1, the line XY subtends the angle P. We can also say that angle P has been subtended by line XY.

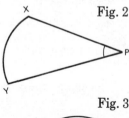

Fig. 2

In figs 2 and 3, angle P has been subtended by arc XY.

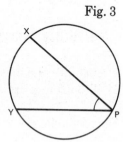

Fig. 3

In fig. 3, arc XY subtends an angle P at the circumference of the circle.

weight

see mass.

whole numbers (p. 9)

A whole number is a member of the set $\{0, 1, 2, 3, 4, \ldots\}$.